WILD RIVER

WILD RIVER

by

ANNA LOUISE STRONG

LONDON
VICTOR GOLLANCZ LTD.
1944

To

JOEL SHUBIN,

my husband
who in living and in dying
made clear to me
the Soviet way of life

Printed in Great Britain by The Camelot Press Limited
London and Southampton

FOREWORD

Wild River is distilled essence of my twenty years in Soviet Russia. While its main characters are fiction, the scenes in which they live and move are fact. Dnieper Dam's construction, the Red Dawn Farm's fight with kulaks, occurred with the details and in the months given here. Even such minor incidents as the students' "one-day university," the competition between right and left banks, the January elections, the Red Army's trench-digging for Kharkov Tractor Works, are all historic truth.

The people Anya meets on her trip to Moscow—Natalya, Anisia, Dunia, Shadiva—are actual people I myself have met. Stalin's personality as here shown may surprise many Americans but would be recognized by all Russians, many of whom will know the exact sources from which I have taken Stalin's words.

Thanks are due to George Willner and Nat Goldstone, whose enthusiasm for *Wild River* made easier its writing, and to Hilda Hulquist, who considered it "war work" to help with my typing. Chief recognition must go to the hundreds of Russian friends, many now dead in battle or of exhaustion in work behind the lines, who, despite all myth of Soviet reticence, made me for twenty years free of the wide reaches of their country and of the intimate stories of their personal lives.

ANNA LOUISE STRONG.

I

Sweat poured from the faces of the men dismantling the generator. No breath of river air came into the engine room from the August night. The long glass wall was curtained for the final blackout. This muffled even the rumble of troops retreating over the dam by the upper bridge.

There were twelve men and a foreman—thirteen pygmies pecking at a giant frame. They worked fast. Their lives depended on it. Eight generators were already loaded on the train for the east. If the ninth was ready in time the men would go with it over the bridge to safety. If not, they would be caught here when the Germans came.

The Germans would come to-morrow; this none of the men doubted. For two months the world-devastating Nazis had pushed deeper into this Soviet land. They came flushed with victories from a conquered Europe. They advanced in bitter battles; the Red Army was the first continuing opposition they had met. But the Red Army was not yet able to hold them; the ravaging hordes came on furiously. They had raped Kiev, the storied Ukrainian capital. They drove now on Dnieper Dam, the electric heart of the Ukraine.

Here lay the power with which Hitler might achieve world conquest. Nowhere in the world was there such a modern electric empire, built on a single plan. The hydroelectric plant was the largest in Europe. Vast irrigated lands were fed from its man-made lake. Through its locks great vessels rose from the sea and passed deep into the continent. Its fingers of power stretched north to the old steel cities, west to the iron mines of Krivoi Rog, south to the Nikopol manganese, east to the Donetz Basin of steel and coal, lighting three hundred miles of roaring towns and giant farms.

Here was the gateway to the Middle East. Here lay the bread and iron for the ruthlessly devouring hordes. The despot of Europe hailed the Dnieper Dam as his means to become world despot.

Could Hitler use this Dnieper power as he used the conquered strength of Europe? The thirteen men in the engine room said: "No!" They, with millions of others, were packing up the people's possessions. What they could not take they would destroy, lest the ravagers use it. This was their iron law in mankind's most decisive war.

To-night they were taking out the last generator. The whole centre of power would be removed or destroyed; of this the thirteen men were certain. They did not know when or how the dam would be destroyed, but they knew that they must be over the bridge to-night.

This last generator was an American one. Ten years ago it had come from the General Electric, from a town in New York of which they could not even pronounce the name. It was the first installed. Five American generators, then four that were made by the young Soviet industry. How proud their plants—yes, their whole people—had been of those first giant generators, as good as the American-made. The whole Dnieper Dam, in its planning and building, had united the engineering skill of the two countries. They owed it not only to themselves but to the Americans not to surrender to Hitler what two great, free peoples had built. This generator had journeyed far from New York to what seemed its final home on the Dnieper. It would start on another long journey to-night.

A tread echoed down the long room. At the far end a tall figure came through the door and strode rapidly toward the workers, not even looking aside at the eight torn gaps in the polished floor. They glanced at him for an instant and hurriedly resumed their work.

The foreman, a tall, blond youth in greasy brown overalls, hastened to the newcomer.

The man who had entered spoke first. "How much longer, Vladimir?"

"Another hour, Comrade Superintendent."

"Break her out faster. We can't care for details. The train is ready to leave."

A flatcar appeared through great double doors at the end where the superintendent had entered, and rolled down the room on railway tracks sunk in the tiled floor. The workmen sprang to it, and pushed it into position.

Laying aside his black leather jacket, the superintendent lent a hand with the work. He had a strength and a deftness that even the foreman lacked. From time to time the eyes of a workman glanced at him curiously and then looked even more quickly away.

The man would have aroused attention anywhere. He was of large frame but quick on his feet. High cheekbones, eyes that blazed blue in a dark tanned face. A handsome, challenging face; full, sensitive lips, compressed to-night, either with determination or with pain. Either would be natural to-night, the men at the generator knew.

They knew him for a strict boss, but a fair one. Temper a bit hot, but quickly controlled. Above all, a man quick to consider workmen's proposals and inventions. Ready to pitch into anything that had to be done. No nonsense about him, he knew the dam from foundations upwards. He had begun at the bottom, drilling the bed.

To-night this was not what distinguished him. Their curious glances and increased energy of work came from the thought in the minds of all of them. They would go to-night over the river to safety. This man would be staying behind. He had something to do—they did not know what—with the final fate of the dam. This set him suddenly apart from them, perhaps forever, yet made him at the same time near as he had never been before.

Again there was noise at the door. The superintendent hastened to meet a thin man in captain's uniform; then he came back.

"Will you watch the door with me?" He nodded to a young workman. "Nazi parachutists have been sighted; they may try to rush us." Then to the others: "Keep on, double time!"

Later there was a scuffle near the entrance and shots were fired. The work kept on; the shooting stopped.

Shortly before ten the generator was loaded. The two at the door returned, the workman much excited, the superintendent calm.

"The Army stopped them," he reported. "One got through; I shot him. The dam's still ours—to destroy." Nodding approval at the finished work, he added: "You're boss from now on, Vladimir. I'll meet you at the door." He strode down the room, crossed between two of the gaps left by the removal of the generators, and stepped behind the curtain that hid the glass wall.

"He's a cool one," exclaimed the young workman. "The Nazi had the drop on us; the darkness hid him. One of his shots went through the boss's jacket. The boss sighted by the flame of the Nazi's gun." Looking with admiration at the curtain, he added: "He's taking a last look at the dam; he was here when it was built."

They pushed the car toward the door where the locomotive waited. The curtain parted and the superintendent joined them. Staring at the torn floor, he said: "I thought we'd never use those tracks again. We used them once—to build!"

"Don't take it so hard, Comrade Superintendent," begged the foreman. "When we come back we'll build it faster and better than before."

It flashed into the young workman's mind that Vladimir was rather tactless. Stepan Bogdanov had little chance to be here when they returned. Apparently the superintendent had not noticed the implication. They all heard him answer in an assured tone:

"Faster? Certainly. Better? It may be. But what we built you'll never build. What we built was built once only. . . ."

Now what was the meaning of that, the youth wondered.

As they started to follow the car to the railway station, he heard the last words of the superintendent, words that made the man seem to him suddenly, not only a boss and a hero, but human in a way he had never seemed before.

"We were wild boys by a wild river . . ."

II

O N T H E H I G H western shore of the untamed Dnieper, a boy of fourteen was dragging a heavy sack across a neglected field. Driblets of grain oozed with every movement through worn places in the burlap. The boy looked at each loss with growing concern.

"The devil!" he remarked to the windy solitude, as he paused to wipe the sweat from his brow with grimy knuckles. "All sacks are rotten, even the kulaks' sacks."

He glanced backward furtively as if in fear of pursuit. There was no one between him and the village which lay on the cliff more than a half mile upstream. Shading his eyes with his sunburned hand, he surveyed the landscape. From the slight rise he could see beyond the huddled houses to the rapids, where the foam whipped in wet gusts against the cliffs. His long thin legs shivered.

In the grey sky cranes flew south, taking the summer with them. On the brown earth the grain, long gathered, lay stacked in ragged sheaves. Only that part of the high rolling prairie close to the village bore this burden of harvest. Nearer the boy, weeds choked even the footpath through the ruined fields.

It was autumn of 1923; the fertile soil of the Ukraine had been desolated by war, revolution, banditry, and famine for nine long years. More than a dozen times had the land changed masters. The Russian Tsar lost it to the German Kaiser. The Ukrainian Rada held it; the bandits Petlura and Makhno. The White Denikin drove across its fields to storm Red Moscow and ravaged its homes in his vindictive retreat. Polish invaders looted it and were driven out by the Bolsheviks. The boy could not even remember the time before all these wars.

He remembered only that people grew always hungrier. Each peasant toiled for himself with worn-out hand tools, strove to raise food and to hide it from his changing overlords. Peace had come at last but the people were exhausted. They had lost half their cattle and working animals and most of their pigs and chickens. The poorer ones—the ones the boy knew best—could not even till their scattered bits of soil. They hired themselves out as farm hands not for wages, but for meagre food, to people like Faber, one of those rural property owners known as "hard fists"—kulaks. Faber had grain in his barns. He had one sack less now. The boy patted the sack with satisfaction and continued down the slope.

Even downhill the going was not easy. The change of movement dislodged a tiny cascade of grain. With an oath the boy halted, scooped the grain from the earth, and moved as if to poke it into the sack again. Thinking better of it, he tossed the pellets into his mouth, together with a generous portion of rich, black soil, and chewed it all vigorously.

For more than a mile the trail kept south by the river, rising and falling a little but always well above the water. Off to the left the floating bridge swayed in the current; a launch drew up to the mooring on the far shore. Finally the path turned inland over a ridge. At this point the boy left it. By a hardly perceptible track on the rocks, he started down the side of the cliff to the river.

He sighed with relief as he dropped below the surface of the field and felt safely hidden. His pace slackened; he tossed his ragged hair back from his dirt-rimmed eyes. Suddenly a gust of wind whirled the river spray higher, soaking the boy's ragged trousers of homespun linen, drenching his bare legs and dirty calloused feet. He shivered. But he was less concerned with his own shivering than with the effect of water on his grain. He shielded the sack with his body, taking the full brunt of the spray, which increased as he dropped nearer the river.

Almost exhausted he found himself at the river's edge just opposite a barren, rocky islet which shut off the view of the main stream. Here even the slight pathway seemed to stop in a chaos of half-submerged rocks at the foot of the cliff. Without hesitation the boy stepped out upon the stones, leaping with agility downstream, close to the overhang of the shore.

Shouting above the noise of wind and water, "Hey, Ivan! Hey, fellows! I got it!" he jumped from the last rock to firm ground beyond the steepest part of the cliff.

Half a dozen boys came tumbling around an edge of rock and ran towards him. They were all from twelve to fourteen years of age. All of them were ragged, all were barefoot, all had been marked by the hunger years. But differences were manifest, sharpened by the approach of adolescence. Hunger had stunted some; others had shot up prematurely into scarecrows, with long thin limbs jutting out of their homespun rags.

The first to approach was a scrawny youngster with sores on his legs and a torn sheepskin jacket over his rags. Gazing with admiration towards the sack and back to the boy who brought it, he cried, in tones verging on adoration: "You got it, Stepan! I told them you would."

"So you talked me over," replied Stepan, with a lordly displeasure that made the younger boy wince. "I knew I'd get it. Old Man Faber will give up more than that from the grain he took from our harvest when Mother died. I had no trouble at all; his dog knows me."

His eyes left the first boy, rejecting the easy devotion, and sought out a stockier, cleaner lad with sandy hair and freckled face, who approached more slowly and glanced at the sack grudgingly, saying nothing until the impatient Stepan challenged him.

"Well, Ivan, did I get it?"

Ivan kicked the sack almost sullenly. "It proves nothing," he muttered.

"It proves that food can be got for the Lair when I want it," argued Stepan hotly. "It proves we can stick it till spring."

"Bread for ten days," admitted Ivan, stirring the sack with his foot with a touch of contempt. "Can you steal blankets also. The militia will hunt us seriously if we steal blankets."

"You'd better get out of the Cossacks' Lair if you're afraid of the militia," taunted Stepan. Ivan stiffened. But Stepan turned angrily away and started up the cliff, leaving behind him, as if no longer interested in it, the sack of grain which had cost him so much effort and which seemed to have lost its meaning since Ivan was unconvinced. But he had not forgotten his recently acquired booty. For when two of the smaller boys edged toward the sack as if to touch it, he seemed to feel their moves from the back of his head and turned swiftly.

"Peter," he ordered the boy with the sore legs, "look after that grain and ration it out for ten days." He glanced sidelong at Ivan, whose ten days' estimate he had thus placatingly accepted. Then he climbed a short distance up the cliff and turned to the right behind a tall rock.

He came out suddenly on a wide uneven shelf some thirty feet above the water, visible neither from the river nor from the adjacent shore. From it opened a large cave, penetrating far back into the cliff, where the grey light of the autumn day barely reached a heap of straw spread thinly on the cold stone floor.

A small fire burned on stones near the cave's entrance, spreading thin smoke against the face of the cliff. On it stood an iron pot of boiling water. Several boys crouched over the warmth; they nodded to Stepan but stubbornly held their places.

Stepan glanced at the boiling water with satisfaction; it showed faith in his successful return. He looked with less pleasure at the boys who had seized the places by the fire when the others had come to meet him. "Lazybones, how can a gang get ahead with boys like you?" The words beat against the roof of his throat but did not come out. These laggards must be disciplined but not angered. A struggle was upon him in which he might need their support.

Almost casually he pushed two of them back to make room for Peter and the grain. "Toss in a full day's ration," he commanded. "We'll have a council after eating."

A glow of satisfaction spread through the gang at the promise of full stomachs. Stepan's eyes challenged Ivan's silently. He wanted Ivan's allegiance; he wanted still more a united gang in the Lair. He intended to settle Ivan in the coming debate. Fourteen bitter years had taught him that revolt springs easily from empty stomachs. Food was a weapon, so he tossed in food.

When Peter left the fire to store the grain sack in the rear of the cave, Stepan pushed two new boys into Peter's place. He looked on benevolently as Ivan shoved close to the other side of the fire. Then Peter returned to take charge of the cooking. The skirkers moved back almost automatically. A glow of satisfaction spread through Stepan. The gang was coming into order. The first round was his and without any argument.

Long before the merrily boiling water had cooked the grain to softness, the boys ate. Stepan gave the signal. He lifted some half-cooked porridge on a smooth bit of wood which he took from his belt, ate it, and nodded. Until then the half-starved faces had hung over the pot, savouring the smell. Now they tore into the food with their makeshift spoons, salvaged in their wanderings—bits of smooth wood, pieces of rusty tin. Stepan looked on with approval.

"Well, let's have it," he said at last when the pot was empty and the boys, not fully satisfied but still not hungry, hung over the fire for warmth. "Where do we spend the winter? I say we stay right here. Who's against it?"

For a moment they were silent, taken aback by the suddenness of Stepan's challenge. Then hot discussion began.

"Why can't be go south?" asked Feodor, a tall, weedy youngster whose bare shoulders shivered through the ragged grey burlap that formed his shirt. "I spent last winter on the shore of the Crimea. There was hardly any snow."

"Hardly any food either," countered Stepan drily. Feodor fell silent, but others took up the argument.

"Sochi is a swell place, and the grapes are ripe there now," declared a pock-marked youngster, spitting into the fire. Others urged the merits of an even farther trip beyond the Caucasus, to the warm climate of Tiflis, the Georgian capital. Still others considered that Moscow, even if cold, was a big city with lots of food. These hungry, ragged boys were a travelled group. Some had wandered for years and knew the climate and food resources of most of European Russia. Some had been even in Soviet Central Asia, wintering in Tashkent and Samarkand.

Accustomed to follow the seasons, they could not understand Stepan's desire to winter on the Dnieper. Stepan himself did not quite understand it, but driven to argue he found easy reasons.

"There's nothing to eat in the south," he declared. "A boatman told me this morning. There's good harvest around here, but farther south it's burned dry. Here there is grain and potatoes and chickens. And I know how to get them. We've got to make a base for ourselves. We aren't just fly-by-nights."

Ivan spoke up for the first time. "This isn't much of a base."

"It's the base where the free Cossacks held off the Poles, the Turks, and the Russian Tsar," retorted Stepan hotly. "Their camp was right here on these cliffs. I bet—I bet they even used this cave. I bet their chiefs used it. That's why we called it Cossacks' Lair. They were free men, and they hadn't anything, but they stuck together and took tribute from the peasants, and held off all enemies. Maybe we——" He stopped short, unable to utter his full dream, and added abruptly: "I guess they were sometimes hungry too."

He tossed his head proudly, as if he were already a Cossack chieftain, to whom hunger and cold were only tests of heroism and greatness. The blue eyes, flashing in the dark tanned face, and the intense voice, resonant with feeling, stirred his followers. With straightening spines they thrilled to words which seemed to give a high, if vague, significance to their way of life. But Ivan stood stolid. Under his realistic survey, the cave took on its true proportions. There was no doubt that the floor was hard and cold and the roof was low.

Stepan challenged Ivan's disillusioning stare before it could affect the others. "If you have a better base to offer, hand it out."

Ivan hesitated. He knew he could not sway the gang as Stepan could, and he resented the spell of Stepan's words. "I asked Morosov to come out," he blurted finally, and waited for the storm to break.

"You asked an outsider to the Lair!" Stepan burst out violently while the rest of the gang held their breath. "You asked an enemy in?"

"Morosov's not an enemy," protested the unhappy Ivan. "He has a good idea. I thought he could explain it better than I can. It's a farm colony for homeless kids."

"You sold out the Lair for a children's home?"

"I didn't tell him the way here," said Ivan. "I said I'd meet him at the stepping-stones and bring him the rest of the way. I think we ought to hear Morosov's idea. It's not a children's home; it's different. It's working on our own land."

"We don't want Morosov here," began Stepan. Then he stopped, sensing the indefinable change that had come into most of the gang's members at the words "our own land." With a pang he admitted to himself that the Lair did not mean to them all the wild allurement that it meant to him. To them the Lair was a temporary and rather inadequate shelter. Morosov's "our own land" might promise more.

Morosov must be faced then. Stepan was not accustomed to shirk. "We'll meet him across the stepping-stones and talk there," he temporized. Then, still feeling the mood of the gang, he yielded what they desired. "No, it's too cold for that. We'll stay by the fire here. Peter will go with Ivan and make Morosov promise never to reveal the way to the Lair. Morosov's a goody-goody but he's no cheat."

As Ivan and Peter went to get the visitor, Stepan threw on the dying fire some of his cherished hoard of winter fuel. The flame revived and sent a comfortable glow through the cavern. This was no hospitality to Morosov; it was preparation for the challenge he would bring.

14

The boy who returned with Peter and Ivan gave no outward sign of bringing a challenge. He was only slightly older than the others; his thin body and over-developed arms were clad in homespun linen as worn though not as dirty as theirs. His deliberate movements and pleasantly serious manner were almost apologetic, as if he knew he was here on sufferance and had come to make a request. Yet there was a dignity in his diffidence that was as confident of itself as Stepan's belligerency. It was as if he knew not only how to fight his way but how to move ahead by other means than fighting—as if, in a world where Stepan chose to be an outlaw, Morosov felt himself at home. Stepan told himself, bitterly, that it was because Morosov knew how to read and write.

They all knew Ilya Morosov. He was an orphan too. Son of a local woman who went to look for a job from city to city, bore a fatherless baby in Astrakhan, came back home and died. The boy had since been working for a kulak, toiling from dawn till dark for meagre food and a chance to sleep in hay. A serf's life, Stepan considered it, a life that he had disdained. Morosov didn't like it either; he talked about "revolutionary rights." He was one of the joint owners of the country; there shouldn't be kulaks, he said. He tried to get things done through village officials. Nothing much had come of his efforts yet.

Morosov brought word of a project—a farm colony for homeless youth. "The county school board has at last agreed. They can't support orphans forever in children's homes. There is much empty land and many homeless young people strong enough to make a living on the soil. The County Commissioners—the *Ispolkom*—give us four houses at Cherumshan—on the river bank a mile south of here. They give land and tools and food until harvest. We're starting with some of the older boys and girls from Kichkas Children's Home. We've a hundred acres of land. We'd like you boys to join for you are old enough and strong enough to work. The more members we have, the more land they'll give us, and the stronger our commune will be."

"We don't like children's homes," Stepan said scornfully. His followers agreed.

"I've tried them from Leningrad to Astrakhan," bragged Feodor. "They're none of them any good."

"I sat on the big oven in the Kichkas Children's Home all winter," added Peter. "They hadn't shoes to go outdoors. We've more food here."

"It's not like a children's home," explained Morosov. "In the homes the Government supports you. The Government has little food and many orphans and there isn't enough to go around. In the colony we will support ourselves and have what food we raise. It will all be ours and we will all work to make it better. That is how life should be in a commune."

The deep sincerity of his feeling moved them. For a moment the members of the gang stood spellbound, each dreaming some part of

Morosov's dream. Stepan broke the spell. "Who runs the colony?" he asked bluntly. "You talk as if you owned it. Don't you have teachers?"

Morosov admitted that [there would be teachers "for a year or two."

"I thought so." Stepan's tones were a blast of contempt.

"But it will all be ours as soon as we learn to run it," argued Morosov.

"That's what they say," said Stepan. "And suppose we go and work for the teachers, what do we get for it? Will they give us clothes and shoes?"

"Not right away," admitted Morosov. "They haven't any."

"Then how are we better off than here? Here we have fire and food"—his eyes went proudly to the sack of grain—"and no teachers to boss us. We might even know ways of getting shoes."

Morosov was taken aback. He had so fully accepted the view that it was good to work and produce that he was unprepared for Stepan's contrary creed. He glanced from face to face, feeling for arguments. "But we have land," he said, as if that were an answer to everything. He added, less firmly: "We hope for several horses by spring and later even a tractor."

"Hopes are not horses," Stepan challenged. "They gave my mother land and she died for want of a horse."

He felt that he had Morosov beaten. "We'll talk it over and let you know," he said loftily, in what he considered the manner of a Cossack chieftain bidding farewell to a Turkish envoy.

Baffled, Morosov withdrew. But he left his ideas behind him. Stepan realized this with dismay when the gang began to talk. Several wanted to try the colony, at least for the winter. It might be only a new kind of children's home bossed by teachers. They had fled from children's homes in springtime, but winter was coming now. The colony offered at least a roof and a promise of food.

"Something might come of it if they have land," declared Ivan. "Here we'll just get into trouble with the militia."

A taunt rose to Stepan's lips but he restrained it. He had been sizing up the boys one by one. If he held firm against the colony he thought that most of them would stay with him. Most, but not all. Not Ivan, among others; Ivan would go. Even those who stayed would do so grudgingly, half convinced.

The gang would split. So Stepan made his decision, for the gang must be held together at all costs. The gang would challenge Morosov in Morosov's colony. It would take control.

"What we got to do, fellows, is to stick together . . . nobody can beat us if we just do that. Some want to try this colony. All right, let's try it. But let's go organized. We'll stick together and make the colony feed us through the winter. Next spring we'll come back to the Lair with all the blankets and warm clothes we can take. Then we'll have a Lair worth something!" His eyes glowed.

The shout of approval that met him told Stepan that the gang was still his at heart. He had found the way to hold them together even if he would not have chosen quite this way. He told himself that, whatever lure the new colony might offer, the gang of the Cossacks' Lair would survive.

III

Twenty boys and five girls met in the Cherumshan houses in mid-October to form their new colony. With them came a farm manager, a carpenter, a shoemaker, and a woman teacher. Most were brought by hunger, some perhaps by ambition, one at least by faith.

Stepan Bogdanov looked about his new field of operations and decided that as winter quarters Cherumshan would do. It stood high above the river but had easy access to it by several ravines. The four houses were small summer cottages whose merchant owners had fled from the Revolution and never come back. The buildings had thus fallen to the county *Ispolkom*, which until now had found nobody willing to repair them in exchange for their use. They were colder just now than the cave by the Dnieper, for the river wind drove through broken windows only partly closed by boards. But they had possibilities; they were made of logs, and it should not be hard to tighten them against winter with heaped-up earth.

Fifteen of the young colonists came from the Children's Home of Kichkas, which gladly sent its most intractable adolescents, even supplying them with pots, pans, and thin cotton blankets as going-away gifts. Stephan had little doubt that his gang could rule the colony with ten organized kids against these fifteen nondescripts. He was cynically aware that he had been invited to enter the colony, not because of Morosov's dream of a bigger, better commune, but because his gang already worried the local authorities so that they were ready to feed the boys till harvest in the hope that the farm might tame them to honest labour and remove their menace to the peace of the countryside. This hope Stepan neither defied nor accepted; he was ready to bargain on any good basis.

He had little fear of the carpenter, Fedotov, or the shoemaker, Andreyev, both of whom were clearly craftsmen out of work for want of materials, willing to take on boys as apprentices in order to get some food for their families. Stepan surmised, cynically but without rancour, that they would settle their families in Cherumshan, and share the orphans' grub with their own hungry kids. Nonetheless he approved of them, especially of Fedotov, who had come a day early and made three bunks. To have a carpenter and tools about was clearly worth while. The teacher was an elderly woman who could be disregarded. She was frankly afraid of the boisterous youngsters, but doubtless needed the food that went with the job.

The farm manager, Yeremeyev, could not be so easily dismissed. He had been chief of the county police. Stepan wondered why a chief of police was willing to run this small farm colony. Then he recalled that Yeremeyev was a former farm hand, who had risen through his fighting qualities in the Red Army. He knew land and farming, especially around Kichkas. Suddenly Stepan saw that this farm colony, if successful, might become the biggest farm in the county and that this was why Yeremeyev wanted the job.

It was known that his appointment had been hotly debated. The school authorities thought his education insufficient; Yeremeyev had only "liquidated his illiteracy" during the Civil War. It was also felt that occasional drunken sprees, in which he went into rages, disqualified him as a leader of youth. But the county police had united to support him—some perhaps because they hoped for his vacant job—and had convinced the school authorities that discipline was as important as learning in the new type of colony they were to organize. Yeremeyev had risen to captain a hundred men in the army, and won battles with them. He had energy and a sincere desire for modern farming, about which he knew nothing. But nobody else in the county knew more.

They might have done worse, thought Stepan. He preferred Yeremeyev to any of the county teachers. Twice the police chief had arrested Stepan; once he had drunkenly cuffed him. But there had been neither malice nor superiority in the blow. Yeremeyev never treated the Stepan gang from above, as most teachers did. Even when he tried ineffectually to curb them, he assumed towards them a certain rough equality, as towards growing members of a citizenry in which one man was as good as the next. He interested Stepan because as ex-captain of the Red Army, he had the halo of victory about him and had shown that he could fight.

Stepan believed in fighting. His father had fought and been killed somewhere in the great World War. Stepan never knew where; he only knew that his mother told him proudly and persistently to be worthy of his father, who had died "for land and liberty." This was burned into his brain. Otherwise he recalled nothing of his father. All memories of early childhood were dim. They seemed to start with a horrible headache that lasted forever. That was the typhus, the louse-borne disease that follows war and famine. When Stepan recovered from the typhus, the memory of the past was almost gone.

So the first thing he clearly remembered was the summer day when

18

the Red Army came through the village. All the boys ran to look and to follow down the long, ragged road to the market square. The soldiers stopped in the space by the great church and Stepan stared at them. They looked better than anything he had ever seen. They were fine troops, not like the shabby Red Guards that began the Revolution. It was the third year of Soviet Government in Moscow and the army had uniforms and shoes. They were driving back the Poles and clearing out the bandit Makhno.

"Hello, kids," cried a tall, laughing soldier, looking straight at Stepan. "Who wants to go with us?"

Then Stepan, eleven years old, cried in a great burst of devotion: "My father died for land and liberty; I want to go."

The tall soldier hit him on the shoulder and said: "Come along, kid!"

So Stepan went with the army. He did not even go home to get his things or to tell his mother. All the things he had—his shirt and trousers of homespun linen and a tattered sheepskin of his father's—were on his back. And what was the use of telling his mother when she was sure to object?

Stepan was very useful in the army. He was one of nine boys with a thousand soldiers. The men liked the kids and joked with them and gave them the best things to eat. The boys were never given firearms but they did the work of scouting. When the soldiers drew near bandit gangs and did not know where they lay in ambush, Stepan and the other boys would scatter into the villages, mix with the market crowds, play with the village boys and learn what was going on. Nobody paid much attention to wandering orphans except to give them food or to keep it away from them. In the evening Stepan would report to the Red Army what he had learned.

He wanted very much to see shooting but when the time came to fight, the soldiers shooed the boys out of the way. "Get to the rear, kids," they ordered. Stepan never saw the war at all or any danger. He didn't think of scouting the villages as danger. He knew that if the enemy caught him they would torture him at once. But how could the enemy guess what a wandering orphan did?

So when three summer months of fighting were over, Stepan went back to his village, feeling cheated. The Red Army had asked him to join and he had joined them, and they had never let him see the war.

Stepan's mother scolded him and wept over him and asked him why he had gone.

"Oh, just to see and know," answered the boy jauntily, for he knew much more than his mother now.

Stepan's mother went to the village Land Committee and told them that she was the widow of a soldier who died for his country and that even her little boy had served with the Red Army and she asked for her portion of land. The Land Committee recognized her claim and gave her twenty acres from the landlord's confiscated estate. It was impossible to work all that land without a horse. Excited by her success, she pestered the Land Committee for a horse as well; she refused to believe that they had none to give. "What is land without a horse?" she cried to them daily. At last they refused to see her. A grudge grew in her against the village authorities who refused her the means of life.

Horses could be had only from the kulaks. Stepan's mother rented one from the kulak Faber, pledging one third of the coming harvest. The ploughing fell on Stepan; day after day he toiled beyond the strength of the scant twelve years. His mother held him to it, in frantic fear lest all her family starve. It seemed to Stepan, as he worked in the ploughing and harvest and afterwards gave a third to Faber, that the cost of the horse was taken out of his own flesh and blood. He hated Faber and all peasants who had horses, and the Land Committee which had given his mother land without a horse. He hated the soil of his twenty acres. At times in his pain of exhaustion he hated his brothers and sisters for the appetites with which they ate. He never hated his mother; she ate little and worked as hard as he.

That was the Hungry Year of 1921; with hunger came cholera. Stepan's mother caught it and it finished her off in two weeks. Her last act was to borrow more grain from Faber to feed her children through the winter. This became a debt on Stepan that all his labour was unable to pay. All the next summer he worked frantically. To save renting a horse he harnessed himself and the weeping eleven-year-old Timofei to the plough. His ploughing was very shallow; his harvest was even smaller than in the Hungry Year. Faber took most of it on the old debt. Timofei died of hunger in early winter. Stepan and the others were taken into the Kichkas Children's Home, where an epidemic carried off the younger three.

Stepan learned little that winter. The Home tried to hold classes but there were more than a hundred children and only four pencils, used in turn by long lines of the more studious. Stepan wasn't interested in such learning. He was more interested in the second-hand but durable shoes they gave him. He ran away in these in the spring and sheltered himself two miles below the village in a cave that he had found in the almost forgotten years of childhood play.

From a teacher named Alexis, a youth just out of teacher training school, Stepan had learned the history of those high cliffs by the river whose wildness he had always loved. Often in past generations they had been held by bold men against encircling foes. This gave a name and a purpose to the gang of homeless boys that swiftly gathered around Stepan; their name "Cossacks' Lair" was the chief thing Stepan got from his school. The boys had lived not badly through the summer by stealing grain, eggs, and chickens. Stepan had believed that they could live through the winter as well. All the work he knew seemed bitter and fruitless. His months with the army had taught him that strong men, holding together and fighting, can take for themselves a good life. He fought to make his gang stick together; this became his purpose in life.

Now, installed at Cherumshan, he admitted to himself that his desire to winter in the cave had been romantic. He would not admit it to Ivan but he knew that Ivan's choice had been best. He did not want to break with Ivan, his boyhood chum and second-in-command. Ivan's allegiance had made the gang's beginning; he had run away from the Children's Home with Stepan. Ivan's many doubts made Stepan impatient, but Ivan's support was his seal of success.

After a supper of thin potato soup the young colonists gathered around the kitchen stove in Cherumshan to plan their future. "We must hold our meeting," announced Yeremeyev, "and decide our winter pro- gramme in the democratic Soviet way."

Everyone nodded gravely. Even as children they had exercised voice and vote in schools and children's homes. Now they were no longer children but joint owners of an extensive farm. Their hundred acres, in four fields at varying distances from Cherumshan, were recognition of a new status: not waifs on public bounty but young farmers working towards self-support.

So when names were proposed for the new colony—"May Dawn," "Lenin's Way," "Glory," and "Road to Life"—Ivan's suggestion of "Young Ploughmen" seemed accurate and adequate to them all. Only the woman teacher added: "Not Ploughmen, but Ploughman—one, not many, for we're all going to work as one." So "Young Ploughman" it became.

"We've got from the county enough rye, potatoes, and sunflower-seed oil to last till February," reported Yeremeyev. "They promise more but we'd better rustle a bit ourselves. We've two iron pots, two lamps, twenty- five bowls, and twenty-five large spoons. Best of all, we've a pretty good horse; I got it from the police. It was left behind by some bandits we were chasing; it was half-starved then but it's all right now. I told 'em it was too slow for police work so they gave it to our farm."

Everyone cheered the slow horse. Yeremeyev warmed to the cheers and then checked them. "One horse is very little; we need many. We're going to have a *big* farm." Stepan noted the words; they confirmed his belief that the farm manager was ambitious.

"Next let's divide the work," continued Yeremeyev. "Who wants to learn to be carpenter?" Ten boys, among them Ivan, held up their hands. "Who wants to be shoemaker?" Half a dozen, among them Morosov, volunteered.

"When are we going to have classes?" the woman teacher asked timidly.

"Whenever you like," replied Yeremeyev with lordly graciousness. "We've got to have lots of education. You must ask the county school board for books and supplies." The teacher subsided rather hopelessly, knowing that the county was distant and the books long since assigned.

"I'll hunt books in Zaporozhe," volunteered Morosov, and the teacher seemed relieved.

The girls were not asked to state a preference. Yeremeyev took it for granted that the task of girls was fixed by nature. It was so clean, to cook, to sew. He had asked the Children's Home for a proportion of one girl to four boys since he figured that one girl could clean and cook for four.

Most of the girls seemed ready to accept their woman's destiny, but one of them protested. A small, mousy creature, very neat, even prim in appearance, waved her hand for attention, and finding herself unnoticed at last stood.

"I'm Stesha Orlova," she announced, blushing at her own boldness. "Aren't the girls to learn any interesting trades? The Revolution gives us equal rights."

Somewhat startled, Yeremeyev replied that of course everyone was equal now, and that in time they might get a sewing teacher who would show the girls how to make clothes.

Stesha, hesitant, was still dissatisfied. "The nuns taught me sewing in the orphan asylum. It isn't interesting. I think we girls should have all kinds of work." Then she sat down suddenly, amid a faint murmur of approval from the other girls and from Morosov. Yeremeyev went on with the meeting.

Stepan noted the faint protest. He took no part in the first discussion; he listened and sized up the crowd. Girls had had little place in his scheme of things, but a girl who protested might have. He resolved to know Stesha better. She might prove an ally in his future struggles in the colony. He assumed that there would be struggles, but what kind he did not yet know.

Toward the end of the evening Yeremeyev noticed that Stepan had as yet volunteered for no work, and asked him what he wanted to do.

"I'll look after the horse," Stepan decided with such calm assurance that everyone agreed, and Yeremeyev wondered why he had not thought of this job for anyone before.

The boys bedded themselves down on piles of straw as far as possible from the broken windows. The girls did the same in another room. None of them cared to sleep in the bunks, for without mattresses these were as hard as the floor and colder. The discarded bunks fell naturally to

Fedotov, Andreyev, and the older woman teacher, all of whom had brought heavy cotton quilts from home.

Curling up in the straw close to the others, Stepan indicated the sleeping arrangements to Ivan with a contemptuous gesture—they were no more comfortable than in the Cossacks' Lair. His eyes raked with cynicism each adult who appropriated a bunk. Even though the boys did not want them, the fact that the teachers took them seemed to prove his argument that the teachers owned the colony.

Hardly had Stepan made this point to his own satisfaction when Yeremeyev disconcerted him by making his own bed in the straw with the boys, spreading his two large army blankets over half the Stepan gang. Whatever Yeremeyev's faults he was not addicted to comfort; it was something he had never known. He felt a pleasantly proprietary interest in his new charges, with whose aid he expected to conquer large areas of land. His habit as an old campaigner led him to seek warmth near others and to care for the well-being of all those under his command. He slept near the Stepan gang, since these were without blankets. The fact that the boys were full of lice induced in him no aloofness. He had often been lousy; to him it was one of the common conditions of man.

Stepan, drawing under a corner of Yeremeyev's blanket, close to the big, warm, smelly body, felt the birth of a grudging respect.

IV

REPAIRS BEGAN SLOWLY. The ten young "carpenters" had neither lumber, nails, nor experience. Scouting around, they found two old shacks which Yeremeyev got permission from the county to dismantle. The boys took them apart, saving every nail. They fought Fedotov for the use of the one set of tools—his most prized possession. Tables, benches, and rough plank beds took shape under their hands. The discovery and repair of an old rowboat gave them proud possession of "river transport" both to Kichkas upstream and to the city of Zaporozhe on the other shore.

Window glass was the serious problem. A war-ruined glass factory had reopened in Zaporozhe, but its product was rationed to a long waiting list. Morosov, who as member of the Young Communists—*Komsomol*—went at times to the city, learned that the glass workers were fighting to "over-fulfil" their October plan. From this excess glass the colony managed to get—after a wait of three weeks—six small panes, one for each important room. They boarded the other windows warmly, plastering them outside with mud.

More than once Stepan pointed out to Ivan that the colony was no better than the Cossacks' Lair. "There we had fire and all the wood we côuld gather. Here we need a permit to tear down old shacks. We shiver a month to get six panes of window glass."

Stepan's first grudging belief that the colony might expand and prosper came when they acquired a small nearby mill. Ancient and unreliable—partly because there was little water in its pond and partly because its aged owner was often drunk—it had closed long ago when harvests declined from the war. It still had primitive equipment and seemed to the boys a prize. They got it from the county and the former owner agreed to act as instructor in return for a ration of bread. The county sent them six more children since they would now have more food.

Several boys aspired to be millers. Morosov had already worked in a small mill under his kulak boss. But Stepan decided that control of the mill and its grain was important. He took an interest in the voting; his gang put in Peter and Feodor. All agreed that the third miller should be Marin, a wandering boy from Siberia who had drifted into Kichkas just in time to join the colony. His joking manner made him popular and Stepan wished to add him to his gang.

Stepan's first move for power thus easily succeeded. But Morosov did not seem to know that he had been defeated. He organized a committee to advertise the mill at peasant meetings, saying: "Come to our mill even if it is small and uncertain. For we are your own children, orphans of the famine. And we ask only three pounds for grinding forty, while better mills take four or five." So peasants began coming to the mill.

The mill's best advertisement came unexpectedly through Stesha, whom the Young Ploughman chose to represent them at the meetings of the Kichkas Village Soviet. Stepan supported her candidacy but so did all the others; if Stepan expected gratitude, he got none, for Stesha took the post as a responsibility rather than a prize. In the first two village meetings she didn't say a word but in the third meeting some peasants denounced the colony, saying that the Young Ploughman had plenty of food but the girls were too stupid to cook it, while the boys still stole food from the farms.

Stesha stood right up in meeting. "How can we cook without proper pots?" she cried. "You peasants have only five or six in a family, yet you have two iron pots each. We have over thirty to feed with two small iron pots and one pail. We get water in the pail and milk the cow in it and cook the soup in it and wash the dishes in it. We have to throw out the water before we can milk the cow, we have to drink up the milk before we can make the soup, we have to finish the soup and wash the dishes before we can have drinking water again. Can the best housewife in this village do proper cooking like that?"

After that nobody talked against the colony in the meeting, but all voted to patronize the colony's mill. And Stesha from that time on was as good a public speaker as any in the colony, as good even as Stepan or Morosov.

When Stesha came back to Cherumshan after that meeting, she told Yeremeyev: "We girls won't cook without proper pots. The peasants make fun of us for living like pigs." All the girls supported her. Stepan admired her for the flare-up. So Yeremeyev promised that at the first opportunity they would buy a large cauldron for cooking soup.

As the weeks went by, Stepan drew closer to Yeremeyev. He enjoyed his work with the horse; to handle an animal gave him a pleasant sense of power. He especially liked his trips as Yeremeyev's driver, which gave him variety and brought him to many hamlets and villages. He often stole food on these trips and shared it with the gang, cementing his authority. He knew that his thefts were the source of village criticism that worried Stesha; this gave him an enjoyable superiority over the girl. It also pleased him to know that he, alone in the colony, knew every place that Yeremeyev went.

Yeremeyev, he realized, was set on a swifter expansion than the small repairs and tiny mill allowed. The farm manager soon secured possession of two more broken-down horses from the county police. He showed Stepan how to doctor them so that they seemed better than they were. Then he took Stepan with the horses to a distant market down river, where they sold the animals to unsuspecting buyers for enough to buy one good horse and a cow.

"It's in a good cause," he laughed. "I'm cheating for the Young Ploughman, not for myself." Stepan was delighted by Yeremeyev's shrewdness and Yeremeyev warmed towards Stepan. He spent part of the money on vodka but he was sober when they reached Cherumshan.

From boatman's gossip on the trip down river they learned a new source of help. The American Relief Administration, which had come two years earlier to fight the great famine, was ending its work and disposing of its remaining food. Yeremeyev at once secured a document, properly stamped by the Kichkas authorities, stating that the Young Ploughman had space for one hundred children and asking for supplementary rations. He did not trouble to add that the actual number of children was only thirty-one, but he stressed the fact that the colony hoped to be self-supporting, for he had heard that Americans are practical people who like to help those who help themselves.

Yeremeyev went a day's journey by boat and half a day by rail to the district headquarters of the Americans. He took Stepan with him to help with the expected supplies. He was a bit worried when the man in the outer office told him that the district chief, Mr. Johnson, wanted to see him. Yeremeyev had heard that Americans were careful in check-ups but he had hoped their scrutiny had relaxed, now that they were leaving the country. Was his slight exaggeration in numbers about to be unearthed?

Mr. Johnson's affable manner set him at rest. The American shook hands and asked through an interpreter whether the Kichkas on the document was the village by the Dnieper Rapids where the Soviets proposed some day to build a dam. Relieved by the American's smile and astonished at his knowledge, Yeremeyev replied that it was.

"You see I know something of your country," smiled Johnson. "I'm a hydroelectric engineer. Your Dnieper is a great river, but it has never been properly navigable because of those sixty miles of rapids. I understand your Government intends to build a dam to regulate the flow and to furnish electric power."

Yeremeyev stared at Johnson with suspicion. If the American were really an engineer, what was he doing in a relief office? Why should he care about a dam so far away from America? Yeremeyev decided that the genial foreigner must be a spy. This view was confirmed as Johnson went on, pleasantly:

"I wanted to get up to see your district but I hadn't the time. That was a tremendous plan for electrification that your Lenin proposed in 1920. Of course he was only playing politics when he said it could be done in fifteen years. Have they made any surveys yet?"

As former police chief, Yeremeyev knew very well that some sort of survey had been made on the river. But he did not propose to tell an American spy. He made a noncommittal answer from which Johnson deduced that the villagers along the Dnieper were not interested in the talk of a dam. Pleased by this confirmation of his own idea of Russian backwardness, the American gave only casual scrutiny to Yeremeyev's documents. He smilingly initialled the request for supplementary food for one hundred children and told his secretary to "toss in any junk in the way of clothing that may be left."

Shaking hands with both Yeremeyev and Stepan, he said graciously to the farm manager: "You and I won't live to see the Dnieper tamed but perhaps this young man will." He patted the boy on the back.

"Our future is assured," cried Yeremeyev to Stepan on leaving. "These Americans don't know the value of food." He wondered uneasily if he were being paid for some inadvertently given knowledge about the Dnieper but he decided that he had really told nothing. Yet he had secured not only flour but lard, sugar, and cocoa—things nobody had seen for years. Stepan was equally elated. Yeremeyev and he could really get things done!

When the American products reached Cherumshan the young colonists sampled them with excitement. For five years they had had neither sugar nor pig fat; they had almost forgotten the taste. For two years they had possessed no soap; they had scrubbed dishes with ashes

26

or sand. Cocoa they had never tasted; the dark-brown stuff seemed oddly bitter when they dusted it on their tongues.

"It's something expensive used for a drink for sick people," explained Morosov. "I've seen it in hotels where Mother worked. City people will gladly buy it."

"We'll sell this fine food in the market," began Yeremeyev, "and buy livestock and bread." Then, seeing the dismay of the young colonists, he conceded: "Some of the sugar, lard, and soap we'll keep."

At once discussion began about what they wanted to buy for the Young Ploughman, and how much they would sell of their precious food. Stepan, Morosov, and Stesha were chosen as a Trading Committee to visit the markets for selling and buying.

The second-hand clothing at first sight disappointed them. They stared at worn-out silk dresses and torn rayon underwear, marvelling that the practical Americans should have such impermanent clothes. Everyone brightened at Stesha's suggestion: "We'll have a dramatic club; they'll do for that." The only warm garments were a half-dozen black clergymen's coats; everyone assumed the odd fashion was the American style. Thereafter these black coats, worn over home-spun linen trousers, appeared conspiciously against the Ukrainian snows.

They were all pleased by a quantity of strong new ticks intended for mattresses; it was the strongest material they had yet secured. Everyone agreed that it was too good for mattresses; they would make shirts of it for the boys and skirts for the girls. It might be unusual-looking, but people would know that they had foreign clothes.

Morosov eagerly seized some twenty-five pairs of second-hand shoes. They were not wide enough to fit the young colonists; they were made for city folk. "But they're of real leather; we'll sell them easily in Zaporozhe and buy leather in return." So at last the shoeshop also began working, with its unskilled boys and its single set of tools.

As the grip of winter fastened itself on the river, the life in Cherumshan settled into organized routine. The trading committee's visits to market resulted in improved equipment. They secured a second-hand sewing machine and quantities of worn-out burlap sacks from which the girls made mattress bags, filling them with straw. And they bought an iron pot, bit enough to make soup for fifty people. A small smithy, found in an outbuilding, became their blacksmith's shop, where two boys hammered old tin cans into bowls and cups.

In two months they were ready to hold a celebration—inviting officials from Kichkas and even from Zaporozhe—in which they declared the Young Ploughman a fully civilized institution, each member of which had a mattress and a bunk. It was also declared a farm commune, "each for all and all for each." After the celebration the young colonists continued to pile their mattress bags together in a corner for warmth. And following the declaration of unity, quarrels increased from the winter confinement and the struggle against the cold.

The problem of laundry came to be an especially sore subject. Stepan's intent to add Stesha to his followers suffered a sudden lapse when she told him how dirty his underwear was. The girls hated to wash it in the frozen laundry, where you could see the river ice through cracks in the walls.

"You girls are clean because you steal the soap from the laundry," he shouted. After this he didn't speak to Stesha for three days.

The boys clothes were especially filthy because of the calf and two little pigs that slept with them on their huddled straw bags. These animals, bought by the trading committee for precious American food, were among the most prized possessions; they had to sleep in the house lest they freeze to death in the barn. The boys took the animals into bed with them; but the girls said that the boys' sleeping habits were "uncultured," than which there was no stronger reproof.

A third little pig slept in the girls' room and was unhappy. Frost came through the shrunken windows; snow drifted through the attic floor. The girls put their plank beds together in the middle of the room around the stove. The little pig had no place to keep warm; he went walking all night under the beds, making noises. One night he found the basket where the bread was and managed to eat all of it. This gave Stepan a chance to get back at Stesha.

"We lost a whole day's bread because you were too 'cultured' to take the pig to bed with you," he sneered loftily. After this he felt appeased.

Morosov and Stesha worried over the quarrelling and tried to stop it but without much success. Even Stesha flamed up when a girl borrowed her shoes—one of three pairs among eight girls—got them wet, and dried them so that they cracked. With all the girls using her shoes, Stesha knew that she would be barefoot by spring. Yet how could she refuse to lend them? Despite all quarrels, they all had to help each other if they were to live through the winter. They were constrained by their common need.

Stepan escaped the worst of the quarrelling by his long drives with Yeremeyev. He handled two horses now. On warm sunny days he took the gang to the Lair for a picnic; the food stolen on his trips and the grain stolen from the mill by Feodor and Peter were basis for a feast. Stepan began to think that he might remain in Cherumshan even when spring came, if he could be both chief of the Lair and an important boy in the Young Ploughman.

This decision was strengthened by one of his trips with Yeremeyev. On the way home from Kichkas Yeremeyev told the boy to pull up at Faber's two-story stone house on the edge of the village. Wondering what business the farm manager had with the kulak, Stepan complied.

Embarrassed by the boy's presence, the farm manager hesitated and then blurted out: "Come in and have a nip and warm yourself. It's a cold day."

So that was it! The old rumour that Yeremeyev, as police chief, had protected Faber's bootlegging flashed into the boy's mind. His personal hatred of Faber rose in him. " I wouldn't go into that house for anything," he declared. "I'll wait for you outside."

Entering the comfortable house, Yeremeyev nodded to the host and demanded: "A bottle of the usual and make it plenty *krupi*—strong."

Faber demurred. "You haven't been round for some time. What are you paying with? There's another chief of police."

"Damn you for a kopek-pincher," cried the outraged Yeremeyev A jovial soul, he had liked to pretend that Faber's free bootleg had been. given him in good fellowship. "I'll pay you. I'm head of the biggest farm in the county."

The boast did not endear him to Faber, who hated all farm communes, even those run by children. "That doesn't raise your credit," he said sourly. "My farm belongs to me while yours belongs to the State." After some argument he agreed to give the strong home-brew known as *samagon*, but only in return for sugar and lard from the colony's stores. Yeremeyev shouted loud refusals but finally agreed.

He was full of apologies to Stepan when at last he emerged from Faber's. "I'll give you an extra ration of sugar," he mumbled with maudlin good humour. "There's nothing wrong in that; you need it for waiting outdoors so long." Then he rolled into the straw of the wagon, pulled his blanket over him, and was soon snoring in a drunken sleep.

Stepan, driving home in the sharp frost of early evening, patted the straw beside him with exultation. He had made use of the time to steal a dozen precious eggs from Faber's barn. It was a threefold triumph because he was getting even with Faber, winning praise from Yeremeyev, and because the farm manager would never dare betray him now. The bootleg and the dozen eggs would be the beginning of a new relationship.

Reaching Cherumshan, Stepan carefully helped Yeremeyev into his bed, to sleep it off without scandal. Then he sought Ivan, gave him an egg and gleefully told him that it came from Faber. Ivan was glad of the egg but demurred at the procedure.

"What do you take such chances for? The food here isn't bad."

"Huh! I'm not taking chances. You don't know what I know!" gloated Stepan.

He had planned to tell Ivan the whole story but now he decided against it. He would find another confidant. After distributing most of the eggs to the gang, he sought out Marin, whose allegiance he had long wanted. He gave Marin an egg and took the last himself. Over the sucking of the eggs he probed for Marin's confidence.

"Who sent you to the colony?"

Marin shook the bushy head of hair that made him look like an African savage and smiled his half-impish, half-angelic smile. "Nobody sent me. I came on my own. All the way from Siberia to this famous colony. I like to see the sights."

Pleased by Marin's method of putting a fine flourish on ordinary happenings, Stepan continued: "Do you like it here?"

Marin patted his stomach. "Why not?" he grinned. "I'm full." He held the eggshell up with adoration. "I'm fuller now!"

"Thinking of staying?" asked Stepan.

"God knows," replied Marin, piously rolling his eyes. "I'll stay the winter. Then—if something better offers . . ."

Stepan felt that Marin was a boy after his own heart. He probed arther: "Maybe you'll go back to Siberia."

"Maybe," replied Marin nonchalantly. "We've land enough in Siberia . . . Land, land, more land than anywhere on earth . . ." He stretched his arms wide to indicate it, then dropped them in sudden deflation. "But there's nothing to farm with. The White Guards took the horses."

Flattered by Stepan's attention, Marin began to chant his story: "The White Guards came to our village and they came right into our house. . . . They took our two strong horses. . . . They took our chickens. . . . They took my brother Vassili to be a soldier with them. But Vassili ran away and came home. . . . So the White Guards came again and asked for the 'deserter'. They threw my old man in the pond through a hole in the ice. 'Give us your son,' they demanded. They did this many times till my old man was covered with ice. He was sick a long time. He's dead now. But Vassili was safe."

"Where was Vassili?" asked Stepan.

"Down in the potato hole, and the trap door was covered with manure," said Marin. "But my old man didn't tell. Afterwards Vassili went away to the Red Army. We never saw him again."

"Could you keep a secret the way your father did?" asked Stepan.

Marin's eyes lit up. "Have you one you want me to keep?"

"Maybe," replied Stepan.

The flattered Marin gave many assurances. Then Stepan told of the Cossacks' Lair and of Yeremeyev's weakness. While Yeremeyev drank, they could steal food in the village. When Yeremeyev slept off his drinking, they could hide the food at Cossacks' Lair, making a hang-out for all kinds of adventures.

"Peter and Feodor will get us grain from the mill. I'm telling you because I'm going to let you help with the horses as soon as we get more of them."

"What a lark," cried Marin, his eyes shining.

30

"Yeremeyev won't dare tell on us, whatever he suspects," cried Stepan. He was on top of his world.

V

ILYA MOROSOV SANG as he skated across the river. He was bound for Zaporozhe for books. Ivan had shaped him a pair of wooden skates in the carpenter shop and the boys in the smithy had hammered old barrel hoops into runners. Morosov tripped occasionally; he was not as skilled in skating as the boys who had grown up on the river. He laughed as he picked himself up and went on singing. Morosov liked books.

Besides, it was something to do for the Revolution. Morosov regretted that he had really done nothing yet for the Revolution, though he had been in it from the start. It had found him a boy of ten in Astrakhan, where his mother worked as laundress in a hotel. He saw the soldiers' strike and the disorders that followed. He watched with fascination when starving Persian workers looted with long knives their Russian bosses' stores.

He had heard the many meetings: who is for the Tsar? who is for the Soviet Power? Morosov's mother voted for the Tsar because the hotel manager offered each of his employees five or ten rubles for his vote. He offered five to Morosov's mother, but when she hesitated he raised it to ten. She hesitated only because she didn't know she had a vote, but when he gave her ten she knew she had.

Morosov could have told her that women had votes now but he didn't talk with his mother much. He preferred to hang around the meetings of Red Guards that declared "revolutionary order" and put down looting and other lawlessness. They elected officers, commandeered weapons, and set up "people's power." Morosov saw how governments are made when he was eleven; he knew that he was for the Soviets. He saw the fighting for the Astrakhan fortress when the Theatre Square went up in flames. He met there an old Bolshevik who told him that the new country would need trained people and that working-class lads, properly trained, are the hope of the world. So Morosov went to school a whole year conscientiously and learned to read and write.

When the boss of the hotel fled away with the other bosses, Morosov's mother, feeling strange and insecure without a master, came home to her village by the Dnieper, got a job as laundress for the district hospital, caught typhus from the soiled linen, and died. Then Morosov worked for the kulak Hackman; his arms grew strong and his body thin from the poor food that was his pay. Morosov hadn't liked working for a kulak; that wasn't what the Revolution was for. Now he worked longer hours for the Young Ploughman than he ever had for the kulak. This work was

31

joy! If only he were strong and popular like Stepan, he could do ever so much more. So far, he seemed to have accomplished little. He envied Stepan's high vitality, which seemed so carelessly used.

Books now! Morosov had trudged to the county school board, but their meagre quota of textbooks had been sent in September to village schools. He had unearthed three books in village markets: a medical book, a discarded arithmetic, and a book of fairy tales. With these they had tried to have classes. The medical pictures were interesting but the words were impossible to read. The arithmetic was full of useless problems about landlords, rent, and interest. What could the colony do with stuff like that?

The fairy-tale book was the favourite. The young colonists discussed whether there were such things as fairies. Some thought that, if printed, it must be true. Morosov and Stesha supported the teacher's view that there were no fairies; Morosov, in fact, disapproved of the fairy tales because they were lies. The general view in the colony was that there had probably once been fairies, just as there had once been a Tsar and holy saints and the house spirit and the devil, but that these had all been abolished. If not entirely abolished, they had been deprived of power by the Bolsheviks.

The fairy tales, of course, had had to be made over. The teacher had read aloud the story about the goose-girl who marries a prince. She did not know how to end it, since to marry a prince is not "happy ever after" in revolutionary days. She told of the marriage as a sin; the goose-girl abandoned honest work and was supported in a palace on money stolen from the common people, her early friends. Since the young colonists liked the goose-girl, they cried out against this shameful ending. Marin invented a better one, in which the goose-girl married a coal-miner, who rose to be Red Director of all the district mines.

Clearly these books were not adequate for the Young Ploughman's education. Morosov had taken it up with the *Komsomol* in Zaporozhe. He had been promised that the trade school of the *Kommunar* Farm Implement Works would help the colony out with some of its books. That was why he skated across the river on this sunny afternoon.

He was welcomed at the Works by the shop-committee chairman, Nikolai Ivanovich, a thin, middle-aged man with dark circles under his kindly grey eyes, who smiled warmly at Morosov, ran a knobby hand through his sparse, greying hair, and said:

"Let's see . . . that colony . . . books . . . how many colonists?"

"Thirty-one," replied Morosov.

"Come over to the school. I'm afraid we haven't much."

An air of order and clear purpose pervaded the half-dozen classrooms, four workshops, and office that made up the trade school of the *Kommunar* Works. More than a hundred boys were studying, learning to handle machines. How long, Morosov wondered, would it take the Young Ploughman to build a fine school like this?

In the office he met two boys of the school committee, not much older than himself.

"We aren't over-supplied with textbooks," explained the taller. "We share one among five boys. We talked about your colony and decided to put seven pupils on a textbook, and release a few for you. We can give you eight books, chiefly arithmetic and reading primers, only paper-bound, but this year's books, modern and up-to-date."

"That's the most important." Morosov thanked them joyously. "We have an old arithmetic but its problems don't fit our life."

Clutching the books, he opened one of them. He could hardly tear his shining eyes from the page. Nikolai Ivanovich looked at him with warm interest. "You've had a long walk; won't you come to the factory dining-room for tea?"

Morosov smiled happily. He liked this man and wanted to know him. Tea at the factory would be a great event. Then he sighed. "I promised to get back right away with the books. It's getting late."

"Let us know how you get on with them," said Nikolai Ivanovich. "It's important for us all to have that colony succeed." All the cold way back to Cherumshan those words warmed Morosov as much as the books.

For a few days everyone in the colony was excited by the new books and perused them so assiduously that the paper covers wore off. Then interest lapsed except among the more studious. They lacked warm classrooms and classroom equipment. The teacher was not able. Yeremeyev paid lip service to education but distrusted boys who had a strange vice for paper and pencils; he admired those who were handy with tools or animals. The boys themselves found their outside work more interesting and the colony had no firm discipline to compel them to learn.

The girls, whose jobs were dull, were fonder of study, seeing in it their only chance to escape the drudgery of their lives. They studied in bed, pulling the covers up to their eyes to keep warm. Some of the boys also studied; on this point Marin disagreed with Stepan. He found in the book an arithmetic problem about Siberia, and was thenceforth converted to mathematics. As for Morosov, he went through the arithmetic from cover to cover, learning how to count the cows in a village, to tell what food the peasants could export, how many deputies a big village could elect to the County Soviet, and even how to calculate the peasants' food tax, according to the land and the number of "eaters." Mathematics had been changed by the Revolution; such arithmetic was clearly a guide to life.

The greatest excitement of the winter came soon after the arrival of the books. Some forty Moscow students, returning from a study of the

Donetz coal basin, were held up for a day by a freight-train wreck. At once they announced that they would hold a "one-day university," with discussions for railway workers, peasants, and children, close to the tracks in the open air. It was just across river from Cherumshan.

A terrific fight took place in the Young Ploughman over who should attend this one-day school. There were only nine sheepskins and nine pairs of felt boots in the colony, worn in turn by those who went outdoors to work. The Stepan gang succeeded in grabbing these and went to the "university" in high spirits. Morosov had to stay at home. Since the girls had their own footwear, Stesha went with two other girls.

The students proclaimed "man's conquest of Nature." The old ways of farming were nonsense. they said. Planting by saints' days is nonsense; processions for rain or to bless the fields are nonsense. Deep ploughing. seed selection. and at times irrigation are the ways of science. Man must conquer Nature and be master of his fate!

The peasants, listening respectfully. crossed themselves when the students spoke of saints' days. They took little stock in this city knowledge. Everyone knew that fields won't yield without blessing and that tractors poison the earth. The members of the Young Ploughman believed the students and were thrilled to meet young folks from Moscow only a little older than themselves.

Stesha was ecstatic. She hung around the students' special car with so much admiration that they invited her in. It was a third-class carriage without upholstery but it seemed to Stesha happy and sociable; she had never been in a railway car before. She stayed with the students while they sang new popular songs. She went back to Cherumshan dizzy with joy. bearing a copy of the students' new book.

A new song appeared at the Young Ploughman. Stesha had learned it from the students. The girls sang it in the kitchen, then the boys learned it; it became the favourite song.

> We are the blacksmiths of our own future.
> Blow by blow
> We shape from hard metal
> The keys to happiness.
> We beat with our hammers
> Shaping our new country.
> Forging our own freedom.

Even more than the song the new book excited Stesha. *Man's Conquest of Nature* was a thick volume of five hundred pages, which only Morosov and Stesha were able to read. Morosov willingly relinquished it when he saw how the reading of it transfigured the girl. Formerly she had been sad in manner, respected but not very attractive; now she went about as if some tremendous new happiness had come into her life. Her joyous

34

air of having discovered a great secret drew everyone's attention. Stepan felt a strange hunger to seize her and take the secret by violence into his hands.

He grabbed the book once and ran away with it. He could read only a few words but he saw that there were pictures of a windmill, a steamboat, a printing press and similar interesting objects. What had such things to do with Stesha? They were for boys. Good enough in their way but not worth all her excitement. He rejoiced to see how she followed him; he savoured her imploring look.

"Take it." he granted loftily. She took it as if it were life he gave.

That evening, when they gathered around the stove after dinner, and Stesha was reading by the single candle light. Morosov asked her gently: "What is it that is so exciting?"

She looked up with shining eyes. "There are laws of Nature instead of a punishing God," she said with rapture.

"Yes?" he invited, made happy by her happiness.

"It is lots nicer to believe in Nature." she went on. "For the ways of God were a mystery and you never knew what He might do to you. But everyone can study the ways of Nature. The more you know of them the better life you can make for the whole world!"

Morosov smiled at her. "Don't keep it to yourself. Read it to us all."

For the rest of the evening and for many evenings thereafter Stesha read aloud while the others pressed close to hear how primitive man used tools and harnessed the winds and waters; how men discovered steam and electricity and wireless; how an American named Edison rose from newsboy to be a great scientist, mastering the unknown; how human speech made man able to communicate thought to his fellows and so raised him above the animals from which he sprang; how the inventions of writing and—after long ages—of printing knit man across time and space and so conquered time and space forever, making all man's past the stuff from which all men may build their future. Into that candle-lit room on those winter nights on the Dnieper there came to those shivering orphans of famine the sense that they were joint heirs, not only of a great land and a great Revolution, but of the far greater march of mankind that began long before history—before any human memory—but that may go forward even beyond the earth and beyond the stars.

Stepan thrilled with the others as Stesha read the story. It made him want to squeeze Stesha and take her excitement for his own. Yet he felt a bit contemptuous that she should be so excited just because there was Nature instead of God. To Stepan God had never mattered. Years ago his mother used to beat him over the head to make him bow to the icon. She would say: "Pray to God for your good meal." Stepan had prayed and paid no attention except to think that the meal wasn't so good. After he came back from the Red Army he felt superior to his mother and refused to pray any more. But he never got excited about it like Stesha. He felt that kind of choking excitement about the Cossacks' Lair.

Next day the trading committee went to a distant market. Stepan filled the big sleigh with straw; Stesha and Morosov climbed in and Stepan drove. There was no metal on the home-made runners; they slid as easily sideways as straight ahead. The occupants tossed merrily against each other. Stepan teasingly drove the sleigh so that it threw Stesha against him. Then he shoved her away. shouting: "Girls should stay in their place."

Stesha's cheeks were rosy with the wind; her eyes shone at Stepan's banter. How handsome his blue eyes looked under the dark and light layers of weather-bleached hair! She was pleased that he liked her enough to tease her. His sudden blows made her shiver deliciously inside. He frightened her a little; she was glad that Morosov was there. She leaned contentedly against Morosov, feeling his solid body a protection against the dizzy delight of Stepan's blows. Morosov, glad of her glowing laughter so near him, wished painfully that he could be gay with her as Stepan was. Stepan was exultant. Stesha was the finest girl in the colony, so educated, and a year older than he, yet she trembled and gasped at his touch.

Suddenly he turned serious and asked her: "Whey are you so excited about God and Nature?"

"Nothing in all my life was so dreadful as praying to God," confessed Stesha, humble and happy that Stepan should ask for her deepest thoughts. "We used to hide under the beds in the orphan asylum to get away from it. But they would catch you and yank you out.

"I was six years old when they put me in the asylum," she went on. encouraged by his listening silence. "I cried when they put on me the long blue dress down to the ankles and the long white apron to show that I was an orphan kept by charity.

"Most of all we hated the prayers on Sunday. Weekdays weren't so bad, just an hour of prayers morning and evening and thanking God at every meal. But on Sundays we went to church without food at four in the morning. We stood for hours on the cold stone floor looking straight at the shining candles and swinging censer. We got dizzy but we dared not look to right or left. At midmorning we stopped for a rest, but not long enough to go home to eat. Then the praying began again and lasted till noon. After this there were house prayers at the asylum and only after these could we go to the dining-room and sing a hymn asking God to give us food. There was evening church too; it began at four o'clock and lasted till seven or—on saints' days—till long into the night. We were so dizzy and so hungry and it was so hard to stand still. That praying on Sundays was the most terrible thing in my life."

"I would have run away," bragged Stepan.

Stesha looked at him with admiration. "There was no place to run to," she sighed. "We knew no other life and we were never allowed in the street except in processions."

"I bet you were glad when the Revolution freed you."

"No, we were terrified. We cried very much. We prayed for the Tsar to come back for we thought it was the end of the world. There was shooting in the streets and we stayed in the cellar, praying and weeping. At night we came upstairs and saw the red glow of burning buildings and knew it was the Judgment and we prayed God not to send us to hell.

"Then everything was quiet and after a week we had a new director, not the old priest but a merry young fellow who gave us all short dresses like regular children. All at once there was freedom; we didn't have to pray or go to church. But even in my new happiness I was frightened for fear God would punish me for this freedom. I was always frightened until I read this book. Here it tells how human beings combine to make the forces of Nature serve them. So how can there be a God to punish us for freedom when nothing is too great for us human beings to do?"

Her ecstasy embarrassed Stepan. Just when he had her under his hands and quivering with his blows she had slipped into an alien world. How queer and uncomfortable girls were! Even Stesha, whose admiring gaze had been so pleasantly exciting and whom he had thought he could do with as he chose!

He whipped up the horses to cover his turmoil of annoyance. The sleigh leapt forward and threw Stesha backward in the straw. She recovered herself and fell silent. Shame came to her because she had talked so freely. Was she crazy? She had never told anyone so much in her life. She had wanted Stepan to like her and now he was angry. She felt bereft and alone.

She turned for relief to the market place that they were entering. "What cute little pigs," she cried. "just like ours, only bigger. I wonder if we are feeding ours properly. I'm going to ask."

Jumping from the cart, she moved rapidly away from Stepan. She strode erect but she trembled; her face burned. She did not even see that Morosov jumped down and followed her a little distance and then, after watching her with eyes full of longing, slowly turned back to help Stepan unload the cart.

Stepan had deftly manœuvred the cart into a good place in the market. He had scooped up a handful of sunflower seeds as he passed a peasant wagon, and was cracking them now in his teeth and spitting the shells out in a steady stream. He had forgotten both his triumph over Stesha and his annoyance with her; he was thinking how pleasant it was to possess a horse.

Ilya Morosov was thoroughly angry with the whole world for the first time in his life. He was angry with Stesha for baring her soul to Stepan, angrier with Stepan for his lack of response, angriest of all with himself because he could talk easily with everyone but Stesha, because he had left it to another to draw out of her all that beauty that he loved.

Then anger passed and he was aware only of Stesha, as she tripped between the carts to follow the little pigs. He seemed to feel each movement of her body—even without looking, even without hearing, even across the market—as if it were his own.

VI

TURBULENT, TOSSING TOGETHER the sun and the rainclouds, the winds of March arrived. Swiftly under their touch the snow dissolved on the hills of Cherumshan and ran down ravines to crack the icebound shore. Then the boys of the Young Ploughman made ready for the ploughing.

They had made their plans throughout the winter, visiting their lands between blizzards. Their hundred acres lay in four scattered fields, the nearest of which was a mile upriver, not far from Cossacks' Lair, while the largest was some ten miles to the west. If, in other countries, farmers had their lands all in one solid area, none of the young colonists was aware of that. They felt very modern and efficient to have only four pieces, and such large ones; most peasants, even with only twenty acres, had a dozen different strips in different directions and spent more time walking to their bits than in working on the soil.

The Young Ploughman had decided to reserve the distant field for wheat, which could be sown by a single group of boys camping out; to plant millet and sunflower in the nearer fields, since these require much hand labour; and to set vegetables in the tiny patches of rich soil in the Cherumshan ravines. Horses were the chief problem. Their two horses might hope to plough the nearer lands but certainly not the wheat field, the hope of their future, without which they could not feed their present members, much less expand.

Carefully they had canvassed all possible ways to get horses. Horseless peasants usually tried to rent from kulaks, but this would never do for a farm commune; besides, it was no way to get ahead. A Mutual Aid Committee had been recently formed in Kichkas, but it was even worse off than the Young Ploughman, having only the four horses of the village officials and at least forty horseless families to help. A nearby State Farm was fairly well provided; Yeremeyev drove over to propose an exchange of services, offering boys' labour at harvest in return for some horse power at sowing. The State Farm manager, an easy-going intellectual, who had studied agriculture but never handled a plough, waved their request aside as preposterous.

"My workmen are so unreliable that I won't be able to get my own land farmed."

As last and only hope there remained the Red Army, which often "adopted" needy farm communes, helping them with horses. Stepan, Morosov, and Yeremeyev were sent as a committee to seek such help. They found a regiment which had adopted another farm near Kichkas and which agreed to lend four hourses after they had finished the already promised work.

As Yeremeyev was expressing gratitude, Morosov interrupted with a suggestion which was to prove epoch-making for the colony's future. He had studied the wheat field and knew that it lay on a high, exposed slope.

"Our field dries earliest in the region. It will be too late if you come to us after the others. If we can have the horses first, we can finish by Easter, when the others will want to begin."

Looking at him in surprised interest, the Red Army man asked: "Are you willing to plough before the field blessing?"

"As soon as the plough can be pulled through the ground," declared Morosov earnestly. Yeremeyev and Stepan agreed.

"You can have the horses all the time before the field blessing," promised the soldier, smiling. "We are glad to help you fight superstition."

For centuries the peasants had fixed by Church festivals the proper dates for all their farming tasks. As the Russian Church calendar slowly became more inaccurate, the sanctified date for sowing grew steadily later and was now thirteen days late for a normal spring. But no peasant dared break soil until after the field blessing, lest he go against religion and incur bad luck. This inflexibly late ploughing was one cause of the low yield on the fertile Ukrainian soil. Ever since listening to the Moscow students, the Young Ploughman had determined to plough "by science," disregarding the saints' days.

When Stesha learned that they had secured the use of four horses by going against religion, she could not contain her joy. "As soon as we unite to conquer Nature," she exulted, "see how everyone comes to our help."

"Not everyone," Morosov gently corrected her. "Not the State Farm and not the village officials. So far, only the Red Army helps."

"Isn't that enough?" cried Stesha. "Soon there will be more."

Her prediction was fulfilled almost at once. At the Farm Implement Works in Zaporozhe, Nikolai Ivanovich heard of the colony's plan and called the shop committee together.

"Boys, the Young Ploughman is fighting superstition. They're ploughing early. Let's help them with a good plough."

The committee endorsed the idea, the administration agreed, and a week before the ploughing the Young Ploughman rejoiced to add to its home-made wooden implements a factory-made plough of chilled steel, one of the first to appear in the district.

Twice in one week Morosov made on foot the twenty-miles round trip to the wheat field, to test the stickiness of the soil. Then the field group set out, with Morosov and Ivan in charge. Stepan, with the colony's horses, was assigned to the millet field, but also handled transport to the wheat.

Since the boys in the wheat field would remain for the whole time of sowing, they set up their camp at once. They built a wigwam of poles, thatching it thickly with grass and straw; it would keep out wind and any but the heaviest rains. They hung a pail from a horizontal pole for cooking. Once a week, Stepan drove over from Cherumshan with a load of potatoes, cabbage, and great loaves of dark, satisfying bread. They allowed themselves more food than in the winter, more food than they had had for years. For sowing is a season of heavy work, and men and beasts must be fed. So they had plenty of potato and cabbage soup every noon, strengthened with sunflower-seed oil. Morning and evening they made "sweet tea" of roasted wheat grains, steeping them in boiling water with a little sugar. On the day when the horses came from Cherumshan they had milk in their tea as a treat.

The first week Yeremeyev worked with them. The weather was good and the bread tasty—baked by Stesha—and work went easily. Then Yeremeyev left for the millet field. Rain came and the ploughs pulled hard in the sticky soil. The rain beat on their thin coats and bare legs and softened their straw sandals so that their feet were cut by stubble. They fell ill with chills and fevers. Worst of all, the second batch of bread was heavy and sour—baked by the younger girls—and gave them stomach-aches. Grumbling rose from boys who limped across the field or lay shivering and aching in the wet wigwam.

"We are leading the whole district to better farming," cried Morosov. "We are ploughing by science and not by religion." So they ploughed in a great crusade. Those who had sheepskin jackets worked longest and then loaned their coats to the others, while they crawled for a little warmth under the damp straw. They ploughed not only for their own harvest and their own record; they ploughed for the future of their country. Before the surrounding peasants were ready to begin ploughing, the boys had finished the wheat field and taken the Red Army horses to help in the millet field. The peasants looked askance at their daring but the county land committee gave them forty acres more to seed that same spring.

At last the peasants assembled in church for the ceremonial procession. First came—aloft on poles—the banners and placards, showing saints and pictures of the sun. Next walked the priest in ceremonial robes, swinging from long chains a smoking censer. Behind him a church official bore the holy water, sprinkling the earth with a long brush as he passed. Then came the choir boys, chanting, and then the peasants, the elder and more important of whom, such as the kulak Faber, carried holy pictures from the church.

Far out the muddy road went the procession, until it reached a high point overlooking the village fields. The priest waved the fragrant smoke over the land and the holy water was sprinkled on the soil. Then all the peasants went home and celebrated with their neighbours, chiefly by getting drunk. When they went out to plough a day or so later, the wheat field of the Young Ploughman already showed green shoots.

One hundred and forty black acres were ploughed and seeded by the young colonists that springtime. It was the largest sown area under one management in the county. The State Farm, with more than twice as many horses, had accomplished only half as much. The Young Ploughman had seventy-five acres of wheat, forty of sunflowers, twenty of millet; they had gardens of potatoes, cabbages, cucumbers, tomatoes, and squash. Life ahead looked bright. Everyone began to plan for the things he wanted. They would not only have bread and vegetables but would trade for meat, sugar, clothes, and even for additional livestock.

Even Stepan almost saw in the Young Ploughman his own future. The rhythm of that great sowing caught him; he worked fairly well that spring. Ploughing was not so bad with the chilled steel plough from the *Kommunar* Works. He had managed to get the use of it; Morosov did not even put up a fight. Besides, the millet field was near the Lair; it was easy to slip away for evening campfires, or to hunt porcupines by the river. If the work at times suffered from Stepan's absences, he made up for them by bursts of enthusiasm during which he could turn out more work than Ivan, almost as much as Morosov, who was older by nearly two years.

His tall vital body—he had filled out with regular food and work—looked clean and handsome, in the second-hand but untorn shirt Yeremeyev had secured for him from one of the village officials. He won many admiring gazes from Stesha; she even praised his industry. He knew that he could get her for his girl if he wanted, but Stepan felt aloof from girls. They were good enough for cooking and cleaning but not to share in a man's real life.

He liked that song so many young folks were singing, the one about the Cossack chieftain on the Volga, who threw the Persian Princess in the river because she seduced him from his loyal soldier band. Stepan sang it in the Lair, changing "Mother Volga" to "Father Dnieper":

> "Dnieper, Dnieper, Father Dnieper,
> Never have you seen such a gift
> From a Don Cossack. . . ."

He imagined himself thus sacrificing Stesha, some day when she tried to allure him from his gang. She would be sinking in the river, imploring him to save her, and he would heroically and firmly refuse.

The fame of the Young Ploughman spread up and down the river. From all directions came boys and girls who wished to join. They came hungry, without underwear or shoes. The young colonists discussed each application in general meeting. Stepan did not want to take the newcomers; Ivan agreed with him, saying that there was not enough food. Morosov argued that other homeless children should have the same chance that they had had. Yeremeyev, pleased to see his large, successful farm grow larger, wanted to take all who were strong enough to work.

In the end, nearly all the newcomers were accepted. It was Stepan's first defeat in colony politics. He could not quite see how it had happened. Even some of his own gang had voted against him. Next time he would make an issue of it and see that they voted right.

As harvest approached the Young Ploughman grew to nearly eighty members. Yeremeyev exulted! "It will be easy to get in the crops with so many hands." But Cherumshan was painfully overcrowded. There were not enough beds, dishes, or equipment. Soap gave out and clothes went dirty. Food gave out; hunger sores developed on arms and legs. The boys and girls fell ill with many minor diseases. Quarrelling arose and spread between the old colonists and the inexperienced newcomers. Quarrelling between the girls and boys revived; it was worse than in the winter. Even Stesha was low in spirits from hunger.

Stepan quite simply ran away to the Lair. He took many members of the gang with him; they returned when they felt like it, for supper, late at night, or even the following day. They shirked their duties and demoralized the work. Because of their past thefts, they had better food at the Lair than in Cherumshan.

A week before harvest the country authorities sent fifty children to Cherumshan, with a brief document stating that the Selidba Children's Home was being reorganized, and its older boys and girls were being sent to the Young Ploughman because of its fine harvest prospects. To accommodate them, the colony was given a large two-story house not far away on the riverbank. Some additional tools were sent with which the carpenters might repair it.

A storm broke loose at Cherumshan when the new group arrived. The Stepan gang led the revolt against the county authorities. They ganged up on the newcomers, drove them into the road and refused to let them come into the houses.

"Stop this nonsense!" shouted Yeremeyev, wading into the fray. "We must take them since the county sends them."

"You want more hands for your big farm," Stepan yelled back with

with hot suspicion. "You're just a big landlord, wanting more and more. We raised this harvest. Why should we give it to fellows who did no work?"

Morosov tried to mediate. "We must ask the county for extra food until our grain is ground. They must feed the eaters they have sent us. But afterwards, we can't refuse to share our harvest. It is not ours alone; the Red Army and the *Kommunar* Works helped us get it."

"Let's quit this place," cried Stepan, turning to Ivan. "There'll be nothing but hunger here. Look how they take in all the hungry."

"Where do you want to go?" asked Ivan, trying to calm him. "I don't like taking these newcomers either, but where is it better than here? Here at least the Red Army and the factory workers help us."

Stepan stormed off to the Lair, taking most of the gang with him. They stayed away from Cherumshan for several days; in the following weeks they took little part in the harvest.

"Why get a harvest for others?" complained Stepan. "Instead of buying shoes and clothes for ourselves we shall have to feed these others all next year." What angered him most was not the physical lack but the thwarting of his vague dream of dominance. He had seen himself as one of the masters, but the county had compelled him to share.

He sulked the more because in the confusion caused by the new arrivals no one came to look for him and because, despite his sulking, the harvest succeeded. At Yeremeyev's demand, the county sent a month's food rations for the fifty extra mouths. The swarm of new members, despite their inexperience, settled like locusts on the fields and got in all the crops. There was a bumper yield of wheat, millet, and sunflower; they had a hundred tons of potatoes, cabbages, cucumbers, and squash.

At the Harvest Festival they triumphed. They slaughtered a pig and invited visitors for a feast. The same county authorities who had sent the fifty extra children now helped them acquire four new horses from the liquidation of the State Farm, whose harvest had been poor. At this, the grudge against the newcomers was dropped by all but Stepan. A city speaker told them: "The Young Ploughman is a light to the countryside."

The young hearts warmed to the plaudits. Their stomachs were full again; they were ready to welcome fame.

VII

To Stepan the Young Ploughman seemed no longer a gate to the future but a place to be plundered and abandoned when the chance should arrive. He strengthened his gang, not as a means to master the colony—this was no longer possible with the increased numbers—but as a means to a double life, in Cherumshan and in the Lair. He used the

Lair to escape the restraints of the colony, and the colony to escape the discomforts of the Lair. His thefts of food, once casual, became vengeful, systematic.

This double life was possible because the Young Ploughman was disorganized by expansion. The newcomers overtaxed all facilities. If the Stepan gang left for a day, the absence might not even be noticed, neither from the sleeping-rooms, which were packed from wall to wall with mattress bags, nor from the meals, which were eaten in three shifts. Their absence from work of course increased the disorder but there was no firm check-up; the chaos of overcrowding was alibi for anything. Yeremeyev, incompetent to handle the suddenly increased problems, took, as autumn advanced, more frequently to drink.

The colony's hope lay in the big house by the river, which the county had given to take care of their growth. When it was repaired, there would be room for all. Ivan, chief carpenter now under Fedotov, was proudly aware that nobody else since the Revolution had been strong enough to reclaim that imposing villa. This important work made the Lair seem to him rather childish. He did not break with the gang but he went to the Lair less often. Marin slipped naturally into his place as second-in-command.

Even in the chaos there were times of warm sociability. Music and drama had come to the Young Ploughman at last. In early summer, before the overcrowding, they had entertained several pupils from the *Kommunar* trade school who needed fresh air and rest. The school gave them an accordion at harvest. They sang old songs and new ones in the autumn evening and danced Ukrainian dances under the locust tree. Marin became chief musician; this increased his popularity. But he often deserted, taking the accordion to campfires in the Lair. These absences were more noticed than those from work.

The drama club was formed after harvest. Its chief organizer was one of the newcomers from the Selidba Children's Home, a girl named Shubina, whose enthusiasm for the colony soon made her Stesha's closest friend. Shubina had the job of cow girl; she rose at four, milked three cows, fed the calves and pigs, strained the milk and put it in the kitchen, and was then free until evening. This gave her plenty of time for the drama club. Everyone loved drama; even the previous winter Stesha and Marin had acted pieces from a textbook, using the gay American silks. With the larger numbers and with Shubina's energy, they were now prepared to try a full-sized play.

Springtime without Sun, from a special textbook for drama clubs, was a play about student life before the Revolution. Shubina was the priest's daughter[1] who secretly helped the revolutionists; Stesha tried for the part but finally decided to make costumes for the show instead. Most of

[1] Village priests of the Greek Orthodox Church may marry.

the boys drifted into and out of rehearsal and then lost interest. Half a dozen remained. Ivan was a faithful but uninspired performer; Shubina liked him because he always came in time. Stepan liked the violent parts; he was a dynamic but erratic actor as the student who killed the Tsarist gendarme. The part of hero fell to Marin, who portrayed with vivacity and daring the student who led a workers' strike and was killed on the barricades.

The play was a great success. When the young actors had given it several times before their fellow colonists—no room in Cherumshan could accommodate all at once—Shubina proposed that they give it in Kichkas to raise money for paper and pencils to equip their school. This was a sore point with the more studious colonists. Because of Yeremeyev's lack of interest in education, the colony never seemed able to afford to equip a school.

"Can we use for the school all the money raised by the drama club?" Shubina demanded in the colony meeting. Everyone agreed; Shubina and Stesha were appointed to administer the expected funds.

A big turnout jammed the Kichkas village school when the play was given. The actors were loudly applauded. Stepan, with his flashing eyes, expressive face, and fiery manner, won more applause than any of the others.

A wide-eyed, golden-haired girl of fourteen years, sitting in the front row, stared at him all through the performance as if he were a wonderful creature from another world. She clapped every word he said. She even applauded when he was led out to execution, when everyone else was silent with the suspense of his final words.

"She's glad they're killing you," teased Marin, a little envious because Stepan got more applause then he, the hero.

"Huh," bragged Stepan, "I bet I can take her out walking."

"Bet you can't," dared Marin. Stepan decided that he would.

None of the boys of the Young Ploughman had thus far been able to go walking with the nicer peasant girls. To "go strolling" with a boy without any immediate errand was the recognized first step towards becoming engaged. Careful peasant fathers protected their daughters' virtue even in the early teens. The standing of the colony boys had improved when they reclaimed the old mill and still more when they had such an excellent harvest. But the thefts of the Stepan gang, which continued even after harvest, had again aroused community distrust.

Everybody in the village, therefore, noticed it next morning when the tall young actor, so dramatically slain the night before, walked the whole length of the village with Anya Kosareva, one of the most respected of the village girls. The actors had spent the night in Kichkas. In the morning Stepan found the Kosarev house, an old but substantial cottage at the extreme northern end of the village on the high bank of the river, where Anya lived with her grandfather. He invited her for a walk. She knew as well as he did the significance of the action. She was fascinated by Stepan and happy to be walking out with so handsome and talented a youth.

They walked, from her grandfather's cottage, by the road that led along the river bank to the market place, with its big, onion-domed church. Then they turned by the crossroad and walked west almost to Faber's house at the end of the village, where the branch road turned to Cherumshan. All along both roads the people stopped to look at the proud, handsome youth with the red-kerchiefed girl.

It was the season of autumn mud. Anya had no rubbers. Her thin shoes caught in the deep mud and came off her stockingless feet. She could not keep up with Stepan's lond strides.

"Don't go so fast," she begged him.

"Huh!" cried Stepan, pleased with everything and especially with himself. "Girls never can keep up with boys!"

She had expected tenderness; her lips quivered. "They can too," she protested. "Only not in this mud."

Stepan laughed. "Come along," he commanded. "I'll help you."

Grabbing her hand, he pulled her rapidly along until she was breathless and stained to the knees with mud. Anger grew in her and she would have turned back, but pride demanded that she see this "strolling" through until he took her home. He had been wonderful last night when he gallantly protected the priest's daughter, choosing death rather than betray his comrade! Why wouldn't he be wonderful now?

When they turned toward home he was very genial; his self-assertion had been satisfied. They walked along contentedly and even slowly. As he suited his step to hers, a delicious languor flooded her and she seemed to be carried along by his motion, without effort of her own. He took her hand again to help her over a puddle; this time his touch cherishingly appropriated her, so that she felt caressed all over and knew that she was now his girl.

She began to tell him how she had admired him in the play.

"So you liked my acting? I'll show you more than that some time." He tossed his bright hair and turned on her the full fascination of his blue eyes. She glowed with happiness and he saw that she was really very pretty, with her large hazel eyes and rosy cheeks. She was much prettier than Stesha. Stesha had shown him little attention lately; she had merely reproved him for neglecting his work. He hoped Stesha would be jealous when she saw that he could go out with a prettier girl.

They reached the market place on the return walk. It was midmorning and there were many people about. The Young Ploughman's horses stood there ready for the journey back. Marin was holding the reins. Suddenly remembering Marin's challenge, Stepan walked over to the cart and presented Anya to his friends. Jumping to the driver's seat, he pushed Marin aside, saying, "I'll take the horses." In casual farewell he added to Anya: "They're ready; we have to go home."

She stood in the square, barefoot, with her shoes in her hands, trembling a little. They had been walking so nicely together. Now that she was his girl, she had been sure that he would go with her all the way home. She had even planned the tea she would offer—some of the small hoard of real tea that Grandpa kept in a special jar. Real tea was very expensive; it came all the way from China. But Grandpa would surely let her use it for her first very own guest. She could not believe that Stepan was leaving her in the market until he had whipped up the horses and driven away. She saw the curious crowd staring at her and smiling. Slowly she went back to her house, biting her lips hard to keep back the tears.

"Well, I did it, didn't I?" bragged Stepan to Marin, loudly so that Stesha could hear. He watched Stesha, hoping that she would show some jealousy.

"You rude boy," cried Stesha indignantly, "to leave her standing in the market."

"What business is it of yours?" demanded Stepan, forgetting that he had tried to make it her business.

"It is any girl's business when a boy is mean to another girl."

Stepan did not answer, but he whipped the horses more energetically than usual all the way home. He was sorry now that he had not stayed with Anya and kept Stesha waiting. A sudden warmth that he had never known before swept him at the memory of Anya's adoring applause and the soft submission of her hand to his touch. Then he reminded himself impatiently that he was through with girls.

The drama club had three rubles for school supplies from the collection they took up at the play. They decided to give another performance, this time in Selidba. They were eager to appear as actors in the village which had known several of them—including Shubina—as orphans in the Children's Home.

They started out on a bright sunny day late in December. They had gone only four of the ten miles to Selidba when a blizzard came up from the river. The horses staggered in the drifts; the young folks were covered by the whirling sleet. Shubina suffered most; she had only a padded cotton coat borrowed from another girl and it was too small for her since she was large in build. She had only broken sandals without stockings on her feet. She buried herself in the straw of the cart as well as she could. When at last they reached Selidba, even the boys in the sheepskin coats had frostbitten ears or fingers. Shubina's arms and legs and face were black with frost; the last part of the way Ivan and Marin had to pound her to keep her from falling into the frozen sleep of death.

At the schoolhouse they hauled her out and pounded her some more until the blood came painfully back into her arms and legs. Then she went on the stage and played the part of the priest's daughter who helped the Revolution. This was what she had come for and it never occurred to her that she should do anything else. Ivan admired her endurance, but even he had no feeling of pity; the other boys stopped thinking about her as soon as they saw that she could walk. The peasant audience applauded loudly; it was the first play they had seen. The collection was only a ruble and forty kopeks, for Selidba was more backward than Kichkas, where boatmen lived who knew about city things like plays.

Shubina slept on top of a peasant oven. On the way home the sun shine brightly, but Shubina shivered much. She kept on shivering while she did her work as cow-girl. Only her head was very hot. Next morning she was up again at four o'clock but went to bed as soon as her work was done.

At midmorning Ivan announced in triumph that the big house was at last repaired. All that was left was to clean up the pieces of wood and straw and plaster—the dirt of nine years and the new dirt that the carpenters had made. Cleaning, the carpenters claimed, was the work of the girls. The head of the cleaning committee, a girl named Olga, flatly refused, for the big house had stood in the winter wind for weeks.

"We won't clean it until you heat it," Olga declared.

Ivan shrugged his shoulders. "We carpenters worked in the cold and so can you. The fuel committee didn't get wood."

"You carpenters had sheepskins and felt boots," retorted Olga. "We girls have only leaky sandals and water comes from holes in the ice." Tossing her head, she retired to the warm kitchen.

Then Shubina got up from bed, where she had been lying in a stupor. "Come on, girls," she cried. She put on her sandals and started across the half mile of snow to the big house with a pail of icy water and a cloth that was frozen stiff. The cleaning committee followed, shivering.

"There's one girl that knows how to work," Ivan approved.

All day Shubina washed floors and windows while her arms and bare legs were soaked with icy water from the floors. Her head grew hotter and her eyes glazed until she could hardly see. In late afternoon she staggered and nearly fell downstairs. Then Olga felt ashamed for letting the cow-girl do her work.

"Go home, Shubina. We'll finish the job," she said.

Dragging herself home across the snow, Shubina remembered that it was time to milk. She took the pail, went to the cold barn, milked the cows, and fed the calves and pigs. She put the strained milk safely on the kitchen table and then fell unconscious to the floor.

Ivan saw her fall; he was coming into the kitchen with shavings for the fire. He ran to her and tried to lift her, but she was dead weight in his arms. He shouted for help and the woman teacher came and helped him carry Shubina to her bed. When the doctor arrived, she had a temperature of 104 degrees, and was raving in delirium that she was completely frozen inside.

After the crisis passed they moved her to the big house. It was heated now and had room for everyone. But Shubina got thinner and thinner. Her stomach would not hold the heavy soups and coarse black bread. It was discovered that she liked milk and could retain it. Many of the colonists gave her their milk ration in addition to her own. Quarrels in the Young Ploughman grew fewer, partly because the big house was more comfortable and partly because they all felt sorry and ashamed on account of Shubina.

Ivan was especially worried about her. He felt to blame because he had challenged the girls. He gave her his milk ration regularly; through the giving of milk his interest deepened. He wanted to know her better, but he was ashamed to go to the girls' quarters to see her for fear the boys would laugh. At last he made a tray on which to carry the warm milk to her, and with this as an excuse he visited her. She was so glad to see him that he forgot his embarrassment. After this he brought her her supper often. He wanted to know about her and how she had come to the colony. Little by little she told him the story of her life.

"Always since I can remember I worked as a nurse-girl, looking after children. Sometimes my masters were kind and gave me dresses; sometimes they gave me only food. Then I cut up my mother's dresses and made them over. They lasted a long time for they were strong linen, but they are all gone now. . . .

"When I was eight years old, I was lifting a heavy baby. The baby slapped me and I let it fall. My mistress grabbed me by the ear and shook me; for a long time I could not hear well. . . . When I was eleven, they sent me on rainy nights on long errands past the churchyard and I was much afraid of ghosts. . . . I hauled water from a deep well. The heavy bucket pulled me off my feet and I was always afraid I would fall in. When I think how I lived in those days I begin to cry. . . .

"When the Revolution came I was working for Penchelin, a very big kulak, the worst I ever worked for. I was always hungry there. I could not read and write, but that was the way with all servant girls. But from the time of the Revolution I wanted to learn. Penchelin would not let me go to school, but a girl in the *Komsomol* taught me secretly. My master's little boy found the textbook under my mattress, so they fired me. After that I worked in many places, but my work always kept me from learning to read. So I went to the Children's Home and asked to learn and I was too old for them and they sent me here."

"Do you like it here?" asked Ivan, remembering with shame how he had fought to keep out Shubina and the other newcomers.

"Better than anywhere," she sighed. "They let me join the *Komsomol* and they let me play in the drama club. If only we can make order and have a real school and a sewing shop, then at last I shall learn a trade and begin to be something. But if not . . . if the fuel-boys don't get the wood, and the school doesn't open, and we have to study in bed, if the lamps get broken and no one can make order, then I don't want to live another winter. I think I shall die."

Moved out of his taciturnity, Ivan let his hand fall awkwardly on Shubina's. Then he drew it away in embarrassment while a dark red flush coloured his face and neck.

"Don't die, Shubina. We will make order. I promise you that we will make it here."

From that time Shubina began to mend, though her convalescence was long. From that time Ivan knew that his future was pledged to the Young Ploughman and not to the Cossacks' Lair.

VIII

An unusual February sun beat through the windows of the shop-committee room. Nikolai Ivanovich opened a window for air. The vagrant breeze stole in, lifting the ragged hair from his forehead. He pushed the hair back, making it still more ragged. "Snow is still with us but another spring is coming," he remarked cheerfully. Then he turned back to the committee discussion.

"Well now, this problem of bootlegging. Absences from work are becoming a scandal. What have you unearthed?"

The swarthy young delegate from the sheet-metal shop reported: "Zaporozhe is surrounded by an ocean of *samagon*. The kulaks distill it in tons from last year's surplus harvest. They flood it into the city through a joint behind the Peasants' House. They seem to have contracts with its manager. If he doesn't handle the stuff himself, he knows who does."

"That shouldn't be such a hard problem," said Nikolai Ivanovich. "The Peasants' House is a municipally owned hostel. If our Works can't bring enough pressure to learn who supplies its manager, we're not much good."

"It'll be a fight," anticipated the young worker.

"What else are we for?" Nikolai Ivanovich nodded pleasantly.

The drive against bootleg rapidly widened. Other Zaporozhe factories took it up. A committee of workers representing several plants invaded the municipal hostel and compelled the manager to name his suppliers.

The clean-up committee swept into the rural districts, gathered evidence and brought pressure on backward village police. The district newspaper supported them. "Progressive workers know what drunkenness means to their standard of living and to the development of our country," boomed a front-page editorial.

Yeremeyev was sitting in Faber's house one Saturday evening, consuming a glass of powerful *samagon*. The door banged open and three city workers entered. They strode to the table and in the moment of shock that followed they poured the contents of several glasses, including Yeremeyev's, into a big bottle that they carried.

"What are you doing?" demanded Faber belligerently.

"Collecting evidence," laconically answered a worker. Then quickly turning he called out: "Hey, you! Where are you going?"

Yeremeyev had hastily risen and was trying to make the door. Finding himself caught, he put on a bold face and introduced himself, claiming that he had come to transact business with Faber and had accepted a glass to warm his bones.

"What business has the head of a farm commune with a kulak bootlegger?" demanded the worker suspiciously.

"We're buying livestock; who else but a kulak has livestock to sell?" replied Yeremeyev. "I'm here in the colony's cart, driven by one of the young colonists. You can ask him if you like."

The cart outside was empty; Stepan had vanished. The worker investigator saw that the straw was disarranged in one corner, put in his hand, and brought out a handful of eggs. Yeremeyev could not conceal his astonishment.

"There's something odd here," judged the investigator.

Just then Stepan came out of Faber's barn with more eggs. He saw the men and stopped in consternation, letting an egg fall.

"You dirty thief!" shouted Faber, who had come to the door.

Glaring in the face of his ancient enemy, Stepan yelled: "You took more than that from us when Mother died."

With a short laugh the investigator stepped between them. "This smells bad, Citizen Manager," he declared to Yeremeyev. "You'll hear from us later."

The horses started back to Cherumshan. Deprived of his drink, and upset because he had been called by the cold term "Citizen," instead of the warmly respectful "Comrade Manager," Yeremeyev began to abuse Stepan for stealing.

"You're a fine one to talk," cried Stepan. "As if I didn't know what you've been buying with the colony's food."

"Damn you for a hooligan and a spy," the man raged uncontrollably, giving the boy a blow. Stepan furiously hit back and Yeremeyev struck him again with redoubled anger. The horses, alarmed, leaped forward and Stepan fell in the snow. When he saw that the cart continued rapidly toward Cherumshan he followed slowly, but with dignity, on foot.

Yeremeyev drove on in seething anger for a quarter of an hour, then, his rage cooling, he realized that if an investigation was coming, it was suicidal to make an enemy of Stepan. Being comfortably lacking in pride, he turned back and met Stepan, trudging along in the starlight. The boy knew quite well what prompted Yeremeyev's return; he had expected him sooner and was contemptuous of an adult who could let anger sway his judgment so long. Deeply satisfied by the knowledge that Yeremeyev would now have to make the approach, he mounted silently and sat waiting, aloof.

At last the farm manager broke the silence. "I've got a hell of a temper, Stepan."

"Uh-huh," agreed the boy.

"Well, we've all got our faults," continued Yeremeyev.

"Uh-huh," grunted Stepan again.

The boy's reticence forced the man to make his overture explicit. "You won't let it make any difference, will you, Stiopa?"

"Guess not," said Stepan. "Guess it won't be up to me."

Yeremeyev warmed towards the lad, thinking at first that Stepan meant that his own guilt forbade him to judge. Then, with a start, he realized that the meaning was different, that others than Stepan would be bothering Yeremeyev adequately. This confirmation of his own worry terrified Yeremeyev. It made destiny painfully clear.

"I'll stick by you if you'll stick by me," he rushed on.

"It's not my business; I'm not a tattletale."

Relieved but chilled by Stepan's coolness, and feeling that in some vague way the boy had reversed the normal relation between farm manager and homeless youngster, Yeremeyev clinched the agreement. "You're a good fellow. I'll see you don't regret it."

"Uh-huh," agreed Stepan, knowing that Yeremeyev had promised to shield his thefts in return for silence about the misuse of the colony's supplies.

By the following noon the committee from the *Kommunar* Works arrived at the Young Ploughman. They asked for an immediate session of the Colony Soviet and reported Yeremeyev's presence at Faber's and his claim that he was exchanging food products for livestock. Morosov, who had been for two successive years an elected member of the Soviet, at once replied that at no time in the colony's history had they authorized Yeremeyev to trade anything with Faber. The food supply was then investigated and a noticeable shortage was found.

The revelations seemed so serious that it was decided to hold a "cleaning" of Yeremeyev in open meeting before the whole colony, a method of public fact-finding which Yeremeyev did not dare refuse. The young colonists were at once called together in the largest room of the big house. One of the *Kommunar* workers was made chairman, while Stesha took notes as secretary of the colony Soviet. The books of the colony were produced, the shortage in food products reported, and Yeremeyev was asked to tell all his dealings with Faber and defend them if he could.

"How often did you visit the bootlegger this winter?"

"Twice," stated Yeremeyev with an involuntary glance at Stepan. A whistle of surprise came from several boys.

The chairman turned to Stepan. "You've driven the cart. How often did he go?"

"It wasn't so often," replied Stepan.

"More than twice?"

"Well, yes, more than twice."

"Maybe twenty times?"

"Oh, nothing like that."

Snorting with dissatisfaction, the chairman attacked Yeremeyev. "You went often enough. What did you give for the *samagon*?" He cut short Yeremeyev's plea that Faber had merely been "hospitable." "We know kulak hospitality." The sarcasm was biting. "We know what you gave because it is gone from your stores." He then asked Stepan if he had seen any food products delivered to Faber.

"I really didn't notice," Stepan evaded.

"Every colonist should notice the colony property," declared the chairman sternly. "Your loyalty in protecting a thief is misplaced."

Yeremeyev decided that he had better make a clean breast of it. "I didn't want to give him the colony food, but I couldn't resist the drink. I haven't enough to do in winter; when sowing starts I'll be all right. I'll make good what I have taken out of my salary."

What should be done about it? The whole meeting discussed it. Shubina said, "He could keep busy in winter if he took interest in starting a school." Stesha contributed: "He wouldn't be tempted if he didn't have the keys to the store-room." Several boys mentioned Yeremeyev's good qualities—his hard work in the fields, his energy in expanding the colony property. "There's lots of good in Yeremeyev," concluded Morosov, "when once this bootleg is controlled.'

"Yeremeyev is a confessed thief and drunkard," was the summing up made by the visiting committee in final session with the colony Soviet. "These faults might be expected in an ordinary farm hand; they are common failings of our backward past. But Yeremeyev should have conquered them; he was in the Red Army and was chief of police. If the school authorities can find a better head for the Young Ploughman, we suggest that Yeremeyev be removed. If not, let him be reprimanded before all the colonists and let the keys to the storehouse be kept by a committee of elected members. They are all advised to be more vigilant."

53

In the excitement over Yeremeyev's crimes, Stepan's theft of Faber's eggs went unmentioned; his many thefts of colony food were not even known. All the loss was blamed on Yeremeyev, who did not himself know how much he had taken. Elated because where Yeremeyev had failed he himself had succeeded, Stepan saw no need for changing his ways. The farm manager's confession had actually hidden all the boy's stealing; Yeremeyev, he thought, was a bungler as a thief.

Yeremeyev was greatly relieved at the outcome. He might even have gone to jail, but everything had been settled in a friendly manner. Stepan's testimony and Morosov's judgment especially cheered him; the colony appreciated his work. He swore that he was done with *samagon*. He had sworn this many times already; but this time he felt surer, since the whole colony would watch.

Feeling behind him the strength of one hundred and twenty-five colonists—they seemed to like him better since the cleaning—Yeremeyev plunged into the fight for a record sowing. Morosov, Ivan, and all the field workers were older now, with a year's experience of success. This balanced the fact that the Stepan gang could never be relied on, and that Yeremeyev, owing so much to Stepan, felt powerless to control the boy. What did that matter? He had enough workers who wanted a harvest. Four hundred acres of rich black soil were sown in that summer of 1925 by the Young Ploughman. Kichkas authorities even came to the colony for assistance; through the Mutual Aid Committee they ploughed fifty acres for the widows and orphans of the village. It was their high point of success.

Recognizing the strength of the Young Ploughman, the county at last acceded to Yeremeyev's request for the great four-story mill left over from the State Farm's liquidation a year earlier. It was the largest in the county and had ground grain for a dozen villages before the First World War. Agents of the former owner wrecked it during the Revolution; several organizations, among them the Kichkas Co-operative, had wanted it since but had feared the cost of repairs. Even the State Farm had repaired only one unit.

"The Young Ploughman will handle it," cried Yeremeyev. He had visions of a spectacular success—the largest farm and the largest mill in the district—which should wipe out forever the shame of his "cleaning."

Proudly the young colonists displayed the mill's machines to curious peasants. They sold most of their record harvest to buy expensive parts. They would all swim in plenty, Yeremeyev assured them, as soon as the mill began to work.

The days and weeks went by; they were unable to repair it. No labour, no devotion, no agony availed. They became at last aware that the parts had not been intelligently purchased; nobody in the colony had really known exactly what to buy. The peasants increasingly grumbled when the mill on which they had counted did not open to handle the rising flood of their grain.

The break-up of the Young Ploughman was even swifter than its growth had been. Their harvest was spent; they faced famine in winter. Frantically Yeremeyev applied in every direction for help. One investigating committee after another arrived, discussed, and suggested. The Kichkas Co-operative took over the mill, paying the colony six weeks' bread for the parts they had purchased with most of their crop.

With covetous eyes on the big villa, so well repaired, the county school board offered to take Cherumshan on its budget as a "School for Young Peasants," a type of institution just becoming the mode. Upstairs they would have a dormitory for fifty of the younger children, with downstairs class-rooms for village day pupils. They wanted the livestock, the shops, the cultivated gardens, but not the distant fields. They had no use for Yeremeyev. Nor did they want the older boys, whose reputation was tainted by the Stepan gang's depredations. They would drop all colonists over sixteen.

An outcry arose from the older colonists. "We repaired that big house," shouted Ivan. Shubina pleaded, "We dug those gardens." Morosov protested, "We ploughed when we shook with chills and fevers and built the colony's wealth." Their clamour spread through the county and reached Zaporozhe. Public opinion supported them, their chief champion being the *Kommunar* Works.

So two organizations arose on the ruins of the Young Ploughman. The School for Young Peasants got the big house, the gardens, and most of the livestock. The older boys and girls were encouraged to form their own collective farm. They were given two of the smaller houses, a cow and chickens, some carpenter tools, all the field implements, and as much good land as they could work. Best of all, in recognition of their repairs to the villa, they were given two pair of horses, their greatest wealth. With these they could get hauling jobs for the rest of the winter and establish themselves on the land in spring. By general agreement, Morosov, Ivan, Stesha, and Shubina were accepted as initiators of the new organization.

The *Kommunar* Works sent a delegation to them, saying, "Comrade colonists, we've left you alone too long in your difficulties. We knew of the bootleg and should have kept track of what followed. We propose to take formal 'patronage' over your new farm." Much heartened, the young farmers accepted.

Feeling that out of their night of defeat they had saved the beginnings of a better day, they chose the name of "Red Dawn Farm."

IX

THE BREAK-UP OF THE Young Ploughman was a deep shock to all the older colonists. Gripping success in their hands, they had felt it collapse. Morosov especially suffered. He could not eat; he dragged himself about, looking pale and ill.

Nikolai Ivanovich sent for him. "Stop brooding. Life finds its way through many failures. Not the organization is important, but what we all learn from its growth and decay. Try to think out the reasons. . . ."

Morosov stammered: "Yeremeyev . . . Stepan . . ."

The older man nodded. "Yes, but look deeper. Drunkenness, thieving, ignorance—these are everywhere in our country. We must progress in spite of them. What were the faults in your methods of control?"

Morosov thought this over. Finally he judged: "We had no way to check what everyone was doing. I wish I knew better how to organize."

Looking at the lad fondly, the man suggested: "Study the sample constitutions recommended for collective farms; that will help you till harvest. Afterwards, if you wish to study social and political organization thoroughly, our shop committee is ready to recommend you to the Party Training School in Zaporozhe and provide your stipend."

Astounded with happiness at this unusual offer, Morosov glowed. "So you think that I . . . Oh, if the others can spare me for the winter, I would like that best of anything."

"Train up someone to take your place on the farm this winter," the man admonished. "That's your first lesson as organizer; your success is measured by the number of replacements you can train."

As a result of this conversation—at once reported by Morosov to his friends—the Red Dawn Farm decided that the large, loose, uncontrolled form of the Young Ploughman had been a major cause of the disaster and that they would organize the firmly knit type of collective farm known as "artel." Each member—they had twenty-two—would be assigned definite work, daily checked and paid for at harvest. Shirking would lead not to random cursing by Yeremeyev but to the grimmer penalty: "He that works not, neither shall he eat."

Unanimously they asked Yeremeyev to remain as their leader. They had all suffered from his weaknesses but they knew that he worked. A better farmer still than any of them, he had not been drunk since Faber's bootleg ceased. He agreed to work with them and share his knowledge till harvest, after which he hoped to enter a training course for State Farm managers. By that time the Red Dawn Farm could do without him, since its older members would be nearly eighteen.

Excited by the offer of the school stipend to Morosov—it was the first time one of their colony had been offered to pay for full-time study—all the young farmers began to discuss what kind of higher training they would like for themselves. The Young Ploughman's dissolution had sharply posed the question of their future, and made each think what he most wanted to do.

Stesha aspired: "I'd like to be a doctor. Am I too old to begin?"

Ivan decided: "Farming suits me; I want to make the Red Dawn Farm a success." Shubina agreed with Ivan but wanted to specialize in chickens and birds.

They brought their dreams to the *Kommunar* Works for their "patron's" advice. Nikolai Ivanovich promised to get them textbooks on farming, chicken-raising, and first aid. All agreed that Shubina should take charge of the farm's smaller livestock, Stesha should be doctor's helper in all sickness on the farm, while Ivan should have a chance to prove that he could take the farm's management when Yeremeyev and Morosov should leave. He had shown as chief carpenter a quality of placid leadership, more by example than by words. If the young people's interest in their chosen work continued, they would later be helped to appropriate schools.

Not yet had Stepan decided what he wanted. He had been the first to know that the Young Ploughman had failed. He drove the disheartened Yeremeyev home, that dark January evening, from the liquidation voted by the County Soviet. When the manager stumbled blindly into his quarters, Stepan drove off to the big house, stealthily roused Marin and motioned him outdoors.

"We're taking all we can carry to-night," he whispered. "It may be our last chance."

Marin's jaw dropped when he heard that the days of the Young Ploughman were numbered.

"Hurry up now," Stepan commanded. "We'll take everything we can to the Lair and be ready for whatever happens."

"Oh, yo," Marin exulted, slapping Stepan on the back in admiration for his foresight.

All night they worked by the starlight on the snow, driving back and forth with provisions to the place where the trail led over the ridge and down to the stepping-stones, then carrying their treasures to the cave and hiding them behind carelessly placed rocks. The thefts were so large that they were noticed in the morning, but no one had time to attend to them in the crisis that followed.

The possession of this well-stocked retreat, which Stepan had thought would make him free in his choices, actually hindered decision. It was hard to choose any regular work when he knew he could be free and well fed in the Lair. He resented the strict requirements of the Red Dawn Farm, which he knew were directed against his own habits and which would make impossible the easy, domineering life that his standing with Yeremeyev and his control of the gang had given him in the large, loosely knit colony. He was especially averse to collective discipline by Morosov, Ivan, and the girls, all of whom seemed to him less able than himself, less daring, less free.

In the blustery days of March, as sowing approached, Ivan tried to get Stepan to join the new artel. His admiration for his old chum had suffered many setbacks but he modestly recognized that Stepan was abler than he, as able perhaps as Morosov, and that the Red Dawn Farm would get along faster with his help.

"You could get any job you tried for on the farm," he pleaded.

"A little farm run by that bungler, Yeremeyev! I wouldn't take the whole of it as a gift."

Stung by the taunting allusion to the new farm's smallness, Ivan retorted: "What bigger plans have you?"

"Don't worry about me," Stepan tossed back lightly, piqued by his loss of influence over Ivan. "There are plenty of ways for me to live."

Learning of Morosov's good luck, he went to Nikolai Ivanovich to ask about jobs in the Implement Works. The shop-committee chairman replied that the *Kommunar* had not yet reached full production and its old workers had first chance at jobs.

"What do you really like best?" he added. "You don't seem to care for farming. Have you any special interest in machinery?"

Under the kind but penetrating eyes, Stepan felt compelled to think it over. "I don't exactly know," he said disconsolately, brightening as he added, "I know I like the river."

The man smiled encouragingly. "There are many ways of liking the river. I love our Dnieper too. It is important in our history. It's the waterway by which in ancient ages the culture of the Mediterranean Basin came into our savage North. Even before history the heroes of old Greek legend sailed up it into unknown wilderness. They came as far as where Kichkas is to-day. They were stopped by the rapids."

Stepan's eyes sparkled. "I didn't know all that about the river. I know how free Cossacks held the cliffs."

"I see we have a common interest," smiled Nikolai Ivanovich. "When I was about your age, I used to travel the river, distributing illegal literature—Lenin's pamphlets and translations of Marx and Engels. I would leave Odessa on the night boat, the side-wheeler *Graf Totleben*; Odessa was district centre for the Bolsheviks. I picked up my rowboat at Kherson in the morning and hid the literature under the big circular seat at the stern and in the compartment at the bow. I took an enormous loaf of bread and a dozen packages of cigarettes to trade for tomatoes and watermelons along the river. I tied up to the end of a string of rafts or barges and was pulled upstream. Last stop was just outside Zaporozhe.

We had a strong centre in the Slobodka foundries between here and Kichkas; it's part of Zaporozhe now. Downstream I drifted without rowing, often asleep in the boat."

He saw that Stepan was enthralled by his story. He was attracted by this vital, handsome boy. He knew his reputation—an unreliable worker and a petty thief. This interest in the river might really be a base on which to build. "You don't really know the river," he continued, "until you learn some way to use it: fishing or boating, perhaps, not as a sport but as a regular trade. Best of all will be the big dam that we're starting year after next. That will be great work for you and tens of thousands more."

The dam sounded exciting, but the time to wait seemed long. "Always promises for the future," said Stepan cynically.

"Yes, always promises for the future," affirmed Nikolai Ivanovich, annoyed. "While you're deciding what you really want there's that Red Dawn Farm. These new artels are important; they're working out the pattern for our future farming."

Stepan was at loose ends; the man's esteem of the farm might have moved him if he had not already rejected Ivan so proudly. He wouldn't take back his words. That night the colony's rowboat disappeared from Cherumshan; Stepan and Marin hauled it over the half-submerged rocks near the Lair and hid it behind the rocky islet. After his talk with Nikolai Ivanovich, Stepan had thought of a new way to use the river.

When the Red Dawn Farm moved into the field to sow, Stepan found himself out of place at Cherumshan. On an alluringly warm day in April the gang moved out to the Lair. There were twelve of them, including Marin, still the gay adventurer, Feodor, now a husky, undisciplined roughneck, and Peter, whose interest in farming was outweighed by devotion to Stepan. They took several blankets from the new school in addtion to their own. They did not steal from the Red Dawn Farm; it was too well organized and two of its members knew the way to the Lair.

"We'll have a horse of our own," Stepan promised, knowing that his prestige was challenged by the Red Dawn's four horses. "A horse to ride and take swimming in the river, not a horse that makes you work." Not knowing how he would get one, he postponed the problem by adding, "First we must find a good place to keep it safely."

The search for a good hiding place for a horse gave the gang a cheerful, desultory occupation for several days. Peter was the one who made a serious job of it. He had long felt himself overshadowed by the gay, adventurous Marin and badly wanted to win renown. Patiently studying the cliff face, he explored it methodically. After several false starts, he found the ideal spot. A short distance downstream, the cliff was broken by a steep gully overgown with bushes; from it came a tiny trickle of water. Following this back and keeping well above the underbrush, Peter found himself on a high, narrow ledge from which a gap suddenly opened into a still higher, hidden gully. He climbed this and came out in a grassy glade, shaded by flowering locust trees and walled in by the perpendicular cliff. It was watered by the source of the little stream.

The entire gang applauded Peter and celebrated his discovery at the campfire. Now that the hiding place was found, Stepan really had to produce a horse.

Luck played into his hands a few nights later. Learning of a troupe of passing gipsies, he went by night to their camp and succeeded in detaching a horse. He had some trouble getting it past the stepping-stones; the horse resented the alien hand. Though fearing pursuit, Stepan had to wait until daybreak gave light. When he brought the horse to the Lair at dawn, the cheers of the gang were the loudest he had ever known. They gave Peter the honour of leading the horse to the hidden glade, where they all took turns riding it.

"The fine thing about this horse," bragged Stepan, "is that the police won't bother us. Nobody cares what happens to gipsies."

"I stole a gipsy's horse in the Caucasus," chanted Marin. "But ay-ay-ay! The gipsy stole him back!"

"When were you ever in the Caucasus?" challenged Stepan, unwilling, even in Marin's fancy, to share the glory.

Marin cocked his head at Stepan and then made a gesture of extreme exhaustion. "My tongue is tired," he said, sticking it out for Stepan to see.

For several days the gang stayed close to the Lair, until they learned that the gipsies, after complaining loudly, had gone on. After this they were less cautious. They took the horse several times to swim in the river—the best sport they had ever had. Some of the boys, on a visit to Cherumshan, bragged about swimming with a horse.

Three weeks after the theft, Ivan came to the Lair one evening. Embarrassed, but very serious, he went straight to the point.

"The police want you. They have asked me to show them the way here. I'll do it unless you go out and face the charges."

"You sneak!" shouted Stepan, furious.

"Don't be childish. This is serious business. They'll find you even without me. I'd much rather you'd go out and face them. I don't want to give away the Lair."

Confident that he could still bluff the village police, Stepan was surprised to find himself before the district authorities. It was the first time in the neighbourhood that gipsies had appealed to the law. Formerly the peasants had treated them as inferiors and even as outlaws, but Soviet officials were trying to assimilate them into normal social life. It had therefore been decided to hold what was known as a "show trial," to demonstrate to both peasants and gipsies their equality as citizens.

60

The court was held in the Kichkas market place to accommodate the expected crowds. A distant judge came from Zaporozhe; the "people's co-judges," taken from lists prepared by Kichkas organizations, were a middle-aged peasant from Selidba and Stepan's former teacher, Alexis, now assistant head of the new school at Cherumshan. This court of three sat behind a table under a large tree at the end of the market place. Benches and chairs brought out from nearby buildings seated a hundred peasnts, while several hundred stood.

The gipsies, it was shown, had followed the trail of the horse to a point not far from the river. Members of the Stepan gang had boasted about swimming with a horse. These boys, questioned by the court in the presence of the villagers, claimed that they had found a horse and that it had disappeared later. Marin added an embroidery of enthusiasm: "Eh! What a horse! Swam like a porpoise! Vanished . . . just like a dream!" Stepan supported the joint story but as if it were an event of little concern.

The judge, who had assumed that the horse would come in automatically with the boys, was annoyed and baffled by the gang's evasions. He began to harangue them about the seriousness of their action.

"In taking a horse you take the livelihood of many men."

"It was only a gipsy's horse," Stepan dismissed the incident. "They are not used for work."

Angry at Stepan's apt insolence, but seeing in it a chance to make the point for which the trial was being held, the judge announced firmly: "Gipsies are human beings like everyone. Gypsies are equal citizens like everyone else." He launched into a discourse about the equality of all people—regardless of race, sex, or religion—under the Soviet Power, proving this so eloquently that the horse seemed forgotten. Even Stepan was impressed to know that gipsies were equal, though it made him uneasy about the theft.

"You see"—the judge at last turned pointedly to Stepan—"it is very serious to take a gipsy's horse. You increase your offence by your manner towards the court and the citizens who have come here to enforce our Soviet justice. We could commit you all to an institution as vagabonds. But we want to help you become good citizens. If there is any sign . . ." He waited.

"What do you want of us?" asked Stepan directly.

"First of all we want the horse. Why waste the time of the police hunting the cliffs when we are convinced that you know where it is?"

Stepan reflected that he was even more anxious than the judge to avoid a police search of the cliffs. "That might be arranged," he bargained. "I'll go to the river with one of the boys. I shouldn't wonder if I can find it."

"It's not for you to dictate conditions," snorted the judge. He added that the return of the horse was not sufficient. The gang must work industriously till harvest in some place where their work could be checked. Perhaps the Red Dawn Farm would accept them. They could not expect a full share of its harvest, for they had taken no part in the sowing, but they could make enough to live and begin an honest existence.

The Red Dawn Farm seemed unendurable to Stepan, especially under the humiliating conditions. He began to argue: "We will work in road building or construction."

Thoroughly aroused by Stepan's stubbornness and determined to break the gang, the judge compelled each member to state before the whole village whether he would work at Red Dawn Farm. All agreed except Stepan. "I'll work anywhere except at Red Dawn," he declared.

"He's incorrigible," pronounced the judge, when the court withdrew to a nearby building to consider the sentence. "We should send him up for two years."

"He stole it all right," contributed the peasant co-judge, "but you can't prove it."

"He would only have demoralized Red Dawn," judged Alexis. "His refusal is a blessing in disguise. We've split him off from the others."

The court unanimously decided that Stepan must take some regular job and report weekly till harvest. They felt only partly satisfied when he secured work as farm-hand with the kulak Krotov, for no Soviet officials approved of kulaks and they would have preferred that Stepan work in some co-operative enterprise. However, few people wanted a boy with Stepan's reputation, and the private hiring of farm-hands was not yet forbidden by law. Krotov himself, a big cattle trader before the Revolution, now professed loyalty to the Soviets, motivating it by religion: "The government is sent of God; we must render to Cæsar what is Cæsar's." Stepan had met the court's condition and they agreed to his job.

In one thing Stepan succeeded. He did not reveal the way to the secret glade. He persisted in saying that he could not find the horse if accompanied; he was finally allowed to go alone. It was a small victory, but it cleared him as he resigned himself to a summer of work. He was defiant rather than discouraged. He would make a brilliant harvest record— better than anyone at Red Dawn—and take mastery over the gang again.

He had not even noticed the girl with tragic eyes who stared at him through the trial from her seat far back in the market place. Anya was much more ashamed of the theft than was the youth who committed it. She hoped nobody recalled that she had gone strolling with a boy who turned out to be a criminal. She had been ashamed to come to the trial, yet at the last moment had been unable to keep away. Her deeper shame was that, knowing all the time that it was wrong, she could not keep from thrilling to his insolent arrogance.

X

THE HARVEST FESTIVAL was the gayest in Stepan's memory. Three good harvests had brought farming back to normal with a big surplus of wheat. Krotov offered his "first-fruits" in church and made his farm-hands go. Stepan had no objection; he enjoyed the big thanksgiving and it meant that the end of his servitude was near.

Two days later came *Yarmarkt*. From all the hamlets the crop-filled carts converged on Kichkas market place. Peasants displayed products and compared records. The teacher Alexis, who had been assigned by the court to check Stepan's summer work, approached the boy.

"Why aren't you more cheerful, Stepan? Your record is good."

"The Red Dawn Farm did better," replied the boy sullenly. "It was mentioned in the Zaporozhe newspaper."

"Naturally. Red Dawn planted early; your Krotov plants 'by religion.' But you yourself worked as well as Ivan or Morosov. I hope you will do as well in the future. What are your plans?"

"Am I free to decide? Is my sentence over?"

"Yes, you are free."

Stepan laughed. "I'm going to get drunk to celebrate my freedom. This is my last harvest."

Alexis began to protest but thought better of it. Getting drunk was the commonest celebration and he himself had declared Stepan free. Opposition might only make him defiant.

Comfortably cheered by vodka, Stepan strolled about the market place. It was hard to get near the attractions. The merry-go-round no longer interested him and there was a long line at the tent of the fortune-teller. The tightrope walkers were good; they juggled hoops as they walked the rope. The biggest crowd was around the "bodiless woman"; she was only head and bust, but smiled and seemed alive. The gaping crowd pressed close to the rail that held them back from her cage. How was the trick done? With pleased superiority, Stepan knew that there was no real woman like that.

There were fewer blind Chuvashes than usual. For generations these alien folk from the middle Volga had furnished the blind beggars that followed the *Yarmarkts* north. A dirty people, most of them had trachoma. "I suppose Chuvashes are equal just like gipsies." Stepan snorted at the manifest absurdity, but he felt a sneaking pride at the number of strange peoples in this country and at the work of the health authorities cleaning up blind beggars through the land.

Content with himself and the day, he reached the end of the market where the young folks were dancing. He stared in amazement: Anya in gay festival costume held the centre of an applauding circle. How she had changed! Instead of the shy, awkward, adoring creature who had stood barefoot in the mud with her shoes in her hands, she was a triumphant golden girl. Her scarlet kerchief had come loose and her long, glossy braids swung around her shoulders as she danced. Her clear skin had borrowed a radiant tan from the summer sun. In the two years that had passed since Stepan had noticed her, Anya had grown up.

It seemed that everyone recognized it. Ivan and other boys were gazing at her with the same admiration that Stepan was beginning to feel. They must be shown that she was his possession. Had she not adored him? He pressed near.

She saw his admiring gaze. Her feet quickened. Stamping, swaying, clapping her hands to the music, she released her tumult of joy. She had been happy before with her harvest triumph and the plaudits of the village. The applause of this boy was the one thing needed to make her triumph complete.

Her harvest was the talk of the *Yarmarkt*. Too young to till for grain, she had planted vegetables. Alexis helped get selected seed and pamphlets from the Commissariat of Agriculture. She had produced vegetables which were not on sale in the market, since the co-operative bought them at a higher price for seed. She was especially proud of a small plot of sugar beets, which were not much grown in this district, since there was no refinery. A pamphlet told her how to make sweet syrup, so she would have sugar, which was still hard to get.

For the first time her grandfather allowed her to wear her mother's festival costume, preserved through all disasters of the warring years. Nobody in the village had a prettier one. The skirt was homespun and home-woven in gay stripes of blue, yellow, and green. The full sleeves of the linen blouse were embroidered in red and black cross-stitch. The loose over-blouse was bell-shaped, of green and scarlet wool edged with city-made gilt braid. A dozen strands of bright beads swung from her neck and sparkled in the sunlight as she danced.

Ending the dance, she met Stepan's eyes and shrank a little from their flame. Ivan came up to ask if she would join him in the next group dance. Agreeing, she started with him back into the circle. Stepan could not endure this; Ivan seemed to get everything. Vodka added to the swagger with which Stepan pushed through the crowd and stepped between Ivan and Anya. She drew away from him, laughing with mingled excitement and fear. Stepan looked her over possessively, from her golden, dishevelled hair to her dancing feet.

"You're my girl, Anya! Come on and dance with me. Later I'll take you to the fortune-teller."

64

His lordly manner reduced her from belle of the harvest to the little barefoot girl whom he could pick up, stroll with, and leave. It reminded her of that day when she stood in the mud of this same market place, almost in this same spot, and surrounded by these same people. His eyes told her that he remembered and dared her to deny that she was his. Had he not shamed her enough already, that he should make her flush and tremble again?

"Do you want to dance with him, Anya?" asked Ivan stiffly.

Stepan moved confidently toward her. Suddenly and fiercely she slapped him in the face, and turned to take Ivan's arm. Tears shone in her eyes; she bit her lips and moved swiftly. Ivan was dancing with her but it seemed to both of them that Stepan after all had won.

Shaking with fury, Stepan stared after her. Then his lips curved in a slow smile. Anya was clearly not indifferent to him. He walked away, through the crowd, whistling, and applauding the attractions half heartedly; his thoughts were elsewhere. At last he went along the road toward Krotov's house.

When Anya returned at sundown from the merrymaking, she found Stepan sitting on a bench in her yard. Rising, he held out his hands full of eggs.

"I wanted to knock you down in the market place, but I decided to bring you a present instead," he said with his most winning smile.

She glowed with relief. She had been in a turmoil of mingled anger and repentance, thinking that she had driven him away. Here he was in a clean blouse, with his blond hair all smooth and shining, and his blue eyes caressing her as they never had before.

"Come in. I'll cook your eggs for tea," she said happily, leading the way into the cottage.

Through the square covered porch they came into the main part of the house. Never, thought Stepan, had he seen a room so neatly arranged. The mud-brick walls shone spotless with whitewash. The hard earth floor was smoothly sanded. On the high top of the great brick oven that filled a whole side of the room a man lay dozing, almost hidden by the hoops of brown onions that hung from the ceiling to dry, placed with such care above the stove that they seemed like ornamental festoons.

Stepan sat down on the long, solid chest of family possessions; it was on this, except in bitter weather, that Anya slept at night. He looked at the family portraits in hand-carved frames, ranged neatly on the large table under the window. For the first time in his life he felt himself in a cherished home. His own early home had been too full of small children ever to seem clean and comfortable. Krotov's house was much larger than Anya's, but Stepan had never sat down in it; he lived and slept in the barn. Even Krotov's best rooms did not show the loving care that was evident here. Stepan felt a vague longing and a restlessness that was almost resentment. The soft pressure of the ordered home seemed to check his easy spontaneity of movement.

To fight himself free of the spell, he began to brag. "I took the biggest eggs in the barn."

Anya hardly heard him. She had hurried toward her grandfather and, seeing that he was comfortably dozing, had begun to replenish the fire. Then, as she turned back toward Stepan, his words penetrated her mind fully.

"Are these your boss's eggs?" she asked, embarrassed.

"His best," nodded Stepan in cheerful triumph.

She gathered the eggs up slowly, and held them out to him. "You'd better take them back."

Stepan lifted the eggs in a rush of anger, as if to hurl them to the floor. Anya's presence and the spotlessness of her floor restrained him. He put the eggs in his cap and laid them on a bench in the entry. "Well, if you don't want them . . ." he mumbled, seating himself on the chest again.

"I thought you had done with stealing," said Anya. "Everyone says you've worked so hard this summer."

He warmed to the soft-voiced praise and still more to the pleading look. "What's that to do with it?" he asked. "These are just eggs."

"But they're not yours."

"They are now," he smiled, teasing her. "What makes a thing 'mine' anyway?" He was watching the golden flecks in her hazel eyes.

She flushed but held her ground. "Well, if you make something——"

He laughed gaily. Now he had her. "The chickens made the eggs and I helped look after the chickens."

She tossed her head indignantly, so that the golden braids flew around her shoulders and fell across the bright red and green of her overblouse. "You can argue better than I can, but you know just as well as I do that stealing is wrong."

"I know people say it is," admitted Stepan.

She pushed her point. "I felt so ashamed at that trial, thinking that the boy I went strolling with was a criminal in front of everyone."

He brightened at the flattery of her interest. "So you were there?"

"Everyone was, and it's nothing to look so cheerful about," she rebuked, steeling herself against the seduction of his smile.

"They never found the place where the horse was," he bragged. "They never even found the Lair."

"What is the Lair?" asked Anya, interested.

"It's a place . . . A secret place . . ." He could not put the Lair into words, so he concluded: "I'll show it to you some day, high up in the rocks above the river."

She prepared tea from real tea leaves. She set out cucumbers, tomatoes, and sour cream, and cut large cubes from the tasty wheaten loaf.

The grandfather came down from the oven to eat with them. His eyes opened with surprise at the tea. Then he looked at Stepan more closely. "Yes, it's harvest festival . . . And your name?"

Anya flushed; she had told the old man only a moment earlier, and she hated to have Stepan see how quickly her grandfather forgot.

"Stepan Bogdanov," the boy repeated. The old man's lapse and the feebleness of his walk made it clear that Anya was without proper protection. Stepan felt more at home in the house; he almost felt as if he himself was the host.

"Bogdanov?" repeated the grandfather. "The family beyond the market. Bogdanov went to war."

"He was my father."

The old man looked approvingly at the tall, strong lad, noticing particularly the dark tan and the muscular development that came from toil in the fields. "You look as if you could work," he nodded, sniffing appreciatively the fragrance of the tea.

"So these are the prize tomatoes and cucumbers," said Stepan to Anya, flattering her with his eyes. "I hardly dare eat such famous things." He helped himself liberally. Anya laughed happily, and they began talking about the market and all the excitements of the day.

The evening passed quickly. The old man obviously approved of Stepan, and Anya seemed happy to be with him. The spotless walls and neatly placed family portraits lay on Stepan's senses like a charm. They no longer made him feel restless and alien. What would it be like, he wondered, to have a place like this, so cosy, so secure? When he left Anya invited him to come again. They were already good friends.

Not for a moment did he think of returning the eggs he had stolen. He added some vegetables next morning while Krotov slept off the effects of the festival. He rounded up his gang from the Red Dawn Farm to celebrate the end of their sentence. That evening was a record-size campfire in the Lair.

"A second harvest celebration," chortled Marin, displaying ten more eggs and a big chunk of hard sugar, taken from the Red Dawn Farm.

"There's enough for another feast to-morrow night," said Stepan. "We'll get mushrooms in the woods."

The talk turned to the achievements of the Red Dawn Farm during the summer. The boys mocked the farm and affected contempt for it. Marin spoke of it as "our forced-labour camp" and "our jail." Nonetheless, under the disdain Stepan felt a new note of respect.

"Ivan says there'll be a tractor in the spring," said Peter.

"Shubina won a prize in the *Peasants' Gazette* contest," proclaimed Marin. "They're sending her a machine that makes chickens! Ay-ay, think of chickens from a machine!"

Everybody laughed. A machine that made chickens was a joke in which nobody could believe. Yet in the laughter there was a half belief, not quite in a chicken machine, but in a life from which Stepan was shut out. Long before the gang curled itself to sleep by the fire, he knew with a pang of loneliness that whatever dream he might have had of reviving the Lair was dead. He hardly knew what he had expected or even what he wanted, but he knew that to the gang the Lair had become only a picnic place. Their serious thought for the future lay with the Red Dawn Farm.

Late into the night he lay staring into the glowing ashes, listening to the frogs, the distant hoot of an owl, and the soft swish of water against the shore. Silently awake among the sleeping boys, he thought back over the whole summer. Where had he made his mistake? Was it in stealing the horse? Was it in working alone while the gang worked at Red Dawn? He could think of no way in which he might have saved the gang and the Lair.

That judge smashed us after all, he thought. Then he saw that this was exactly what the judge had intended. Not the punishment of them as indivudals, but the smashing of the gang. The judge had won; the contempt which Stepan had felt for him became a storming hate.

Next morning they all rose late and gathered mushrooms. Without exchange of words, all realized that they would return to the Red Dawn Farm that night. Marin alone felt the need of explaining: "Why should we let others eat our harvest? We raised it; they owe us our bread for the winter," he laughed.

Most of them, through inertia, would have stayed to feast on mushroom soup the second evening, going back to the farm late at night. Stepan chose otherwise. In mid-afternoon he suddenly gathered up his mushrooms. "So long, fellows. Going to have supper with my girl." While they still stared in amazement, he strode away.

He went to Anya's house and offered her the mushrooms. Touched that he had spent time gathering them for her, she invited him to supper. "You picked them and I'll cook them," she smiled, bringing him close in a common task of home. Before he left, she agreed to go to the Lair with him to pick mushrooms the following Sunday afternoon.

Three times during the week Stepan slipped away early from Krotov's fields and went to prepare the Lair for the expected picnic. He foraged for wood and stacked it in the cave, rolled a big log to make a good seat where they could get the best view of the river. He stole eggs and even a chicken. He believed that Anya had refused the stolen eggs for fear of incriminating her cherished home. They were on better terms now, and he did not think she would be so particular in the Lair.

On a crisp but sunny afternoon he brought her to the picnic. On the path above the river where he had so often hastened with burdens, they strolled and skipped in happy leisure, enjoying the view and the warmth of the sun. The cornflowers were gone, but yellow daisies with dark-brown centres dotted the fields. *Aniutini glaski*, they were called—Aniuta's Eyes. Stepan teased Anya by holding one of them up to compare it. "They're darker than my Aniuta's," he complained, pretending to be disappointed. His laughing glance told her otherwise.

An enchanted stillness seemed to enfold the whole earth, broken only by the murmur of the river and the calls of young people far off on the water, boating in the sun. "We've a row-boat, too," Stepan suddenly remembered. "The wind is right to sail to Kichkas and drift back." As they crossed the stepping-stones, he bragged that the way from this point was secret. No girl had ever visited the cave.

"You're the first to know the way here."

Anya thrilled with pride. The wildness of cliffs, the rhythm of uneven motion on trail and stepping-stones, released her to a new and almost frightening sense of freedom. She explored the cave with little cries of discovery; she sat happily on the big log to admire the view. When Stepan brought out the stolen eggs and chicken she felt unreasoning triumph at his successful theft. She was afraid of this strange feeling, which swept her away from the respectable way of life she knew. Was it only a week ago that stolen eggs had shocked her? They ought to shock her now, for eggs and bread are things to be won by honest work. Why did it seem to her here that food, like the sun and the river, was something to be seized, to be enjoyed, something by its nature free?

She did not even ask him where he got the rowboat, which clearly didn't belong on that deserted cliff. She relaxed in Stepan's mastery of this world of the open air. They held their coats to the wind and let it blow them slowly up the river as far as Kichkas, where the current at the foot of the rapids became too strong. Then they furled the coats and drifted downstream slowly through the drowsy afternoon, with his tousled head on her lap and her hands lifting the light sunburned strands from the dark roots of his hair.

When Stepan made the fire and prepared dinner, Anya watched in a trance of happy adoration, as once she had watched him in "Springtime without Sun," because he had snatched her out of her life of routine, and freed her to a wider world. They ate the broiled chicken gaily. She laughed at the grease that got on her fingers and Stepan, laughing back, licked her fingers clean.

Her happiness communicated itself to him. He wanted to shout with joy that she should sit thus tranquilly in his Lair. At the same time he wanted to shake her out of her tranquillity, so that she would shout with him or dance as at the harvest festival, only more and more dizzily until she swooned from dancing. He would catch her when she fell and she would be glad that he was strong. He trembled with the conflict between the desire to seize her and the fear lest something he might do should make her angry. He did not know the sources of her joy or of her anger, and was awkward because he did not know.

Suddenly he leapt to his feet, ran perilously up the slope to a rocky point that thrust far up into sunlight. Standing erect, he gave a long shout that echoed along the cliffs. He shouted again and again until his breath was gone and he was momentarily exhausted. Then he leapt down the rocks and threw himself on the log next to Anya with a force that made the heavy timber shake. He panted for lack of breath and with the violence of strong, unformed desire.

Shaken by the feeling that came to her from his actions, Anya said hesitantly: "Why did you shout?"

"I was saying good-bye to the sun," he answered, hardly knowing what else to say.

She saw that the sun was really setting. Dusk grew around the log where they sat; the cave was frighteningly dark. Only on the high point where Stepan had shouted was there sunlight; even as she watched it was gone. She thought of the twilit miles between them and the village. With the dusk Stepan had become an almost terrifying stranger, whose actions she could not predict. She rose hastily, clenching her fists to keep from trembling.

"It will be dark before we get home," she worried.

"Uh-huh," agreed Stepan without rising.

Panic swept through her. "Why don't you hurry?"

"That's all right," Stepan assured her. "We can stay in the Lair. It's warm and there's plenty of food."

His unconcern made him stranger than ever and heightened her fear. "We can't stay in a cave all night," she cried sharply.

"I lived here all one summer," he began lazily. Then he suddenly knew what he wanted. He jumped up and ran after Anya, who was walking slowly down the trail towards the stepping-stones. He wanted Anya and the Lair together; Anya, his dream of home, and the Lair, which gave him freedom. He must have them together, these two best things in his life. Then everything would be all right with him.

Throwing both arms around her, he pleaded in desperation. "Stay with me till to-morrow, Anichka. You'll love the Lair at night. You'll feel free from the whole world."

Her panic mounted sharply at the onslaught and at the dizziness that seemed to be flooding her body with a languorous wish to stay. With her last energy she fought frantically. "I'm afraid of you," she gasped. "I'm afraid of the way you live. I hate your Lair. It's only a dark old cave!"

Stepan released her as if she had struck him. She sped away over the stepping-stones and up the far side. He stood there, shaking and defeated, while the long twilight deepened into dark. Ivan was right. The gang was right. Anya was right. The Lair was only a dark cave.

He was homeless as he had never been before, in all his orphaned life.

Slowly, in the starlight, he felt his way down the cliff without looking back at the Lair. Slowly he loosed the rowboat and pulled out into the stream. He glanced indifferently at the lights of Kichkas and the dim glow over Zaporozhe. Lying down in the boat, he stared at the stars. Then the lapping of the water against the wood soothed him and he fell asleep as the current bore him south.

XI

Nikolai Ivanovich was working late in his office. The voice of the Zaporozhe procurer—the district attorney—came to him over the telephone as the warm June night began to cool. "I think I have the information about the implements. Would you care to talk it over to-night?"

"Is midnight too late for you?" asked the shop-committee chairman. "I still have the housing report for the City Soviet to finish."

A laugh came over the wire. "There's no late or early in this town since we all began working for the dam. Midnight is perfect. I'll be there."

Nikolai Ivanovich coughed a bit as he checked the housing report. His face was dark with fatigue; the work on the great dam had increased his labours many-fold. The first explosions, thundering, in the spring of 1927, in the canyon of the Dnieper, had shaken the life of Zaporozhe to its foundations. Thousands of workers had poured in from all over the Ukraine in the year that had followed, seeking jobs and bringing with them many problems. The shop-committee chairman had a dozen public duties now besides his regular work.

As a member of the housing committee of the city government—he had been elected deputy by the workers of his plant—he was trying to plan new homes for thirty thousand workers somewhere in the two-mile stretch between Zaporozhe and the river. Should they build temporary barracks, single cottages, apartment houses, or a mixture of all three?

The main emphasis should be on the future Socialist City [he read from the concluding section of his report]. Streets well laid out with trees; transportation not only to the dam but—even more important— to the tremendous industries that the dam will later serve. Blocks of apartment houses alternating with parks; smaller homes farther out with space for vegetable gardens; barracks immediate but only temporary. It must be a model for other Soviet cities to copy, for our dam is the first giant of the Five-Year Plan.

Laying aside the report, he got out the file on the stolen implements. Thefts had been troubling him for several months, but especially this spring. Implements left the factory on flatcars or in boxcars, but did not arrive at the farms to which they were sent. They were not always the same implements—a plough, a harrow, recently a large reaper—and they disappeared in different ways. Sometimes so casually that it was not possible, with all the inexperienced help, to be sure whether the implement had physically vanished or whether a green checkman had made a mistake in the list.

The losses amounted now to nearly two dozen implements; it was beginning to look like a system. Moreover, reports had come to the district committee of the Party, of which Nikolai Ivanovich was also a member, that a number of kulaks were getting new farm equipment from an unexplained source. So far the facts had not been tied together, but the procurer seemed to think that he had connected them now.

"Clever stealing," said Nikolai Ivanovich to himself as he went over each theft in detail. "What a waste of ingenious thought!"

While awaiting the procurer, he picked up another of the jobs the dam had given him. As a member of the Zaporozhe Council of Trade Unions, he was interested in the recruiting drive for construction workers, handled by the Labour Exchange. Ilya Morosov would be coming about this to-morrow, or rather to-day, for it was after midnight now. He did labour recruiting in the villages as his summer-vacation work for the Party Training School, where he had finished his second year. Already he had secured more than a hundred workers and sent them organized in brigades, which greatly facilitated the task of handling them. He was coming to ask Nikolai Ivanovich what chance there was of getting some implements for a collective farm, to enable it to release ten men for the dam.

"A good boy, Morosov," mused the man. "We'll need a special drive to produce implements above the plan for just such cases." Drooping with weariness at this additional work, he made a note of it in to-morrow's calendar.

His thoughts turned naturally to the young folks who had taken charge of the Red Dawn Farm when Morosov went to the Party school. Ivan Bobrov, a methodical, industrious manager; Shubina, patiently expanding the poultry farm; Stesha, helping in the summer with the village day nursery and studying in the pre-medical school. "It's good we took that patronage. Young life goes ahead on so little. Some food, some sunlight, a word at the right moment, and suddenly life flowers."

What was the name of that other boy who refused to work at Red Dawn and asked for a job in the Implement Works two years ago? Yes, Stepan. A difficult youth, but one of fire and power. "He could make something of himself if he could get untangled. There are plenty of jobs now, right in his line—the river. I wonder where he disappeared to."

The door opened to admit the procurer, an energetic man in his late twenties, whose embroidered-linen blouse was wrinkled and untidy

72

from a long day of work in the heat. Dropping his overstuffed brief-case on the table, he began to apologize for being late.

"Never mind," said Nikolai Ivanovich. "I've used the time not badly. Wait a moment while I make a note to ask Morosov to look up a lad named Stepan Bogdanov—a fellow at loose ends who might organize a construction brigade for the dam." He wrote it down with a broken bit of pencil.

"Stepan!" exclaimed the procurer. "You needn't hunt Stepan. If he's the fellow that used to run that gang near the rapids, I know where he is. He's been handling the distribution of your stolen implements. I have him in jail."

Nikolai Ivanovich dropped his pencil in consternation. "That's too bad," he said finally. "I lost sight of him too long."

The procurer laughed. "Trust you for knowing everyone. But this Stepan is a bad one. Clever, too! There was a small group of hooligans here in the city who caused some trouble by petty theft, chiefly food, clothing, shoes—things they could use themselves. They had no outlet for anything of serious value. Sometime last autumn this Stepan blew into town from somewhere and got in touch with them. He built up their distribution; he has contacts among the kulaks. It seems they stole implements to order. The buyer for each was arranged in advance."

The older man's face grew steadily graver during this recital. "That's really serious," he concluded, as the procurer paused. Sighing, he added: "That Stepan asked me for a job two years ago. Our industry wasn't ready then to absorb him. Well, what are we going to do with him now?"

"He's good for a five-year sentence. He's a bit young, barely eighteen. Still there's no doubt that he's the real ringleader. Without him they were disorderlies and small-time thieves. He made them a menace to the countryside."

"I'd like to have a talk with him before you try him."

The procurer nodded. "When do you want him?" he asked.

Nikolai Ivanovich considered. "Give him a night or two in jail to think it over, but not long enough to establish new habits and contacts. I must find out about him from Morosov. This may take a few hours for checking. Send him here day after to-morrow, any time in the forenoon."

Picking up his brief case, the procurer paused for a last word. "I don't like these circles under your eyes. Take care of yourself. You're too long in this hot office. We don't want to lose you to the sanitarium again."

"I'm going home right now," agreed the older man. He rose wearily and moved to the door, coughing a bit. "I wonder how that boy got mixed up with kulaks," he sighed as he drew a deep breath of the soft June night.

Two days later Stepan came to the office. At Nikolai Ivanovich's request, the guard who brought him from the county jail remained outside in the ante-room. Stepan tried to hide his apprehension under a jaunty manner, but his restlessness betrayed it. He knew that he was in for some serious punishment; he was not sure just what and this vagueness worried him still more. He respected the shop-committee chairman, but certainly he did not want to hear him preach.

With a pleasant nod, Nikolai Ivanovich indicated a chair. "I'll be ready in a moment. I've a little work to finish."

The matter-of-fact approach puzzled Stepan but set him curiously at ease. It was almost as if the old man didn't know he had come from jail. He watched suspiciously while the man arranged a few papers, signed a handful of letters and took them into the other room, put through a telephone call to the director of the Works about a factory problem. This normal routine of work seemed suddenly pleasant to Stepan now that he was shut out of it, perhaps permanently. He wondered if Nikolai Ivanovich remembered the time when he had been here seeking a job. What did the man want with him, anyway? Recalling that it was from this factory's shipments that he had stolen the implements, he understood that the shop-committee chairman represented the complainant in his case. He stiffened, ready to face attack.

He was taken aback by the casualness with which Nikolai Ivanovich stretched himself in his chair and said: "Well, the war has begun between the working class and Nature for the control of the Dnieper. I was thinking about you the other night and wondering why you haven't been to see me about that job you wanted. There are plenty of such jobs now. Just as I was planning to hunt you up the procurer came and told me he had got ahead of me; he had you here in jail."

Stepan stared at this man who spoke of jail so easily, without emotion. The shop-committee chairman went on. "I had hoped you might help us out by organizing a gang for Dneprostroi.[1] It seems the procurer has other intentions. He expected to send you north."

Bitterness rose in Stepan. Was the old man tantalizing him by suggesting jobs and snatching them away? "So I'm for the White Bears, am I?" he said in sullen defiance, looking Nikolai Ivanovich full in the face.

"That's the nickname they usually give it," agreed the older man calmly. "Headquarters, Bear Mountain, for work on the Baltic–White Sea canal. If you're talking geography, the white bears are five hundred miles farther north. It's a canal important to the defence of our country, a construction job like other jobs, but under somewhat harder conditions, isolated by great stretches of northern woods so that you cannot get away. It will be harder to steal there; the opportunities are limited. There will be more incentive to work and more pressures to see that you do. That's what it's organized for. But life is life there as elsewhere; it's not so different as you might suppose."

[1] Dnieper construction.

74

Stepan's heart sank. He had been ready for threats of harsh punishment which would single him out from others to some bad eminence. Instead of this, he seemed to be caught on the same web of life which thus far had defeated him—life under worse conditions. He wanted to hate Nikolai Ivanovich but he couldn't. At the bottom of his soul he felt that he was hearing the final truth. Then the man suddenly held the boy's eyes and spoke sadly but firmly.

"If you want to destroy yourself, nothing we can do for you can stop you. Wherever you are! That choice lies with every man."

He stopped definitely, as if the word were now with Stepan. Out of the boy's whirling thoughts one rose strangely persistent. It had nothing to do with his lawbreaking or the threatened punishment; it seemed more important than either. Never before in his life had he been called a man!

"If I want to destroy myself . . ." he finally stammered.

Nikolai Ivanovich nodded and then spoke calmly and analytically, as if he were thinking some problem through with Stepan. "I cannot understand how you, the son of a poor peasant who died for land and liberty, born of a peasant mother who starved through a kulak's exactions, you who yourself followed the Red Army and in boyhood bore on your back the weight of kulak oppression, could have teamed up with kulaks now."

That stung. Stepan flamed up. "I haven't teamed up with kulaks! I'm exploiting them as they once exploited me. I'm making profit from them." He wondered uneasily if Nikolai Ivanovich knew what immense sums the kulaks were eager to pay for farm machinery. Two or three times as much as the *Kommunar* Works got from the collective farms. Why were they discussing kulaks, anyway, instead of the thefts?

"You combined with kulaks to defeat the will of the Soviet people," came the answer. "I think you do not quite understand the full seriousness. Do you know what is meant when we say 'a crime against the State'?"

"It's a crime you get exiled for," replied Stepan.

"You don't know just why?" asked Nikolai Ivanovich. Stepan shook his head. The man continued, thoughtfully choosing his words. "If you had stolen food, or clothes, or something you yourself thought you needed, even something as important as a plough or reaper, that is ordinary stealing. You would be punished for it, probably by some months of work making roads or bridges for the common good. But we would not consider you an enemy of our society—only an undisciplined member who needed to be brought into order.

"What you have done is more than that. You are fighting the Soviet people. We have chosen to build a Socialist commonwealth, in which our natural resources and productive plant belong to us all. Our people chose this many times by their votes and still more by four years of bitter fighting, in which we not only defeated internal enemies, but drove out the invading armies of the capitalist world. We have neither enough public wealth nor enough skilled people to have Socialism immediately. So for a time we tolerate these private profiteers who live by exploiting hired labour, by moneylending, by private ownership of small-scale means of production. We do not suppress them by law for we still need the food that their enterprises produce. But we never give them the help of the State in their profit-grabbing. We know that if they could they would smash our public ownership for the sake of their private gain."

So far Stepan understood and agreed with all of it, but what had it to do with him? He listened carefully as the man went on.

"When our *Kommunar* Works makes implements, we do not sell them, as in capitalist countries, to the buyers who will pay the most. We sell them first to State and collective farms, in which each machine will improve the standard of living for many families instead of for one. Our factory people work extra hard to produce machines above their quota, hoping that every one of our machines will improve and unite the whole life of our country. But you have been taking our machines and selling them—perhaps for some fancy profit—to these private profiteers who use them to exploit more farm-hands, to build private capitalism among us at the expense of our public wealth.

"You have no cause to love kulaks; you and your family suffered exploitation by them. Yet you strengthen them against the Soviet people. That is your crime against the State."

Watching Stepan's response, the older man saw that his tactics were, at least in part, mistaken. He had explained as dispassionately as if he were lecturing on political economy, as if he asked Stepan, not to repent or to declare any allegiance, but merely to understand his own acts. The boy had a good brain; he was weighing and accepting the analysis. But he had also a fighting will and he was drawing the opposite conclusion from that which Nikolai Ivanovich desired.

"So that's why I've got to go to the White Bears—because I might be wrecking the country," he snapped with bravado, throwing his head back as if the magnitude of his crime gave him a twisted sense of importance, in which he was ready to take on the whole State.

"No!" Nikolai Ivanovich came back sharply. "You couldn't wreck the Soviet people. You can cause a little mess in one small district. But the trouble you cause us is nothing to the trouble you are causing yourself."

From the boy's expectant silence the man felt that he was on the right track. "You have a good brain," he continued, "a good deal of ingenuity and a talent for leadership. The procurer was telling me the other night how cleverly you organized those thefts. It seemed to me a pity that you should use those abilities to your own destruction instead of using them in useful leadership.

"In less than five years these kulaks who lord it over the village now will be finished. The production of our State industry is rising fast and will rise much faster. Tractors, harvester combines, and all kinds of modern machines are pouring into our State and collective farms. That will sweep this small-scale, backward farming from our soil much faster than you dream. You cannot stop us; you cannot delay us by a split second. But we are short of skilled people, of good organizers and leaders; you might be one of them and rise with us."

A fit of coughing stopped him. He drew a deep breath. This was proving harder than he had expected. He had said everything he could think of and could do nothing now but wait.

There was a long silence, while the words of the older man sank into the boy's mind. At last Stepan flung back his shoulders. "I guess you're right, but what's the use of talking? My next few years are settled anyway."

"Your future is never settled until you settle it."

"Why not? I have to go to the North, don't I?"

"Probably. Even there you have chances to grow, to organize and lead."

Stepan seized on the first word, "probably," and ignored the rest. "Do you mean to say it isn't certain about Bear Mountain?" he demanded passionately. "If I could stay here . . . If I could organize a gang on the Dnieper, the way you thought before all this . . . The river . . ."

The shock of a new hope broke through his defences. Unexpectedly, he broke into tempestuous sobs. Angry at his lack of self-control, he strode to the window and stood with his back to the room. The older man said nothing; this was not the time for words. He waited until Stepan turned around in full control of himself, but with eyes of questioning appeal.

"Nothing is certain," declared Nikolai Ivanovich, ignoring the outburst since Stepan wished it ignored. "I myself have been wanting you on the Dnieper. I think it likely that a boy of your age with your liking for the river would do better here. I was slow about it." His voice had a tone of regret. "Now we would have to convince the procurer and perhaps a judge. It depends on the kind of ties you have with the local kulaks and with the gangs you've organized. There'll have to be investigations to see whether your relations with our district can be useful or a clean break with this whole neighbourhood is better. If you like, we can take it up together with the procurer. He thinks pretty badly of you, but you will find him a not unreasonable man."

Stepan lifted his head and squared his shoulders with a firmness untainted by his former defiance. "When can we see the procurer?"

"Don't forget that you are staying at the jail," smiled Nikolai Ivanovich. "We'll meet there at the procurer's convenience. Don't be impatient; he may take time. He must make investigations. There's a guard waiting to take you back."

Shaking hands with Stepan, he gave his attention to the pile of work on his table. The boy walked toward the door, but before reaching it he stopped, looked at Nikolai Ivanovich and saw that he was busy, and hesitated as if he did not quite dare to interrupt.

"Was there something more you wanted?" asked the man at the desk.

"Why do you talk so easily about jails?" blurted out Stepan. "I never met anyone who took them that way before."

"Because I'm an old hand at them," smiled Nikolai Ivanovich. "I spent eight years in a jail under the Tsar. Much worse than the kind of jails we have. Solitary! Intended not to reclaim but to destroy."

Drawing a deep breath, Stepan looked at the older man with admiration. "They couldn't destroy you, could they?" he exclaimed. "What were you in for?"

"Fighting the form of society in which I lived. Same as you, but I fought the Tsar on behalf of the people. We won; that's history. You were fighting the Soviet people. You'd never win."

Stepan nodded slowly, then turned and walked to meet the guard in the outer office. He was aware of a strange new comradeship. He was still uncertain whether his own lot for the next few years would be on the Dnieper or in the Arctic camp of exile. This no longer seemed of first importance. Wherever he might be he was part of a great people whom nothing could stop in their march.

Even the procurer no longer seemed his natural enemy but an employee of his country, a man with an important job to do.

XII

FOR A LONG TWO WEEKS nothing seemed to happen. Stepan remained in a cell with several others, but without any of his previous companions. His cell-mates talked of their crimes and probable punishments. About none of this did Stepan want to think. His active mind was busy with methods of organizing a construction gang on the Dnieper. As one day monotonously followed another the hope of this seemed to recede. The procurer did not even send for him.

What worried him most was that no word came from Nikolai Ivanovich, whom he considered his chief champion and friend. The painfully slow passage of time in prison dimmed even the sharp memory of the old man's expression, intonations, and phrases. The perfect understanding which had seemed to penetrate all of Stepan's problems and aspirations took on the remoteness of a dream. At times he even wondered if the shop-committee chairman had been teasing him with hopes, merely to abandon him.

His own excellent intellect saved him from the worst despair. In the darkest moments he said to himself: "Even if he was playing with me, even if he has ditched me, the things he said were true." There came to him a new and bitter strength that was independent even of Nikolai Ivanovich.

On the fourteenth day of his imprisonment, the jailer told him that a visitor waited in the outer office. His heart leapt with hope that it might be the friend of whom he had been thinking; it sank when he found only Ilya Morosov in the visitors' room. He wondered if that goody-goody had come to gloat over him, now that his vaunted daring had brought him to grief.

Morosov's first words changed the picture that had taken shape in the long days and nights of jail. "I have a message from Nikolai Ivanovich. He is ill and has been sent to a sanitarium in the Crimea. He wanted you to know that he spoke to the procurer and asked me to help collect your 'characteristic' from among the people who have known you. I have now handed this in. The procurer is busy getting characteristics of the gang of thieves that worked with you. You should hear from him in a few days."

Stepan winced at the uncompromising allusion to his "gang of thieves," but he felt relieved. "Thank you, Ilya," he replied. "I wondered why I didn't hear from Nikolai Ivanovich. I'm sorry that he's ill." He wanted desperately to know what people had said about him but he did not know whether Morosov was allowed to tell this and his pride forbade him to ask.

All the rest of the day the sharp thought bit into him that his own immediate future would be determined by the opinions held of him among his earlier associates—all those whom he had either fought or disdained or swayed to his will. Their views, collected by Morosov who had never liked him and filtered through fine meshes of investigation by a procurer who had no reason to spare him, would decide his life.

What would Morosov say of him? "The fellow that wrecked the working schedules and demoralized the Young Ploughman." At the time when he had done this he had enjoyed provoking Morosov's dislike. What would Ivan say? Or even his good friends Marin and Peter? What could anyone say that would seem to a cold, impersonal procurer a reason for leaving him in a neighbourhood where he had done little but harm? He saw himself as the stable community must see him, and did not like what he saw.

Had Anya been questioned about him? What could she have said? How he stole his boss's vegetables; how he took her to visit the Lair; how she had been afraid and run away? Stepan shrank more from the thought that a cold-eyed procurer might learn of that moment when he had run up the rocks and shouted good-bye to the sun than over all the possible reports of his misdemeanours. Of course Anya wouldn't tell about that, but he hoped that the procurer knew nothing at all about Anya. Even if she should give him an excellent characteristic that made the procurer decide in his favour, he did not want to be saved in such a way.

The absence of Nikolai Ivanovich disturbed him. He had counted on the man's influence. He had little hope that the procurer would of himself reconsider his intention to exile the gang of thieves. Nikolai Ivanovich could do anything! Yet this man, busy with the affairs of a great plant and with a dozen important community problems, and exhausted to illness, had taken time for that long talk with Stepan and had remembered to speak to the procurer, to Morosov, and to send a message to the jail. His heart leapt with worship—and with happiness that he had such a friend and champion, even if he couldn't be here.

No! The old man was here with him. He had left his words. Stepan's spine straightened as he recalled what had been said about each man's free choice in his own fate. The things people would say of him would be bad enough; they might send him north. They couldn't settle his life for him.

"They fix the conditions but not what I do with them," he thought with a rushing sense of freedom. "It is I who decide my life."

On the sixteenth day of his imprisonment the procurer sent for him. Stepan tried to tell himself that what had seemed a lifetime wasn't really long. A thin, brisk man sat at a desk, scanning a small sheaf of reports. As he asked Stepan in a businesslike manner to be seated, the boy was sharply reminded of the other office in which he had sat two weeks before. There was even something about the procurer's manner—a dispassionateness, as if watching and analysing—which recalled Stepan's good friend. In Nikolai Ivanovich this observing manner had been warmed by his smile of deep understanding; in the procurer it was chilled by the cynical curve of his lips.

The man finished the page that he was reading, checked something on it with a pencil, and sent a level, piercing glance at Stepan. "You know, of course, that I consider that you and your whole gang should be sent north."

Stepan nodded. Touching the papers on his desk, the procurer went on. "Nikolai Ivanovich has great hopes of you, and I have learned to respect his hopes. At his request I obtained a fairly full characterization of your temperament and past life from those who knew you best: Morosov, Bobrov, Yeremeyev, a girl named Anya Kosareva, and others. I find that you have an excellent brain and some ability in organizing, and are capable of working hard when you wish. Against this are the facts that you usually avoid work, are unable or unwilling to co-operate with others, were the chief disrupter in the Young Ploughman, and wreck anything that you cannot boss."

Picking up a paper he read a marked sentence: *"He will work hard and fight hard if he can be leader; if he cannot, he will distrupt."* . . . He gave no clue to the author. Who had said it? Morosov? Ivan? Yeremeyev? Stepan thought bitterly that that single phrase had probably sealed his fate.

To the procurer the phrase was apparently not so decisive. "There is nothing bad in liking to run things," he continued. "Just now our country needs people who can be good leaders much more than it needs those able to be led. We have millions of unskilled peasants looking for jobs and ready to take orders; we have relatively few who know how to organize. But leadership is a serious matter. It requires not mere bossing but adjustment and co-operation. These things you might learn here or possibly better under a stricter régime in the North.

"So far I see no reason to change the decision to send you to Bear Mountain . . ."

Stepan's compressed lips gave no outward sign of the sudden sinking of his heart. His clear eyes watched intently as the procurer went on: ". . . except for this——" He picked up a slip of paper and read from it: *"Most of all he loves the river!"*

Was it Anya who had said that, Stepan wondered? It must be Anya; only to her had he shown so completely his feeling for the river and the wild cliffs on its shore. Had Anya really understood him, even when she ran away? Or had Nikolai Ivanovich said it? The old man knew. It wasn't likely that he had written a characteristic. It must be Anya after all.

"This might indicate a reason why you would work better on the Dnieper than in the Far North," the procurer was saying. "Against your love of the river is the undoubted fact that you have antagonized most of the people with whom you have associated on its shores. Your first gang has left you; they are working at the Red Dawn Farm. Your second gang consists of thieves. I doubt if you know any honest people who would want to work with you."

The summing up, given in a chilly manner, analytically, left Stepan little hope. Suddenly, the procurer hurled a direct question, fixing him with that penetrating glance. "If you were given a chance to organize a construction gang, how would you set about it? Have you any ideas?"

Convinced that the procurer had decided on exile, and merely asked as a last deference to Nikolai Ivanovich, Stepan flung out with bitter resignation: "Ideas? I've nothing but ideas. It's all I've thought of for the past two weeks—how I'd organize a construction gang."

For the first time the procurer looked at him with a curiosity that was almost interest. "Let's hear your ideas."

"Well," began Stepan with a touch of defiance, for he did not expect

81

the procurer to believe or care, "I think most of the fellows that helped steal the implements would be glad to work on the dam. They really weren't much interested in stealing. They were at loose ends and just picked up things that were handy. I was the one that thought of taking the implements; I knew how the kulaks wanted them and how much they would pay. The rest of them were rather worried about stealing such important stuff till I talked them into it. It would be lots easier to talk them into working on the dam."

The procurer's interest deepened. He knew perfectly well that Stepan was the ringleader, but he had not known that the boy was so conscious of the technique of leadership. He was especially surprised at the frankness with which Stepan admitted this to him. The shop-committee chairman had been right: there was something in this fellow.

Unaware of the growing change in the man's attitude, for the procurer was a close-faced man, Stepan went doggedly on: "Of course you couldn't rely on this bunch alone. You'd have to mix in some fellows that know how to work. I'd want some from the Red Dawn Farm, if you'd let me have them. Marin and Peter could each handle six; they're used to working in groups of six at the farm."

As he rushed ahead, his plan of work again began to glow with reality. It seemed something that could happen overnight. Then he became aware that he was weaving this dream, not, as he had done for a fortnight, untrammelled by anything but his own imagination, but in the presence of the man who had power to permit or refuse its fulfilment. He scanned the procurer's face but it told him nothing. He was not used to people whose faces said nothing. He came unhappily to a stop.

"You have been doing quite a bit of constructive thinking," said the procurer slowly. "I am not sure that your ideas would work. You propose to reclaim a gang of thieves right here on Dneprostroi. It would be a very useful thing. I think you underestimate the difficulties. You have big dreams but dreams must be pinned to realities. Do you really imagine that this Marin and Peter, assuming that they are honest, industrious workers now on the Red Dawn Farm, would leave it to work with a gang of thieves?"

Stepan flushed. His former ascendance over Marin and Peter had made him so sure of them that he had not thought of this view of the case. He stuck to his plan stubbornly: "I don't know how they'd feel about the other thieves——" He did not even shrink as he thus honestly classified himself. "I know they'd rather work with me than with Ivan, and I know they like the river better than the farm. I guess it would depend on how you put it up to them. I think they'd come if they could be my chief assistants. Would everybody know that it was a gang of thieves?"

"Everybody that cared to," nodded the procurer. "You would be working under sentence at Dneprostroi, just as if you were in the North.

82

You would not be free to change jobs, as other workers are; you could leave only with police permission. Your trade union would be told of your crime and sentence, and the administration would deduct part of every pay cheque for your fine. Your living standards under such conditions would be no better than in Bear Mountain—possibly not as good. In some ways it might be harder for you to be among your former acquaintances who will know your crime and your sentence."

"I hadn't thought of that." Stepan recalled how bitterly he had refused to work under lesser disgrace at the Red Dawn Farm.

"You still prefer the river?"

Stepan answered firmly: "Yes."

"You still think that Marin and Peter would be glad to work with you under these conditions?"

"I don't know," admitted Stepan miserably, but then his trust in his friends revived and he was ashamed for doubting them. Lifting his head he affirmed: "If I said I needed them, I know they would."

"We'll take the next week to see if you can realize your project," the procurer granted. "There's no party leaving for Bear Mountain for a couple of weeks, anyway. You'll stay in the jail but I'll give you access to the other thieves, to discuss with them the question of working at Dneprostroi. I warn you: they'll all say they want to work here in order to avoid going north. Make the conditions plain to them and test their answers. If you ask anyone to stay you become personally responsible for his conduct, and may be held liable if he again runs afoul of law. Consider them seriously. Meanwhile I will see if Dneprostroi has a place for you, and find out what Marin and Peter say. The word of any Red Dawn Farm boys will count. Decision will be reached a week from to-day."

Stepan knew that he was dismissed. His hopes seemed nearer but he left with a heavier step. To work on the dam had been glamorous as a dream. Now that it might be reduced to reality, it was dark with responsibility and chequered with conditions. It was no simple job to be mastered by energy and a winning manner. It depended not only on himself but on complex relations with other people. What sacrifices would Peter and Marin make for him? Could he base his life on his judgment of youths whom he knew only as thieves? Facing such questions, he knew for the first time not the exaltation but the heaviness of leadership.

He waited for two days before taking advantage of the procurer's permission to speak to members of his gang. Thinking them over one by one, he asked about each: "Would I stake my future on him?" Then he talked to them individually. Two of them did not want to work on the dam; they were angry at Stepan for getting them into trouble and hoped to escape on the way north. The other nine were eager to work on the Dnieper, but as Stepan talked with them he realized that they had not really accepted the conditions but expected to evade them. Failing that, they seemed to think a job on the Dnieper would be an easy place from which to run away.

How could he make such boys into dependable workers? He had thought of them hitherto as profitable and subordinate companions; as such they did fairly well. The procurer's problem, which had become his problem, was to fit them into life as useful citizens. Stepan's heart sank at the thought of giving such irresponsible people power over his future.

Despondent, he was almost ready to renounce the lot of them, except for Maxim. He felt sure that Maxim, whether or not he liked the work on the dam, was personally loyal to him and would not let him down. He really trusted none of the others, but he felt that he had to show some gang to the procurer or he himself might not be allowed to stay. Besides, he could not bear to think that by refusing his former companions he might condemn them to exile for thefts in which he himself was most to blame.

An older and much chastened Stepan faced the procurer candidly the following week.

"There is only one I feel sure of. There are two that don't want to stay. Four more I would take a chance on because I can handle them. The other four want to stay but I'm not at all sure I can make them work or keep them from running away. I'd hate to have my future depend on them. All the same, I don't want to refuse them and have you send them north."

With a wry smile he added: "I don't know what you're going to do about it. You were right; it was harder than I supposed."

"You did as well as I expected," stated the procurer. "The most important thing is that you yourself have now a clear picture of each of them and have made up your mind how you would handle him. But you haven't shown me a good construction brigade."

"I've failed, then," said Stepan heavily. "I've shown you all I've got." Then he asked the question which was still very important to him whatever might be decided about his work. "What did Marin and Peter say?"

For the first time in their relations, the procurer's thin lips curved into a pleasant smile. "You have better friends than I thought possible. Not only Marin and Peter, but three other boys who were in your earlier gang would rather work with you on the Dnieper Dam than stay with the Red Dawn Farm. I don't know how much of it is a liking for you and how much is dislike for farming. But there is it; they have chosen. You have five honest, hard-working friends. With their help I think you might be able to discipline all nine of your recent associates. I'll take a chance on it if you will."

The sudden relief was almost too much for Stepan. He started to let out a whoop. He checked it and almost sobbed. Then he reflected that he was now leader of a construction brigade on what was going to be the biggest dam in the world. As such he might appropriately shake hands with anyone, even with a procurer who had been about to exile him to the North.

More cordially than Stepan had expected, the procurer shook hands and gave a parting admonition: "Get this straight! Don't forget what saved you. Not I, not even Nikolai Ivanovich, but five youths who think you are good to work with. Their choice gives you the chance to be a foreman. They are as much a part of the job as you."

After Stepan left, the procurer took up his pen and wrote a letter to the man who was awaiting his report in a sanitarium on the shores of the Black sea.

DEAR NIKOLAI IVANOVICH,—You still know how to pick them. I thought you had gone sentimental over that handsome young thief. I recalled, however, that when I was a green apprentice seven years back at the *Kommunar*, it was you who incited me to work on the committee for factory inspection and later recommended me for a scholarship in law. I felt I owed you a thorough consideration of your new protégé.

As you surmised, the boy has something in him. He was astoundingly frank in admitting his primary responsibility for the serious political aspect of the thefts. He proposed to turn his thieves into construction workers—a project on which I have some doubts. But he seems to know what he is doing, and he knows how to arouse loyalty; we actually unearthed five members of the Red Dawn Farm who are eager to work with him.

When you return, you should find him working at "forced labour" on the dam as leader of a gang of fourteen. I'll tell the trade union to watch his work; they'll see that he doesn't have it easy. He will thrive best on a hard fight.

XIII

THE ODOUR OF FRESH sun-baked lumber came pleasantly to Stepan's nostrils as he waited in line at the Labour Exchange. He looked curiously about at the many indications of new and perhaps interesting work. Through the rough frames of unfinished barracks he saw the rock-crushing plant, the concrete-mixing towers, and the glistening railway spur. Just beyond lay the steep drop to the river.

He could see Kichkas easily across the river a little to the north. Downstream, farther away, were the cliffs of Cossacks' Lair. He stared at them sombrely. He had not visited the Lair since Anya ran away from him; after two winters the Lair was still an ache in his breast. He had brought away the best it had given him; Marin, Peter, and the others had met him at the jail that morning and stood beside him now in the warm summer sun.

"I never did like farming," cried Marin, striking Stepan on the shoulder. "We're building a Giant! The biggest dam in the world! The whole Soviet Union is looking at us!"

He had to shout above the noise of construction. The air vibrated with sound: the short, sharp puffs of engines, the whistles of locomotives and rolling of wheels, the rasp of saws cutting into timber, and above all these, like distant machine guns, the rat-tat-tat of pneumatic drills biting into the river granite.

A deafening siren cut off Stepan's answer. Everyone jumped. Over near the river's edge men were running. Stepan was shaken by apprehension; he saw that some of the gang were terrified. Quickly he glanced through the windows of the Labour Exchange and observed that the girl clerks sat placidly, paying no attention to the siren.

"It's nothing, fellows," he said confidently. He did not tell them what it was, for he did not know.

"They're getting ready to blast," remarked a stocky man in a clean, khaki-coloured blouse, hurrying past the waiting line and pushing into the Exchange ahead of the rest. Thirty shots of dynamite went off in the river bed, louder than all the noise there had been before. Below the bank arose a great cloud of dust, from which was heard the clatter of falling rock.

"How can we work in a place like this?" asked Vassili, a pock-marked thief whom Stepan had not wanted to retain.

Vassili's pale face and twitching hands strengthened Stepan with the sense of his responsibility as leader. "Huh! You'll get used to more than that," he rejoined, nonchalantly lifting his shoulders and walking to the edge of the bank to look down.

Below him lay the heart of the great construction. Close to the bank a crater of torn rock, extended almost a third of the way across the river, from which it was reclaimed by an encircling dyke of logs and rocks. From this hollow the explosions had come. Across the river a similar excavation was protected by a similar bulwark built out from the cliffs of the other shore. Between the two shore-bound and roughly circular craters, the river swept in mid-channel, more swiftly because confined.

Gangs of men with heavy drills were moving back to their stations after the blasting. The rat-tat-tat in the river bed again began.

Marin called "It's almost our turn, Stepan." Reluctantly Stepan left the facinating first sight of the men attacking the river and went into the Labour Exchange.

Applicants for work were scattering to different placards on the large, waist-high barrier, behind which worked a dozen clerks. Stepan began to spell out the signs, and felt ashamed to be so slow at it. Marin was quicker; he read the signs to Stepan. They indicated different kinds of labour; wood-workers, rock drillers, concrete layers. Stepan decided then and there that, as a construction foreman, he must really learn to read and write properly.

What job would he get? He did not even know what the different kinds of work involved. Behind the barrier, talking to a girl clerk, was the man who had told about the blasting. The man looked up and realized Stepan's perplexity. Leaning over the barrier he spoke.

"Is this your first time here?" Stepan nodded. "Assigned to any special brigade?"

"Well, in a way," began Stepan, and told how he and his gang were sent by the procurer.

At Stepan's first words the man seemed disappointed but as the explanation progressed he grew relieved. "That's all right. I thought you had signed up with someone else. I'm looking for drilling gangs. I'll take the whole fourteen." Misunderstanding Stepan's hesitation, he added with a touch of scorn: "Afraid to work in the river bed?"

"Is that where you work?" asked Stepan, brightening. "I saw it from the bank and I'd like to work there. Does our being under sentence make any difference?"

"All the better for me," replied the drill boss. "You won't run out on me. These seasonal workers from the farms are the devil; when you most need them they leave. How long do you have to stay?"

"A year," answered Stepan shortly, annoyed and yet relieved at the casual attitude towards his sentence.

"Sign them up as drillers," the drill boss called to the girl at the counter. "From the procurer. Ought to be in your files already. Look 'em up and give 'em a barracks."

"Come to the cofferdam office at three-thirty," he told Stepan. "The cofferdam is that big dyke of logs and stones out in the river. The office is under the bank. Ask for A. Kopilov, drill boss of the north section. You'll go to work at four sharp on the swing shift."

The young woman turned to the files but these were in chronic disorder, for the office workers were inexperienced newcomers, like everyone else. Between attending to impatient demands at the counter, she tried ineffectually to locate something about this "forced-labour" group. Finally she went out to lunch, leaving the Stepan gang waiting.

"When do we eat?" asked Marin. Inquiry showed a nearby dining-room, but it was only for construction workers and they were not yet registered. Stepan and his gang were all hungry; it seemed they would go without lunch.

A middle-aged man in white blouse came into the space behind the counter, laid his brief case on a desk and began to look through the files. A moment later he answered the phone and then called Stepan. "Are you the bunch sent here by the procurer?"

Stepan assented. The man turned back to the phone, showing a bald spot ringed by grizzled hair. "Yes, they're here. I'll tend to it."

Hanging up the phone he spoke to Stepan. "Have you any skill or choice in work? We'll get you registered and assigned to a barracks."

Stepan replied that he had agreed to begin drilling that afternoon under Kopilov. The man laughed appreciatively. "That Kopilov gets round. Wish all our drill bosses were as energetic. Then all you need is a barracks and——"

"Lunch!" interrupted Stepan. The man nodded and the gang relaxed with relief.

The bald man made out two orders, signed them, stamped them with a seal, and handed them to Stepan. "The first is for your barracks. Over to the third row of trees and down-stream half a mile. I think the roof's on, but that's about all you can hope. The second is for lunch this noon; Kopilov will assign you to a dining-room after this."

As Stepan started to leave the older man detained him. "The procurer says you know Nikolai Ivanovich." When Stepan's face lit up, the man seemed pleased. "He's a good friend to keep hold of. I knew him in trade-union work long before the Revolution. Trade unions were illegal then but he could organize under any handicap."

"I wish he were here. I'd like to tell him about my new job."

The old trade unionist nodded. "Why don't you write him?" Seeing Stepan's embarrassment he thundered: "What! You can't write? Shameful! A man of your age! Join up at once; we have classes in every section. You won't stay brigade leader long unless you learn. Come back for anything you need, but not till you've joined a class. I'm Petrov, of the trade union's central committee. I drop in here during lunch."

The dining-room was jammed; there was a waiting line. At last they reached the cashier's desk, exchanged their signed slip for fourteen tickets, and found places on long benches at the rough unpainted table. One wall was torn open to the air; through it they could see that the dining-room was being enlarged.

"Everything growing like mushrooms," remarked the irrepressible Marin. "Dam, barracks, dining-room, all splitting their pants."

The waiter slapped soup on the table in heavy white earthenware bowls—"peasant soup," containing large chunks of potatoes, cabbage, and beets and a small hunk of fat meat. He brought plates of *kasha*, a buckwheat cereal covered with gravy, in which swam another thin slice of meat. Glasses of *compote* were added—sliced apples with skin on and core still in them, boiled in an almost sugarless syrup with a few raisins

88

and dried apricots. All this food was planked down so casually that the soup and *compote* slopped over the edges, while the meat and *kasha* slid across the plates.

The Stepan gang had never learned fastidiousness. "Wow! Three courses!" grinned Maxim, sinking his teeth into a large cube of the dark, satisfying wheat bread. "We're going to like it here."

After lunch they walked down wide dusty streets and found their barracks. It was one of a dozen facing the four sides of a city block and backing towards a central outhouse used in common by all. None of the buildings were finished; walls were up and roofs were on but neither doors nor windows had arrived. Lumber for plank beds, tables, and benches lay about. These unfinished houses were already filled by the pressure of workers for quarters. The one assigned to the Stepan gang was occupied by sixteen men who had overflowed from the barracks next door into what seemed vacant space, and had got a stamped "order" signed by their section boss to reinforce their squatters' rights. They waved this truculently, making it clear that they would not give up without a struggle the living space they had seized.

"Let's throw them out," cried Maxim, starting towards the barracks, tossing his sandy hair like a flag for advance.

"Come back," commanded Stepan. The ex-thief reluctantly returned and the gang went into conference. "We haven't time for a fight," judged Stepan. "We must be at the cofferdam. We want a good record our first day."

"Where do we sleep to-night?" demanded Maxim, amid nods of agreement from the former thieves.

At this critical moment Marin returned from the outhouse, with a grin of triumph on his face. He exchanged whispers with Stepan, who at once ordered the gang to move up the street. As soon as they were out of earshot Marin told them—he had learned it in the outhouse—that most of the squatters worked on the midnight shift.

"There'll be only a few of them when we get back to-night," plotted Stepan. "We'll throw them out and barricade ourselves in, and post sentries while we sleep. We'll get it all settled to-morrow; our paper is the right one, signed by the Labour Exchange."

Everyone cheerfully agreed. For the first time since they had met that morning, the five Red Dawn boys and the nine ex-thieves felt themselves a single unit, knit by the prospect of a good fight.

Uncertain of the exact time because they had no watches, they reached the cofferdam office half an hour early. Kopilov was pleasantly surprised.

"From now on," he told them, "listen for the special whistle half an hour before each change of shift. It's meant for all you peasant workers; none of you have any clocks. None of you ever counted time. Now you must count it accurately. That's the first thing to learn. This dam has a definite schedule for every part of the work. If you're late on your part, you hold up the dam, and that holds up our whole country. The Soviet Union is counting on us. Now let's get to work."

They went down into a torn universe of broken rock. By planks tossed across chaos they moved towards the centre of the river. High above them roared a locomotive; around them a steel host of cranes and steam shovels swung great arms at incredible angles. Stepan saw with a thrill that he was below the surface of the river; he could hear the waves swirling higher than his head against the outer wall of the dyke. He was below even what used to be the river bed. Far down, far down these great foundations had to go.

"Watch that other gang," shouted Kopilov. They had reached the working place.

Stepan saw a group of men around an implement that was making that machine-gun sound in the heart of the rock. The man who held the drill was shaking with it. Near him stood another man with a long thin metal rod. A dozen men were clearing the rock's surface, preparing it for drilling or taking away debris of past explosions.

"The direction and depth of drilling are marked on this chart," explained Kopilov. "Your helper measures the depth with that rod. When you have drilled enough, you write on the rock the number of cartridges needed. That's for the powder gang; they come through later and set off all the charges at once. The shift is changing now; I'll show you how to operate the drill."

Simple enough to Kopilov, the explanation completed Stepan's confusion. How could he read a chart? What were cartridges? And a powder gang? How would he ever know his way about in this terrific chaos?

The gang spread out and awkwardly took up the picks and shovels. Stepan laid his hands on the drill; Marin stood beside him with chart and measuring rod. The drill began to shake; Stepan's body shook with it. Under his feet he heard the now familiar sound—but louder, sending a shudder through the earth.

He was cutting deep into the bedrock of the river, which no one had ever penetrated, which the waters had buried for ages from the touch and the sight of man. The virgin heart of this bedrock was yielding to his hard pressure. He was making over the Dnieper; he was making over the world. With savage joy he probed for the solid foundation that would hold against high water for a thousand coming years.

XIV

THE SAVAGE JOY became a still more savage pain. After the first half-hour Stepan's hands blistered; it was torture to hold the drill. This was as nothing to the recurrent agony that shook his body until it seemed that he would be torn apart. When they stopped for supper he could eat nothing. He sat doubled up on a rock. After supper he yielded the drill to Marin; then all the gang took turns. Stepan held it oftenest and longest. When they went to the barracks at midnight and threw out the squatters he could not sleep. Next morning he limped to the Labour Exchange and made their tenancy secure.

By the third day he recovered enough to ask about the courses in reading and writing. He had made up his mind to get ahead fast on the dam; reading was clearly the first step. There was a small evening class already but Stepan was working evenings. Kopilov told him that the trade union would supply a teacher to any ten workers at their most convenient hour. Stepan roped in the nine thieves, all of whom were illiterate, and got in several more from the swing shift for an afternoon class before work.

No one knew who started the idea of a contest between the two classes. "Socialist competition" was in the air. Stepan became chief promoter. To show his gang better than the others would help wash out the difference he keenly felt between them and workers whose record was unstained. Petrov at trade union headquarters helped him work out the terms of the competition. Its aim was that everyone in both groups should read and write simple Russian by the November holidays. The reading test would be an article in the dam's newspaper, the *Dneprostroi Worker*; the writing test the preparation of a short item for a new wall newspaper, the *Likbez*—Liquidation of Illiteracy—to be launched at the holidays. The best group would have a banner in the demonstration.

"We're going to win that banner!" boasted Stepan. "We'll work our heads off!"

"Why not consider a bigger competition?" smiled Petrov, shrewdly estimating the lad's enthusiasm. "Not merely between two classes but among all the drilling gangs on the left bank. Stamp out all the illiteracy among the drillers by November 7th. That'll be worth fighting for."

"It would be fine," approved Stepan, "but I couldn't organize it. I don't know enough people yet."

"Get in touch with the *Komsomol* of the cofferdam. They'll help you put it through."

Young Andreyev, the tow-headed secretary of the cofferdam unit of the *Komsomol*, was delighted with Stepan's proposal. He was a conscientious youth, not very efficient, who had been unable to think of anything for his unit to do in honour of the approaching holidays. The *Komsomol* was not yet very strong among the construction workers, who had come from the rural districts more interested in making a little money than in study or civic affairs. If the new energy brought by Stepan really helped stamp out illiteracy at the cofferdam it would be worth celebrating.

"There'll be a lot of organizing to do. We ought to have some help from the city headquarters," proposed Andreyev.

"How do you get in touch with them?" asked Stepan, ready to start at once.

"Could you go down to the city office? I'm working on the day shift. We'd save time if we could get everything started at the regular *Komsomol* meeting here to-night."

"I'm not a member," doubted Stepan.

"That doesn't matter in the least," said Andreyev. "Tell them you're starting a competition against illiteracy. "They won't throw you out."

The city secretary was enthusiastic. "We might get you help from the students at the Party Training School." Reading the names aloud, he came to Ilya Morosov. To Stepan's remark that he knew him, the secretary asked: "Do you think he would be good?"

A flash of jealousy made Stepan hesitate. This was exactly the work in which Morosov would shine. Morosov might capture the fame of it. "What would we need him for? Would he run it?" he asked.

Sensing the antagonism, the secretary replied: "You local people would run it, but Morosov has experience that might show you how. I'm not sure that he would do it; these students are everywhere in demand."

Stepan was now quite sure that he wanted Morosov. "Could he come out to-night? We've got to get started at once."

The secretary was already at the phone. Unable to reach Morosov, he left a message. "We of the city office think it important, not only for immediate results in education, but for the growth of the cofferdam *Komsomol*. The demand starts from non-Party workers and we must do everything to help."

At midnight, when Stepan came off shift, he found Andreyev and Morosov waiting to consult about future plans. The *Komsomol* had decided to launch the drive on Sunday, at a general mass meeting of cofferdam workers.

"Would you make one of the speeches, Stepan?" asked Morosov. "The competition was your idea." Stepan was flattered but apprehensive. He had never spoken at a big workers' meeting.

He felt the small attendance on Sunday as a personal affront. Morosov and Andreyev were fairly well satisfied, since a quarter of the cofferdam's workers came. Stepan had promoted the meeting for two full days and considered that everybody should now realize the importance of learning to read and write. In his annoyance at the absentees, he forgot his lack of experience in speaking and hurled his words out energetically.

"Fellows, the whole country's looking at our Dneprostroi. Not only the country but even the whole world. We're building the biggest dam in the world and we can't be kept back by illiterate people. I came on as brigade leader, head of fourteen. I couldn't even read the papers that gave us barracks and tickets for our meals. I'm not going to be that way any longer. I'm going to learn everything about the dam, and maybe some day be an engineer. Besides, we cofferdam workers want to get ahead of the rest of Dneprostroi and have a banner about it November 7th!"

He was vociferously applauded, as much for his flashing eyes and magnetic voice as for his words. When a resolution was unanimously passed that everyone should become literate by November 7th, Stepan thought the job practically done. Organizing was a simple thing to do.

He was stunned when the committee stayed to plan the work and Morosov listed what still had to be done. "First we must get exact check-up: how many can read, how many are totally illiterate, how many half-literate. We'll learn this to-morrow by a sub-committee of three, one on each shift. We must find the most convenient hours for all of them and get teachers and classrooms. Since there won't be enough teachers, we must launch the slogan: 'Everyone who reads must teach one other.' Every *Komsomol* member must keep pushing the idea on the job, get help for those who lag, and cricitize the wilfully lazy in the wall newspaper. The best ones will become the editorial board to get out the *Likbez* special number on November 7th. We'll ask the trade unions for a special place in the demonstration."

What an amount of complicated work to put over so simple and excellent an idea as learning to read! Just as he, Stepan, had been learning how to blow up the bedrock of the river, Morosov had learned a special technique for penetrating the bedrock of the social structure, blowing it up and making of it a new foundation. For the first time Stepan felt for Morosov admiration untainted by jealousy.

As they left the committee Morosov fell into step beside him. "That was a fine speech you made, Stepan. You stirred them up. We've every chance to carry it through."

Warmed by the appreciation, Stepan asked: "Is this the kind of work you do now, Ilya? Have you left Red Dawn? The boys tell me they got the old State Farm and a tractor and an incubator."

"I handle their city connections and go there often," replied Morosov. "The farm does very well now with its land all in one piece. Several peasant families have joined; they have nearly forty members. Anya Kosareva may come in; I've been urging her to start a vegetable department."

'What does she say about it?" Stepan's pulse quickened.

"Last year she wasn't interested. She didn't like all the turmoil over the new tractor. Your old boss Krotov stirred up a lot of talk about the 'devil machine.' Anya farms scientifically but she's conservative socially; she feels what the neighbours say. The talk died down and the farm is plainly succeeding. She's become good friends with them, especially with

Stesha and Ivan, and this is drawing her closer to the farm. It would be a good thing for everyone if she should join."

So Anya was drifting toward Ivan, and Ilya was helping it along! This thought checked the friendliness Stepan had begun to feel for Morosov, but did not prevent their co-operation in the drive against illiteracy. Stepan spent eight hours a day promoting it among the workers. Morosov, from his school, telephoned about teachers and classrooms. The city office of the *Komsomol* gave every possible help. All these forces working together brought victory.

"We are 100 per cent. literate!" was the proud boast flung to the breeze by their big red banner at the November celebrations. A critic might have found the claim exaggerated, for some of the claimants could still read only very simple words and write little more than their names. All of them could read the safety signs on the job and accidents had fallen off. All could read the directions posted about the construction and the newspaper headlines discussing the dam; this made their work more efficient. Stepan and some of the better students had learned as much in that two months' drive as more casual students in a year.

Marching at the head of the demonstration, Stepan and the other cofferdam workers got fine places to see the main event of the day: the laying of the first concrete on a pier in the river bed. To a loud blare of bands a brightly burnished locomotive steamed away from the concrete-mixing plant, pulling a train of giant buckets of ready concrete. With a gread red star for headlight and red-bannered sides, it puffed to the spot where stood a tall, similarly decorated crane. Like a giant bird, the crane stretched its long neck and stuck out a thin tongue of steel cable with a strong hook. A moment later, the first bucket was swinging from the beak of the mighty bird, which turned with its prey back to its original position and proudly lowered the concrete far down into the river bed.

Everybody shouted. The year of preliminary work was finished; the real construction had begun. The first man-made rock was joined by reinforcing irons to the living rock deep within the bed of the river.

Elated with the day and with their own success, Stepan's gang was moving toward the dining-hall, when Peter caught sight of a group of familiar forms. "Look, Stepan," he pointed in excitement, "the boys of the Red Dawn Farm!"

Stepan's delight in the celebration was at once tremendously increased. For two years he had avoided the Red Dawn Farm and most of its members, at first because he disliked farming and later with shame because of his sentence for theft. Now he had begun to succeed; he had learned to read and write and he had organized a competition. Ivan had come a long way by horse cart to see the great dam's triumph in whic Stepan shared. The pang of jealousy that shot through him at the sight

94

of Anya with Ivan was eased by the thought that she would see his triumph too.

"Hello, Stepan," called Ivan, approaching in a friendly manner. "It won't be long before your dam is giving us light and power at the farm! We've all come to see it."

Anya greeted him cordially. "I'm glad to see you getting ahead so well. I was worried when you disappeared for so long." She gave him her hand warmly.

As his eyes met hers she felt for an instant as if she stood again in the Lair with him, thrilled but terrified by his untamed power. Then she saw around her the cheerfully friendly faces of the Red Dawn farmers and the vision of the Lair passed as swiftly as it had come. A constraint came into her manner. She reminded herself that this tall, vital youth had twice disturbed her deeply and each time left her without explanation. This time she must stay free of him; her placid relation with Ivan had grown until she had begun to think of marriage and of the Red Dawn Farm as her future home.

With the touch of her hand the tension was communicated to Stepan. The memory of that last meeting was still for him a pain. It had marked the end of boyhood and the beginning of his darker wanderings. Here she was planning a life on Ivan's farm as if there had been nothing between them. He would not let himself be hurt by her again.

"Come on, everybody. I'll show you the place where I'm working," he cried, resolutely breaking through his embarrassment and assuming command of the group.

They followed him down into the chaos of rocks, planks, rails, and machinery. He showed them the pneumatic drill that he had first used and the heavier electric bore which made deeper, wider holes. He let them lift the crowbars with which some members of his gang moved big rocks, the sledge hammers with which others broke them to pieces, and the *nosilka*, the wooden stretcher on poles with which they carted off the dirt. Like an old hand, he talked with authority about surveyors who marked the places for him to drill and the powder gangs that followed him to set off the dynamite cartridges.

Flattered by their admiration at his familiarity with technical matters, Stepan expanded beyond his own job and showed everything he knew about the dam. "The sand comes from the Black Sea—from Eupatoria." He proudly pointed to the great pile by the concrete mixers. "The cement in those heavy bags is from the Donbas. We crush the granite from the river bed to make a special kind of gravel, not round like pebbles, but with sharp edges that grip firmly. It's all mixed together into the concrete that we laid at the celebration to-day."

On the way to the dining-hall, he boastfully pointed out the first-aid station to which the members of his gang went in case of accidents, the clinic and hospital for serious ailments, the big trade school, high on the bank, where they taught every kind of skill that was needed from concrete-laying to engineering.

"That's where I'm going to study this winter," he boasted, "now that I can read and write."

All over the construction site they saw other workers similarly exhibiting the dam to their home folks. The half-literate peasants of a hundred villages—some of them had come more than a day's horse-drawn journey —learned that day that men of their own kind, from their own farms, were building the world's greatest dam.

Some of the glory of the dam was reflected on Stepan. The young, successful members of the Red Dawn Farm, several of whom had been in Stepan's gang before the days of the Young Ploughman, began to feel his old ascendance. Again he became more glamorous to them than Ivan, as the dam was more glamorous than the farm. Anya felt this. She moved closer to Ivan, as if to protect him and to assert her independence of the spell.

"I've about decided to join the Red Dawn Farm," she volunteered to Stepan as they entered the dining-room, "if I can get Ivan to put a good vegetable department on the budget. He thinks the farm will make more from wheat and from seasonal work on the dam. The girls agree with me, but Ivan has a man's disdain for our women's work."

"I'm interested in your vegetables, Anya," protested Ivan. "But vegetables on a large scale take too much labour."

Stepan's eyes darkened as Anya and Ivan sat down together. He moved away from them, took his place at the other end of the long table between Shubina and Stesha, and began to ask the girls about their work.

"I heard about your machine that makes chickens. I understand it really works."

The light that came into Shubina's face surprised him. How she had improved in the years at the Red Dawn Farm! She was large and healthy-looking, with firm red cheeks, quite unlike the pallid girl who had nearly died. There was something of Anya in her manner—the calm poise of a farm girl. If her pale gold hair had been more vivid it would have been like Anya's too. Her happiness was pleasant to look at when she talked about the farm.

"Nobody really believed it would make chickens; I didn't believe it myself," she laughed. "But there it was, a prize all the way from Rostov, addressed to me, marked 'INCUBATOR, Capacity 100 Eggs.' There was a little booklet telling how to use it. The words were technical and I couldn't yet read very well. I got Morosov to read it on one of his weekends at the farm.

"I didn't tell Ivan or any of the boys about it for fear they would laugh. I set it on the far side of my bed in the room where I slept with Stesha and three other girls. I put in some left-over eggs that I could get without any questions. Every day I turned the eggs and looked and listened carefully to the machine and wondered if it was really making chickens.

"The twenty-one days went by and nothing happened. I said to myself: 'You fool, it's good you told no one. You merely spoiled the eggs.' Late that night I was awakened by a pecking and a cracking. I jumped out of bed to look. The eggs were splitting in the middle and the chicks were coming out! I was never so excited in my life!"

"She didn't sleep for the rest of the night, and didn't let us sleep either," smiled Stesha. "In the morning we called Ivan and all the boys. 'Where did you get those chicks?' they asked her. 'Not that machine! No, we won't believe you!' It was the sensation of the whole farm."

"Of the whole village," declared Shubina proudly. "I was the centre of the attack the priest made on our farm. 'Unholy—to make life by machinery. Resist the devil; keep your old holy life.'" Her pale blue eyes glowed as she added: "What was my old holy life that I should wish to keep it? I wanted a new life.

"We don't use left-over eggs now. We supply pure-bred hens to Kichkas peasants so that farm women will have a good return for their hard work. It took a while to convince Ivan, but now he's all for improving the breed for the whole village. He's slow to start but he sticks when he's made up his mind."

She sent a warm glance to the far end of the table, where Ivan was absorbed in a conversation with Anya. Stepan saw that her face clouded a little. So Shubina was interested in Ivan and thought that there was something between him and Anya. Stepan saw his former chum in a new light, as the most successful young farmer in Kichkas, well worth the admiration of a girl.

He frowned. He did not single Anya out in the farewells, but said good-bye to the visiting group as a whole. That night he lay awake in a restlessness of defeated longing until Marin, noticing his tossing, loudly whispered to him to go to sleep.

XV

"WE DON'T WANT to be just drillers," Stepan announced to the gang a few days later. "Let's learn concrete-pouring next."

"What's the matter with drilling?" asked Maxim. "It's well paid. You thought it was fine when we began."

"Drilling's all right," said Stepan, "but it's just tearing things apart. I saw that at the celebration. The work they cheered was the concrete-laying. When you blow out the rock you've only a hole in which something has to be built. It's the concrete that lasts forever. I want to learn everything there is to learn about concrete, all the kinds there are and how they're made."

"You're going to be God making rock," jeered Marin, but he liked the idea of a change and they all agreed.

Stepan enrolled in the trade school; its evening courses were fortunately adapted to workers' attainments. He learned chiefly from lectures and practical demonstrations; in reading he was still painfully slow. He had been proud of his quickness but in this new field he felt awkward in mind. He knew none of the necessary arithmetic, and except for his two months' class in reading had never learned habits of study. The work on the dam had not unduly tired his strong young body, but when he added the hours of unaccustomed brain work he felt exhausted. He grew thin and worn as he went at it bitterly, relentlessly, trying to compress into one winter the achievements that more leisurely students spread through two or three years.

At first he thought that in a month or two he would know "everything about concrete." Then he would stop and celebrate. As the weeks went by, he saw that each new bit of knowledge was not an end but a widening highway that led to other knowledge. He was appalled but quickened to see how much there was to know. In the excitement of this new conquest he had no time for anything else. To Andreyev's great regret he dropped out of the life of the *Komsomol* as soon as the banner was won. He had not even time to think much about Anya. When his mind turned to her he fretted over the thought that she might marry Ivan. He brushed this worry roughly aside, telling himself that in order to succeed with her or with any girl he must first succeed with himself.

As winter wore on he watched with new eyes the changing moods of the river. In boyhood he had thrilled to the roar of the spring high water, the fascinating revelations which the summer ebb made in the river bed, the winter struggle of the rapids against the icebound shore. These changes in the river now became conditions to be studied and to some extent controlled. The final victory over the Dnieper in what Nikolai Ivanovich had called the war of the working class with Nature could be won only by a careful strategy combining swift advances with the orderly consolidation of all gains.

In winter the work was still largely preparatory. Then spring high water swept over the cofferdams and buried the working site under the flood. Only when the high water had partly subsided and the great pumps sucked dry the enclosed spaces could Dneprostroi swing into the fullest momentum of work. By this time—the summer of 1929—Stepan's gang was pouring concrete.

The whole picture of the dam site had been changing. Stepan had helped make the changes and had changed with them so that he no longer thought how the working place looked yesterday but only how it looked to-day. It had become to him natural that solid rock and even the shape of the earth itself should be only material, all the time being shifted. There was no ground level, even for measurements, at the dam; they took sea level for calculations. On the job there were many levels, varying from to-day to to-morrow. Locomotives passed over your head at a height where you would expect only birds to fly. Cranes stood in bottomless depths, where it seemed impossible for man to descend. All these levels were man-made, connected by transoms of bolted planks, by crosswise riveted girders, by the wooden geometry of hoarding clutching at the upper air, by chasms of shafts that burrowed into the rock.

In one of these chasms the fourteen figures of Stepan's gang stood in waterproof overalls on the concrete, straining their necks upward, watching for the next bucket of concrete to be delivered by the crane. The granite which they had blasted from the river bed the previous autumn was returning to its ancient and everlasting home. It was coming back in a changed form, mixed with sand and cement and water, moulded to the uses of man, and stronger than before.

Slowly and carefully the bucket swung down to them. They could not even see the crane operator, sitting high in his cabin, and he could not see what was going on below. The movement of the bucket was directed by Peter, now a careful rigger. He stood much lower than the crane and signalled with both hands and all ten fingers: to the right, to the left, forward, back, up, down, fast, slow. Suddenly he made a sharp horizontal motion with both hands. The bucket stopped just above the concrete. Stepan and Marin hastened to it and struck a special lever with their legs, then jumped aside as the bottom of the great bucket opened, letting out the heavy mass. Again Peter began to talk with his hands, and the bucket swung upward while the Stepan gang jumped up and down in rubber boots, tamping down the concrete.

This was their life, night after night, through the hot weeks of summer. For Stepan the best moment in the twenty-four hours came at midnight, when they climbed by long ladders zigzagging from the deep box in which they had been working and saw all the planks and girders and chasms lit by electric lights. Some day these lights would flash to hundreds of cities and thousands of farms from the dam they were building.

One midnight he found Andreyev waiting for him. "We have been missing you. We want your help in another competition."

"Walk along with us to the barracks," suggested Stepan. "What's the trouble?"

Andreyev fell into step as they left the brilliance of the dam and came to dusty streets, dimly lit by a few street lamps and the stars. "Both banks

99

are far behind with concrete-pouring," he explained. "We did four hundred cubic metres a day in July and are doing six hundred in August—just half what is needed. If we don't finish our fourteen piers on the left bank before winter, so that the river flow can be turned between them at low water, then the work on the central channel and with it the whole schedule of the dam will be postponed for a year. That mustn't happen."

He coughed as the feet of the walking men stirred clouds of the summer's dust into his nostrils. Then he drew in the grateful fragrance from the line of trees planted the previous autumn, already higher than the stakes to which they were fastened. "The Party has sounded the alarm and called on the *Komsomol*. All our members on the dam will promote competitions; we are even bringing in members from the city and the farms to help. We must strengthen every gang so that we can absorb the flood of seasonal workers in September. We want you at our Sunday conference to work out plans."

Stepan agreed. The conference was well attended; while Stepan had been buried in work and study, the number of workers and their understanding of the dam's problems had grown. Discussion was practical and technical. Fourteen piers must be raised to a height of one hundred feet, and the spaces between them to forty feet. This meant doubling the work of the rock-crushing plants and more than doubling that of the concrete mixers. After considering in detail how many workers were employed, how many could be added, how much the production of each gang could be raised, they unanimously voted that the left shore should finish its full programme by November 6th, twelve weeks away.

"We will make it our present to the country for the twelfth anniversary of the Revolution. We challenge the right bank to do the same."

Stepan was chosen on the committee to draw up the terms of competition with the right bank. Since the old floating bridge was taken up and the only connecting bridge was now several miles upstream, they decided to signal the progress of each day's work from shore to shore by coloured lights. A green light for each hundred cubic metres, a red light for each three hundred—the signals would glow till the end of the twenty-four hours. When the norm for the day was surpassed on either bank, a great red star would blaze all night.

"We must compete not only between the banks but among the gangs on our bank also," suggested Stepan. The committee agreed. Three banners were made, one showing an aeroplane, another a locomotive, and the third a snail, to rotate weekly among the gangs on the left bank. These showed the best, the second best, and the worst. If the lowest gang had nonetheless fulfilled its allotted programme, the banner of the snail would not be used that week.

Stepan bent himself to securing the aeroplane banner as many times as possible. He had a seasoned, well-knit gang. Vassili and one of the other thieves had run away in spring, been caught, and sent elsewhere, but he had replaced them with acquaintances from Kichkas. He succeeded in keeping the group unchanged even under the influx of seasonal workers in late August, when many of the other gangs were diluted.

He won the banner easily that week.

When Ivan appeared at the head of a group of seasonal workers from Red Dawn, Stepan determined to beat them so thoroughly that Ivan could never aspire to rival him again. Since the norms had been readjusted by the contest committee to take account of different degrees of experience, he must surpass his own past record if he would inflict on Ivan this crushing defeat. He could not hope to infect his gang with his own bitter desire, but he had another motive at hand with which to arouse them. The procurer told them that the year of "forced labour" was over; they could work anywhere they liked and without deductions from their pay.

"We're all free men now," cried Stepan to a joyful barracks. "Let's celebrate. Let's show the whole Dneprostroi collective that we're the fastest gang on the dam!"

All the next week they worked at steadily increasing speed. Stepan was well acquainted with the locomotive driver who brought the concrete and induced him to favour the Stepan gang by delivering buckets every time they signalled, even out of turn. He reached the record of twenty cubic metres per man per shift, the highest yet attained by any gang. Ivan was far below.

Coming to work early on the fifth day, Stepan was dismayed to find that his crane had developed some slight trouble and had been sent off for repairs. He would lose several hours at least. Glancing swiftly about the site, he saw that his own crane man was arriving and that none of Ivan's gang had appeared. Quickly he arranged to steal Ivan's crane at the change of shifts, transferring the numbers so that it would appear that Ivan's crane had been taken for repair. The working site was so large and there were so many similar cranes that even if Ivan suspected the theft he would take some time to determine where his crane had gone.

A lawless exultation seized Stepan, such as he had not felt for more than a year. It spread to his gang when they learned what he had done. Laughing and singing in the depths of the form, they redoubled their efforts and reached at the end of six hours their previous record for a whole shift. At this moment their crane returned and the presence of two cranes on a single spot was reported to the chief of the shift. He came angrily over to Stepan.

"Bobrov's gang lost nearly a whole day's work because of your stealing their crane!"

"Better they than we," retorted Stepan jauntily, not in the least abashed. "We've done their work for them; we're the winning gang. We've passed twenty cubic metres and we'll do twenty-four, a double norm!"

"To hell with your record! What do you know of the general plan of construction? Your disorderly act has unbalanced the work."

The shift boss strode away, annoyed that he himself had been caught napping. Stepan's section was sufficiently ahead of the others. Ivan's work was behind in any case; this further delay would affect other sections. He should have seen this earlier and sent the crane to Ivan for the sake of the general plan even if there had been no theft. Conscious of his own lack of supervision, he did not press matters against Stepan, lest he reveal his own negligence. While no official reprimand reached Stepan, the news of what he had done spread swiftly among his fellow workers, some of whom condemned him, while others laughed at his cleverness and applauded it.

The first red star shone out the following night on the opposite shore. The right bank had surpassed its plan; the left bank had not yet done so. Soon the workers on the left bank learned that Stepan's theft had upset the graph of work and that this had caused the whole bank to lag slightly behind the plan.

At the weekly rotation of banners, Stepan's record was highest of all. Not only had his gang the greatest production for the week but on one day they had attained twenty-four cubic meters per man, the highest record yet made by anyone. The figures were received in stony silence. By vote of the whole production conference, the areoplane banner passed, not to the Stepan gang, but to the one that stood next in line.

Stepan stormed angrily away from the meeting. For the next few days the work of his gang fell off. Finally Andreyev spoke about it to Petrov.

"Stepan's gone sour. Something ought to be done."

"Why don't you speak to him? He's a bit arrogant but too good a worker to lose."

"He wouldn't take it from me," answered Andreyev. "He might from you."

Petrov asked Stepan to come to see him at the trade union office. He had no trouble in leading up to the subject; Stepan broached it first.

"My gang beat them all," he fumed. "We had the best weekly record and the best daily record on either bank. They took away my banner because of some damned red tape about a crane."

"When your fellow workers have a unanimous opinion about you," said Petrov slowly, "it's wise to ask yourself why. It wasn't red tape. You disorganized the graph of work so that your whole bank failed to make its norm."

"That's up to the superintendent," argued Stepan hotly. "He's responsible for the general plan, not me. I'm laying concrete. I did my job."

"I think you've missed the point of our socialist competition. It isn't that one small gang shall win and another be beaten. It's that the whole work shall go ahead. The dam belongs to all of us. Its success or failure is success or failure for us all. Let's put it this way. You wanted your gang to win. That's good. But the left bank is your bigger gang. You must help your bigger gang win."

For the rest of the day Stepan thought this over. When he considered his work from the standpoint of the whole left bank, he realized many lacks. Andreyev had been asking him to train in some of the seasonal workers. So far he had refused, but now he saw that something of this kind must be done. Andreyev, he thought, did not appreciate the fine group spirit in his gang, which he did not want to lose. There must be a way to help other workers without injuring this.

He must arouse the gang again and change their habits. In the past they had picked out whenever possible the easier and faster parts of the work, leaving the more complicated bits for the following shifts. Now they must shoulder their share of the "dirty work." Under these conditions it would be harder to win the aeroplane banner.

"We're not just doing our own work, fellows," he argued. "We could pour concrete on this spot till it reached the sky and slopped over, but that wouldn't give us a dam. We've got to push ahead the whole left bank, win the red star, and keep her shining."

Soon the red star was shining nightly. Toward the end of September a new slogan appeared. "This month we'll make a world's record." Members of the *Komsomol* in the engineering offices had learned that the world's record concrete-pouring for a single month was 54,000 cubic metres, made on the Wilson Dam in the Tennessee Valley of the United States of America; they thought Dneprostroi could better this. They passed the information to their fellow members among the concrete workers and published it in the *Dneprostroi Worker*. Both banks of the river were aroused.

Three records were made that last week in September: Stepan's gang won the aeroplane banner; the concrete-pourers of the left bank won the red banner that rotated among all departments of the dam; Dneprostroi as a whole won the world's record, laying 57,000 cubic metres in the month. The giving of the banners became the centre of a special celebration, attended by the chief engineering personnel and even by some of the American consulting engineers.

One of the American engineers turned to his interpreter. "That's a handsome young workman they're applauding. You are starting a new kind of hero; I'd like to meet him."

"I'll bring him over," replied the interpreter, "as soon as I can get through the crowd."

Stepan was joyously shaking hands with large numbers of his friends, as well as with many workers whom he had not met before. They were joking with him about the aeroplane, telling him to "keep her flying." He knew that the applause and the friendliness were increased by the knowledge that he had made good his previous disgrace over the crane theft.

His happiness reached its height when he saw Anya pressing toward him through the crowd. Even at that moment of glad recognition he had time to note that she was not with Ivan, but in the midst of a group of husky girls whose brightly coloured kerchiefs, donned for the celebration, gave a touch of gaiety.

"I've been working on the dam for a week, Stepan," she smiled as he shook her hand energetically. "I came with a gang of girls. I've told them all that to-day's hero comes from my village and that I've known him several years."

"I'm glad I don't shame the village any longer," laughed Stepan with teasing eyes.

"How about coming around this evening and telling us green workers how you do it? We're living on the left bank, too."

Stepan agreed happily; the invitation was the final seal of triumph. Why was Anya on the left bank when her home was across the river? Was it possible that she had come because of him? He was elated.

The joyous light was still in his eyes as he turned to meet the next-comer, an interpreter who said that an American engineer wanted to congratulate him. Feeling that everything was happening at once, Stepan turned toward the American and found him oddly familiar. Wasn't this the relief administrator who had been so friendly to the Young Ploughman and so condescending about the projected dam?

"Aren't you the Mr. Johnson who gave us food six years ago when I came with Yeremeyev from Kichkas?" he asked.

The American had forgotten the episode; it had been only one of many in his previous Russian visit. He would never have recognized the boy of fourteen in this picturesque hero of the aeroplane banner. With Stepan's reminder he seemed to have a vague recollection of a man and a boy from the Dnieper rapids, on whom he had dumped the left-overs of the American Relief.

"Of course I remember that colony," he beamed with pardonable exaggeration. "You have gone a long way since then. I seem to recall that I said something long ago about the building of this dam."

"You said that you and Yeremeyev would never live to see a dam on the Dnieper, but that the children of the colony might," grinned Stepan.

"Imagine your remembering that," replied Johnson, amused and with growing interest in the youth. "Well, you've a great country. It's gone ahead much faster than anyone supposed. I wish you'd come around to my house to dinner and tell me what you've been doing. My wife, I'm sure, would like to have some company. It's rather lonely for her here."

Stepan's head whirled. He had heard rumours of the amazing American houses across the river, with four or five rooms just for two people. To go to one of those places for dinner would be something to talk about.

"I'd like very much to come. When shall it be? It would have to be Sunday for I'm on the evening shift."

"Why not make it this evening?" Johnson suggested. "I'll drive you over in my car and send you back later."

An auto ride would be the final dizzy rapture. Stepan had never ridden in a passenger automobile. Once or twice he had ridden to town on trucks, but the closed car of the American was a height of luxury to which he had hoped to attain only after at least two Five-Year Plans. He assented joyously.

As he got into the car he remembered his promise to visit Anya. With eyes on the splendid machine, he told himself that Anya herself would not want him to miss this opportunity. He would go to her barracks when he got back from the American's, even if it should be two or three hours late.

XVI

STEPAN SAT SILENT and awed on the drive across the river, looking at the car and at Mr. Johnson as if he half-expected them to vanish. The American could talk no Russian; the interpreter sat with the chauffeur in the front seat. This left Stepan free to take in the new impressions as he whirled through the familiar countryside at this startling speed. Instead of being jostled or having to hang on, as when he rode trucks or mechanical conveyances at the dam, he sat in a comfort which he had never associated with speed, a comfort unknown in his barracks or in any home he had seen.

When the American leaned forward to use the cigar-lighter, Stepan's eyes widened. What wouldn't these Americans invent next? His eyes fell on the shining chromium fixtures on the dashboard; leaning forward, he craned his neck to admire them. He had seen enough gauges to know that those dazzling gadgets measured pressures, temperatures, or speed. He had never imagined such beauty of finish. Nor had he thought of them as things to be owned by an individual; they had been instruments for measuring public enterprise.

Crossing the river upstream they sped down through Kichkas. The American colony lay a short distance below. In a small grove of trees, some distance above the river and the confusion of construction, stood a cluster of frame houses of a type Stepan had never seen before. They had been planned by an American architect and had a foreign air, with the large windows and shiny metal fixtures on the doors. The car drew up at one and they got out.

Here, then, was that wonderful American life which he, Stepan, must some day overtake and surpass! Stalin had said it; it was in all newspapers and speeches, in the very air he breathed. "We must rapidly overtake and surpass the capitalist lands or perish." America was the foremost capitalist land, the only land whose technique all Russians admired. Some day the workers of his own country would make and own all the good things the Americans had. Stepan was sure they could do it. Had they not taken into their hands all the resources of one-sixth of the world? How far had they come from the years of famine to the building of the great dam! This very day, in this American home, he would see his own future, which would be attained with much struggle but was definite and sure.

How many rooms seemed to open from the cheerful hallway! And all so orderly and comfortable. Were they all Mr. Johnson's? Into which should he go?

"You will want to wash up for dinner," remarked the American courteously, ushering him into the bathroom.

Never in his life had Stepan seen such magnificence as the white-and-green-tiled walls and floor, the built-in bathtub, washstand, and toilet, all seeming like white marble, the many different-coloured towels on shining metal rods. He would hardly have ventured upon the polished floor if the engineer had not pointed the way. Left alone he began to try out the unfamiliar equipment. He had seen faucets, but why should they have two in one bowl? When hot water came out of one of them, he almost cried out with surprise. Hardest of all he found it to manipulate the toilet; he had seen some that worked with a chain, but never one that had a little handle of chromium steel. At last he managed all of it and came out triumphant and talkative into the other room.

"I never saw anything like that bathroom!" he marvelled. "Some day I'm going to have one! All of white marble and chromium."

"Every house in America has one," laughed Mr. Johnson when the interpreter had finished. "Would you like to see our kitchen? Mrs. Johnson will show it to you."

Mrs. Johnson was a vision of luxury. The green silk dress and frilly white apron seemed meant for a festival rather than a kitchen. But what a kitchen! It was worth dressing up for, thought Stepan, wondering at the white enamelled sink with sloping drainboards, the gleaming white stove, the Frigidaire. He marvelled almost as much at the compact arrangement, well suited to the flow of work. He had learned on the dam to recognize the efficient placing of equipment, but he was amazed to find this kind of planning in a kitchen.

"I've brought you the hero of the day," announced Johnson to his wife as they returned to the living-room. "He's champion concrete-pourer from the left bank. He's won an aeroplane banner that means he's speediest of all. You should have seen them applaud and crowd around him as if he were a football star at home!"

"How handsome he is," murmured Eva Johnson, throwing Stepan a dazzling glance.

Stepan knew that the Americans were talking about him, and he understood well enough the message from Mrs. Johnson's eyes. They hinted that he interested her as a man and that she was a charming woman who wished to arouse desire. This was suggested not only by her eyes but by her smile, by the delicate gestures of her soft, well-cared-for hands, and by the faint perfume surrounding her slim, supple body.

He was both pleased and embarrassed. Admiration in the eyes of a girl was nothing new to him, but a deliberate, provocative gaze from such a wonderful woman! And a married woman at that. Had her husband seen her glance at Stepan? Didn't he object? To his surprise, he saw the American was smiling benevolently at his wife.

Far from being jealous, Johnson was glad that he had thought of inviting Stepan to dinner. To flirt with this handsome young man would be Eva's first relief from boredom in this isolated place, so far from all her friends, where she had none of the stimulus he got from work. How lonesome she must have been to lavish on this young workman the charm reserved at home for socially important guests.

Since his host seemed at ease, Stepan felt free to release his own admiration. How soft yet how exquisitely placed were the dark bronze waves of her hair. He had never seen hair of that colour; he was used to sun-bleached heads. How much care she must have taken to make it curve about her head just like a picture, every strand in the most beautiful place. Did she know how richly its red gleamed above the green of her gown? Perhaps she had even picked the dress for that purpose; Americans could get any colour of silk they chose. Stepan could hardly refrain from touching it, the wonderful American material.

Even the comfortable room seemed to have been made to fit Mrs. Johnson, with its rich colours and its invitation to ease. It was all American except for a bright Ukrainian shawl, which she had known how to place so that it gained an unfamiliar beauty. Besides this, the Americans had a special room just for eating. As he went into the dining-room, he was dazzled by his first sight of an orderly dining table, with fine china and gleaming utensils all set in regular places on the smooth white cloth. His previous standard of home-making, represented by Anya, gave way to the vision of a perfect American home with Mrs. Johnson as the perfect home-maker.

"You should have seen how he looked at the car," Johnson teased his wife. "Almost as admiringly as he looks at you. That's your real rival."

The interpreter, who had been invited to stay to dinner, gave Stepan an edited translation, from which he understood that his interest in the automobile had been remarked.

"It's the first time I ever rode in a passenger car," Stepan explained.

"We have lots of them in America," boasted Johnson. "Most American workers drive to work in their own cars."

A dozen questions rushed to Stepan's mind at this amazing revelation. But Mrs. Johnson had captured the interpreter's attention, and begged, with a winning smile at Stepan: "Tell us all about your exploits. What is an aeroplane banner and how did you win it?"

"The dam was lagging behind its plan," began Stepan, thinking she wanted the full story. He continued, with many technical details which the interpreter did not translate, knowing that they would not interest the American woman. He told of stealing the crane, since it was no longer something to be ashamed of, but a lesson he had learned. To his surprise, she was more delighted by this story than by the record in concrete-laying. She must have misunderstood him; what had he said that amused her so?

"What a nice bandit," remarked Eva Johnson to her husband. "I didn't know you had such interesting incidents on your job."

"At last we all learned to pull together," continued Stepan, telling how the seasonal workers had gained new skill and become part of the rising momentum of work, "until finally in September we beat the American record." He hoped he was not being impolite to his American hosts. But after all they had a share in this great dam, too.

"Isn't it amazing how they get interested in the whole project! This country knows how to create morale," commented Johnson.

"I think he's sweet," sighed Eva Johnson. "I wish you'd make your work sound exciting like that." This interchange was not translated.

The arrival of the salad course interrupted the discussion. Eva Johnson was proud of the vegetable salad she had taught her cook to achieve in this land, which as yet produced no head lettuce but only the long green leaf. She hoped Stepan appreciated her special mixture of raw vegetables—sliced tomatoes, shredded cabbage and lettuce, grated carrot, and other bits from the local market. Then she saw that he was only toying with it and pretending to eat. Under her glance he picked out a bit of tomato, politely swallowed it, and began to hunt through the salad again.

"Don't you like salad?" she laughed.

"I never ate grass," apologized Stepan. "Do the Americans eat it when they have so many good things to eat?"

"We like it and it's good for you," smiled Mrs. Johnson, "but you don't need to eat it."

Stepan gratefully laid down his fork on the plate and turned to the interpreter. "Will you please ask Mr. Johnson to tell me how American workers organize their competitions? I'd like to do an American-style competition on the dam."

"We don't have this kind of competition," sated Johnson.

"What kind do you have?" persisted Stepan.

"Well, we have competition in games. I was telling my wife that the crowd cheered you just like a football champion."

"We have games too," replied Stepan, "but they are not nearly so exciting as competing in work. In making a dam you make something that lasts for many years and that everyone knows about and uses. Don't you compete in work?"

"In a way we do," the American tried to explain. "As an engineer I compete against other engineers. If my work is better than theirs I will get the job of working here on the Dnieper. If not I won't."

"A great engineer will always choose great work," nodded Stepan. "I'm glad you chose to work here." It was quite understandable that everyone should want to work on the Dnieper, even the superlative American engineers.

Eva Johnson sent a wry, amused glance at her husband. They both knew how construction work had fallen off in America and all over the world recently, and how lucky they had been to get this job, even in an alien country. It was nice of this handsome lad to admire them for it.

"Great engineers no doubt don't need competitions," said Stepan thoughtfully. "The wish to achieve great work will make them do their best. Our workers are still backward; we need incentives. We have to have people tell us what the work is for and how important it is to the country."

"I don't see how you get anything done in this country," Johnson remarked, "when you haven't any tools."

"What do you mean?" exclaimed Stepan. "We have lots of tools."

"You don't even know what tools are," laughed the American. "You don't even have any claw-hammers to pull out nails. If a workman wants to pull a nail out he hunts around half an hour and finds someone with a pair of pliers."

"What is a claw-hammer?" asked Stepan, abashed.

"I'll show you one," replied the American. "We have them even in the house." He rose informally, went into the kitchen, and returned with a claw hammer.

"I never saw a pick in this country," he continued, after showing Stepan how the hammer worked, "except for the few we brought to Dneprostroi. Your workmen beat the earth to pieces with heavy iron bars. Instead of a proper bob to determine a vertical line, you hang a brick or a piece of old iron. Your hand-levels are so crude that they only measure within a centimetre."

Stepan defended his country. "I know we're far behind you in technique but still we've done a lot since you were here in 1923."

"That's so," admitted Johnson, "but at frightful cost in human labour. There are endless little improvements that would speed up your work a lot. Your shovels have a short handle that gives little purchase, and a small, flat blade that raises little dirt; in America we have a long handle and a large, curved blade. Then this terrible *nosilka* of yours to cart away dirt. All the Americans laugh at it but it's really a crime. It takes two husky men to handle a fifth as much as one man could take in a decent wheelbarrow."

Stepan was appalled at the catalogue. "Catch up and surpass America" was all very well as a slogan, but there seemed such an infinite amount to be done. What a campaign he could stir up in the newspaper for proper tools! He would find out more about them from Mr. Johnson.

He must save it for later, for they were rising from table and going into the living-room. The Ukrainian maid was bringing in the tea. The delicate cups interested Stepan, because he was used to drinking his tea from a glass. But he could drink tea from anything, especially when it had such a delicious aroma.

"What wonderful American tea!" He inhaled the fragrance. "Do you bring it all the way from where it is grown in America? It is very different from ours."

The eyes of his hostess twinkled. "Shall I tell him, Bob?" Her husband grinned. "We don't grow tea in America; we get it from India and China. This happens to be your own Russian tea from Georgia, bought right here. Only I use a particular flavouring that you can get in the store." She signed to the Ukrainian maid to bring in something from the kitchen. She held it up to Stepan—a tiny clove. "One of these is enough for a whole teapot," she smiled, as if imparting an important secret.

Stepan did not know which was the more marvellous, the variety of American technique or Mrs. Johnson's amazing knowledge. He had been wondering what kind of work she did. Probably her post was as important as that of her husband. Did she work for the dam, or for some big factory kitchen, since she knew so much about food?

When he asked about it she laughed with delight. "You'd better look out, Bob. The hero of concrete is choosing me to work on his dam. That's more than you offer." She smiled provocatively into Stepan's eyes and murmured: "I just came here with my husband. I'm only a wife making a home for him. Isn't that enough?"

"It's the most important work in the world," affirmed her husband chivalrously, "to make a home for a man which inspires him to do his best."

At the moment it was Stepan who was inspired by Mrs. Johnson. Deeply stirred by her gaze, he remembered Anya and realized that the

110

hour was late. He told the Johnsons that he had to see some friends that evening on the other bank. The American called the chauffeur furnished by the administration.

"Come and see us again," he told Stepan in parting.

"Do come," added Eva Johnson, giving his hand a soft pressure. "I loved hearing about your important work. It would be still nicer if you knew a little English. Perhaps I could give you some lessons; I've plenty of time."

"I'd be delighted," rejoiced Stepan. "I'd like to know a foreign language and the American language would be best of all. I can't come easily now; it's a long way around by the bridge. The two banks will meet by Christmas; then I'll come often across the construction."

As he drove back to the other bank Stepan no longer noticed the chromium fixtures that had excited him a few hours before. They were buried under all the new impressions. How long would it take to understand these bewildering Americans? He was particularly fascinated by the marvellous woman, whose amazing knowledge was used for no public work but merely to inspire one man. He envied Mr. Johnson. How glorious to have such a woman all for yourself like that!

XVII

THE ROAD OF ANYA's heart lay clear before her. Stepan had shown himself worthy; she no longer needed to repress her feeling for him. She had seen the light in his eyes when he greeted her and took it for granted that he would come to her directly from his dining-room. As soon as she finished dinner she hastened to put in order the corner of the barracks which the girls had arranged for social purposes—the Red Corner.

"Come over and help me, Vera," she called gaily to an older girl, who was reading in a far corner on her bed.

Vera laughed and joined her. "It's a wonderful feeling, isn't it? Don't let it sweep you away." She smiled sympathetically at Anya's joy.

Abashed that her feelings had been so transparent, Anya began energetically stacking books and papers on the long, red table. She straightened the picture of Lenin on the wall above the table and rearranged the screen to shut off the view of the dozen beds that filled most of the large room. The barracks had been as crude and unattractive as all the others when the girls had taken possession. It was homelike now, with the bedspreads, plumped-up pillows, family photographs and posters that they brought from home, and this decorated space near the entrance set off to receive friends.

She picked up a vase of greenery, gathered freshly that afternoon, tried it on a different corner of the table, looked at it from various angles, then moved it back.

"Take it easy," laughed Vera. "He'll get here just as soon if you don't fuss so much."

Anya sat down, controlling her restlessness. She admired her brigade leader and wanted to stand well in her eyes. How had Vera noticed her feelings so quickly? Had Vera's marriage taught her all these things?

"Was he your reason for coming to work here?" inquired Vera.

"Not entirely. There's no future in working our tiny garden and scattered strips of land. I'd been thinking of joining a collective, the Red Dawn Farm. Grandpa refused; he's eighty and set in his ways. I might have insisted but I didn't feel certain myself. The president of Red Dawn wants to marry me; for a time I thought that was the best thing to do. After I saw the dam last year at the celebration, the farm seemed rather tame. Seeing Stepan made Ivan seem dull to me, too. Stepan used to be wild and I was afraid to let myself like him. I wanted to see him at work and make up my mind."

"You are young to make so serious a choice, Anya. Only eighteen."

"My mother was married earlier."

"Our mothers had no choice; their men were chosen for them. It's different to-day. We do our own choosing. It's not an easy thing—to choose."

"I've found it hard already," agreed Anya complacently.

Vera continued thoughtfully: "Only when you know what you want of life can you rightly choose the mate with whom to share life."

"If Stepan and I love each other, can't we learn what we want of life together?"

"Of course you can," Vera agreed tenderly. "But this personal passion is a tidal wave; you can drown in it. It is hard to decide clearly when you are swept off your feet by an emotion that makes you want to give up everything, everything in the world to please one man. That doesn't last, Anya. Love lasts but not that wish to abandon your own life. If you want the happiness of a full life and a full marriage, don't let yourself be swept away by that wonderful feeling until you know your way of life."

Watching, she saw that Anya's interest was aroused and went on reassuringly: "You can be thankful at least that neither of the young men who interest you is a peasant in a family home. This father-and-son relation, this rule of the old over their sons and their sons' wives and children—it's terrible what it does to people's lives. I came to the dam to get away from my husband. Until he's man enough to stand up to his father, I'd rather be on my own."

"Was his family hard on you?" asked Anya sympathetically.

"The moment I was married they treated me worse than a servant," nodded Vera. "There were nine of us in the house, with his parents and brothers and sisters. They dumped all the heaviest work on me. The daughters of the house sat easy on a cart and rode to market, but I had to toil in the fields even beyond my strength. Even when I was carrying my baby. That was how I lost my child; I gave birth prematurely in the field."

She clenched her hands, controlled the feeling that memory released, and continued evenly: "My husband felt sorry for me and tried to protect me, but he hadn't the courage to break up his father's home. So I left him until he can put his own wife and children before his father's demands.

"In the old days you had to endure it. It was impossible to split the homestead then. If there was only one house, one horse, one cow, it was ruin for both father and son to divide the property. But now we could leave the old man and join a *kolboz*. The law would give us our share of the family land, and even some of the implements and livestock. We could have brought our bit to the collective."

"Was your man against the *kolboz*?" asked Anya.

"Not he! All the young folks want to join. You should have seen the row the old man made. 'Immoral, godless generation! Breaking up the home the minute you get married! If you split the property, how am I to live?' I told him he could join the *kolboz* too and use the new machinery, only we'd all be equal and he'd have no one to boss.

"He shouted: 'I'll never touch a devil tractor. I believe in God and I'm too old to change.' Then he got the priest and both of them told my husband God would curse him if he broke up the family. I said the old man's family killed my baby but the priest said life and death are the will of God.

"The dam gave me my chance to get away from it. It's opened a new life to me; I've joined the Party. Now that I see all the wonderful opportunities to study and advance in anything you like, I'll not go back to the village. Perhaps some day my man will join me here."

Engrossed in the conversation, Anya hardly realized that time was passing until several girls returned from strolling and began to get ready for work on the midnight shift. She saw that it was late. Why had Stepan not come?

A dark, saucy girl named Darya looked meaningly around the Red Corner. "Why, where's the champion? We all expected to meet him."

"He didn't come."

"Maybe he's found someone else. All the girls will want him now."

At that moment they heard the sound of an automobile. The American car drew up at the barracks, where no auto had ever halted before. Stepan was at once surrounded by a bevy of girls calling in mock admiration: "Hail to the champion! Already he's an American engineer! Won't you drive us to the dam in your auto and show us how to work?"

What a reception! How childish the crude joking seemed after the heights from which Stepan had come. He had planned to gloat with Anya over his exciting evening; it seemed to him she should have arranged the surroundings better. He strode into the barracks, and, instead of apologizing, as he had intended, for his lateness, merely remarked: "I went to the American colony for dinner."

Anya had already taken off the nice dress in which she had hoped to receive him; she was in overalls ready for work. Stepan had spoiled everything and wasn't even sorry. "You might have let me know that you were going, so that I wouldn't have wasted the evening waiting."

"I hadn't time to think of it," answered Stepan. "It seems you don't appreciate my leaving a wonderful evening just to come back and keep my word."

So Stepan had come from a sense of duty. This knowledge cut Anya to the heart. Not wanting to quarrel, she suppressed the retort that sprang to her lips, but the effort gave a tension to her manner as she responded: "Tell me about it. There's still a little time."

Sighing for the lost evening, she sat down and tried to pay attention to the account of the automobile, the bathroom, the kitchen. The confusion in the barracks distracted her; everyone was getting ready to go on shift. Stepan rushed to the most important of all—the American woman who presided over that perfect home.

"She's invented a delicious tea. And it's all for the American. She doesn't do any work at all except look after him and his house and inspire him."

"A fine job for a grown woman," snapped Anya, looking at her work-roughened hands and winking hard to keep back the tears. After the months she had thought about Stepan, the hours in which she had admired him as a hero, must he use the scant minutes of their first conversation—while she waited for the whistle—to praise a foreign woman who did no work?

"You wanted to hear about it," Stepan stiffened. "I'm going to have an American house myself some day. With bath and ice-making machine of white marble. We've nothing like that in our country."

"If the Americans have anything worth having in their houses"—Anya's tone expressed her doubt—"we'll all of us get it too, after the dam is built."

Anger seized him. To have left the Americans in order to share his rapture with Anya and to find her disdainful! He burst out: "It seems you're only a plodding peasant and don't want to be anything else!"

"I don't want to spend hours without work waiting around to inspire a man, if that's what you mean," she retorted.

She hurried away, even before the whistle blew, to keep him from seeing her tears. Stepan went indignantly back to his barracks.

Each thought of the other often in the days that followed; each waited for the other to make the first apology and approach. Their different times of work conflicted. A new schedule had been introduced, known as the "unbroken week"; work on the dam went on without stopping, one fifth of the people taking time off each day. Stepan had a different rest day from Anya as well as a different shift. These difficulties could only have been surmounted by joint planning. Since they had parted in anger, the hindrances kept them apart.

"Don't weep your eyes out for a man who doesn't want you," Vera advised Anya. "Make something of yourself. If you do, he'll probably come round later. If he doesn't, find somebody else! You've a lot of life ahead of you."

"What can I study in order to surpass the Americans in culture?" inquired Anya.

"So that's what you're thinking?" Vera gave her a sly smile. "Forget the Americans. Decide what you yourself most want to do. Perhaps you like most of all the work of construction. Then study, as I do, to be an engineer. Maybe something else interests you more. Life on the dam is many-sided. Look about you and see."

What a great variety of work, thought Anya, when she looked at the dam from this new standpoint. In the bed of the river there was every kind of craft, from the pick-and-shovel men to the highly skilled crane operators. In the offices were draftsmen and engineers. On the site of the power station were many kinds of installation men. Besides this a great factory kitchen cooked meals for more than ten thousand workers and sent them in giant thermos containers to the different dining-rooms; here also many specialists were employed. In all these directions there were opportunities. What kind of job should she choose?

The day nursery and nursery school especially fascinated her. Three of the women in her barracks had children. Anya frequently relieved the mothers by taking their children to the nursery or bringing them home. One day Vera said to her: "You seem to like handling children. Would you be willing to serve on the day-nursery committee? The trade union has asked our brigade to appoint a member."

"What would I have to do?" asked Anya.

"Anything you think of to improve the nursery. The city health authorities furnish the medical personnel and the dam administration supplies the building. We women are responsible for general supervision. You ought to be doing some social work."

Anya began to visit the nursery regularly. She discovered its various sections, from small babies up to kindergarten age. "They all look adorable," she raved to Vera, "sleeping on the porch in their little cribs. They are even sweeter in their bright-coloured play clothes, and with their little dishes in the dining-room. I never knew there was so much to learn about children. I don't see how they ever grow up in our villages where nobody knows these things."

"Lots of them don't grow up," said Vera. "Mine didn't."

Dropping her hand gently on Vera's, Anya ventured: "I've been wishing I could fight the high rate of infant mortality in our villages. It's much lower than it used to be before the Revolution, but it's still too high, much higher than in the advanced countries."

"Still think of catching up with America?" smiled Vera.

"Why, no, I wasn't thinking about America at all. I was wondering how I could learn more about public health and care of babies. I might even make it my future work."

"Why not begin by organizing a course among the mothers who use the day nursery? The trade union will pay for a teacher and the health department will send you one. This winter you might take a special course in day-nursery management. I shall be spending the winter in the engineering school."

During the next weeks Anya became so interested in her study classes, her work for the day nursery, and her full-time job on the dam, that she almost ceased to be lonely for Stepan. She confided this to Vera.

"We're lucky, as women, to be living after the Revolution," Vera declared. "Neither our life nor our happiness depends on any particular man."

"Stepan could add to my happiness," protested Anya.

"Yes," agreed Vera, "but he can't take it away."

Anya thought it over and admitted that this was so.

In the second week of November an event occurred in Moscow which was rapidly to affect the future of Vera and Anya, of Ivan and Stepan, of every human being in the Soviet land. Stalin declared to the Central Committee of the Communist Party that 1929 was "the year of the great turning point," that the spectacular advances of the first Five-Year Plan had made the Soviet Union a country of large-scale industry, that full industrial development was held back by a medieval farming, and that the time had come to smash the kulaks and make the collective farm the dominant type of agriculture. After sharp discussion Stalin's policy beat the opposition from both the right and the left and was overwhelmingly adopted. Newspapers all over the country headlined the decisions and they were excitedly discussed in public meetings and in private conversations.

Vera approached Anya the following week. "The concrete-laying is practically over for the season. It's time to think of our next work. I'm ready to recommend you for a post in a new day nursery that will open next spring on the right bank. As soon as your name is approved by the

116

trade union, you will enter a special school to prepare; your salary as student will be the average of what you've earned here."

Anya began to express her delight, but Vera interrupted. "Are you sure that's what you want now? Many of us are changing our plans since the Party Conference. Instead of entering the engineering school, I'll be helping to organize collective farms this winter."

"But you're such a wonderful brigade leader, and you swore you'd never go back to the village," exclaimed Anya. "What changed you? Did the Party mobilize you?"

"Nobody mobilized me," laughed Vera. "The Party asked the trade unions to furnish twenty-five thousand good organizers to help in the villages. I wouldn't miss being in on the greatest farm revolution in history! I think I can qualify. I'm a fairly good organizer and I've felt the bitterness of our medieval farming in my own body. I'll know how to fight it."

"Does it really seem to you more important than being an engineer on a great dam like this?" asked Anya.

"It's all of it important. I'll be an engineer later. Perhaps in industry, more likely on the farms. But now—is our second Revolution. The farms are our next important front."

"But the farms change so slowly, Vera. Even Red Dawn is small and narrow in its interests. That's why I came to the dam."

"The farms will match the dam now," laughed Vera, excited as Anya had never seen her. "The peasants are ready at last; since October they've been moving like an avalanche into the collective farms. Instead of those small artels they're organizing giants. The machines will be ready too; next year Stalingrad begins to turn out tractors. It's the end of the patriarchal farm; we're breaking through to freedom. I couldn't stay out of it now."

A new vista opened before Anya. "Will those large farms, those *kolhozes*, have special sections? In vegetables, perhaps?"

"They'll have everything their members can think of. The best brains from the universities, the best organizers from the cities are pouring into the farms this winter, with all the best new ideas. Doesn't it interest you, too?"

For a week Anya thought it over, read the papers carefully, consulted specialists. Then she spoke to Vera.

"Recommend me, please, to a winter course in sugar beets instead. I like beet growing and I did it very well two years ago. Our country is short of sugar. We should grow more beets in this part of the country. We must bring beets north."

XVIII

Life at Red Dawn Farm was boiling. It had begun to simmer even before harvest. As autumn deepened into winter, the farm became a cauldron of all the seething hopes and fears of the countryside.

For three years, under Ivan Bobrov's cautious guidance, its growth had been unspectacular but steady. Families of poor peasants and farm hands had joined until it had fifty members instead of the original twenty-two. Its lands had grown in proportion, and so had its other facilities. It had two fairly good tractors, though in the absence of a machine shop or skilled mechanics these were often out of repair.

Peasants in hamlets round about had followed its example and organized similar artels; seven such groups, of ten to twenty members each, in a radius of five miles from Kichkas, looked for advice and help to the larger Red Dawn Farm. None of these small groups was very prosperous. They had begun with very little. Some had been formed of homeless farm-hands who lived at first in a central barn; others were of poor peasants, owning three or four horses among ten families. By pooling scanty equipment and securing Government loans they had escaped financial bondage to private moneylenders; favoured by low taxes and priorities on new farm implements, they had slowly gone ahead. The largest—twenty members at Selidba—had a rather battered Fordson of its own.

Cheerfully these small artels responded to the 1929 slogan of the Communist Party: "Organize larger farms; prepare for new machines." They applied for amalgamation with the Red Dawn Farm after harvest. After some discussion they were taken in.

The eight farms worked as one during the fall ploughing. It was a task to make a seasoned organizer quail. Crop rotation, organization of labour, animals, and implements had to be planned for one hundred and twenty families living in seven hamlets and possessing over two thousand acres in a score of different fields. Draft power included oxen, horses, and Fordsons; implements ranged from the wooden plough known as *sokha* to the tractor-drawn plough of steel.

"How can we manage?" groaned the hard-pressed Ivan.

It went better than he expected. Help came from many sources. The first-fruits of the nation-wide attention to farm problems were the arrival of a group of volunteer mechanics from the *Kommunar* Works; they repaired all the implements, especially the three tractors, which, greased and adjusted, moved with an efficiency unknown before. Next came a farm specialist from the Commissariat of Agriculture, making land maps for all the collective farms of the county, showing type of soil and previous crop history. He advised them on crop rotation, helped get selected seed, and put them on the list for future tractors from the new Stalingrad Works.

"Throw away your wooden *sokhas*," he advised. "They're a waste of horsepower. Take your best ploughs and put three horses to them. Then you'll plough deep and fast."

Never had there been such well-worked acres as Red Dawn ploughed that autumn. Shubina's chicken farm also expanded; farm wives from several hamlets became her assistants. Stesha's day nursery established branches, and the women thus released organized field kitchens and served hot meals to the ploughmen in the fields.

"That Red Dawn has either meat or fat in its soup every day in the field work," marvelled the poorer peasants. Formerely only the well-to do ate meat and fat regularly; common men got it, if lucky, during harvest.

Excursions of peasants came almost daily in late autumn to see what Red Dawn's life was like. The peasant women particularly wanted to see the nursery and kindergarten and the homes where the members lived.

"Is it true that you put all your babies in wagons and send them away to the State?" they asked Stesha. "We hear that you weave a common blanket two hundred feet long under which all members must sleep."

"Look and see," answered Stesha quietly. "Some of our farm-hands sleep in the barn, since they had no houses; but they are getting homes like other folks. We have a nursery room where the baby gets good care while the mother is working. When you work for the kulak you put the baby down on soiled laundry or in the dirt of the floor where you raise dust. Our way the baby will be healthier when you come at night to take him home."

Many of the visitors were favourably impressed by the nursery. Others said: "Unnatural mothers, to let their babies out of their sight. Even if my baby sits on soiled laundry, at least I see what he does."

Rumours of all kinds were energetically spread by enemies. Late in autumn the Kichkas Children's Home was moved to better premises down river. The rumour started that Red Dawn would send all the day nursery babies away with the Home. Panic swept even those women who had been members of the small artels for a year but who had never used a day nursery before. Flinging down their tools in the potato patch, they cried that they would not give up their babies. Work was paralysed for most of the day.

"My God," cried Ivan, "who wants your babies? We are socializing land and implements, not people! We don't want your kids for a gift." At this some of the women cried louder than ever, feeling insulted. Stesha finally calmed them.

A gaunt-faced peasant widow named Artiukina defended herself: "How should I know but what I'm told? I cannot read; I think the priest speaks truth. My father was a literate man; he feared neither priest nor devil. So also will my children be. But we who are dark, why should we not believe in God and all these rumours?"

By the end of November, two hundred more families, from ten hamlets, had applied for admission to the Red Dawn Farm. Ivan was terrified.

"We can't possibly handle so many," he stated when the farm's Soviet met to consider the applications.

Stesha, now member of the *Komsomol*, supported the Party policy for large-scale collectivization. "It's our chance to remake the whole countryside," she declared with enthusiasm.

"It's hard enough to combine eight artels into one; that's enough for one season," argued Ivan. "Remember how the Young Ploughman failed when it got too big. These newcomers have neither experience nor food. We'll all starve if we take them in."

Several delegates from outlying hamlets supported Stesha but Ivan's prestige prevailed. It was decided to refuse all applicants except those who could feed themselves until harvest. This automatically ruled out farm-hands and poor peasants, who lived part of each year on borrowed food. Some kulaks were admitted over Stesha's protests. Ivan said shortly: "They are successful men; it is a triumph for us that they want to join."

The rejected farm-hands did not take the refusal quietly. The kulaks from whom they were accustomed to borrow felt the approaching conflict and refused loans to any but their close supporters, especially denying those who had applied to Red Dawn. These poorer families faced starvation. A storm of recriminations swept the district. News of it reached the *Kommunar* Works.

"Go clear this up," Nikolai Ivanovich told Morosov. "Take a woman organizer with you. Vera Voronina comes from one of those hamlets; she's a good brigade leader who volunteers to help."

With Morosov and Vera present the Farm Soviet reconvened.

"For three years we struggled," Ivan argued. "Now we have a sound farm that can feed one hundred and twenty families. You ask us to feed two hundred more. Most of them are farm hands bringing nothing; others are stupid folks who killed their livestock because the kulaks told them: 'In the *kolboz* you'll have to share; better eat it now.' Must we starve together with people like these?"

"You forget your opportunity," insisted Morosov. "Three hundred and twenty members will give you a majority of all families in the township. You can redistrict the land and make a model farm on large fields of the best soil. It will be hard at first but the support of the country will be behind you."

"Will the Government feed those two hundred extra families?" persisted Ivan.

Morosov's eyes flashed. "Are you going against us now? You have done a good job here, but all that's useless unless you forge ahead. This isn't 1925, when the Young Ploughman failed. This is the year of the great turning-point! This is like 1917 when we went with rifles to take power. Now we must take the front of husbandry.

"A peasant is not an independent person; his whole farm depends on the condition of the nation. Our country must be strong so that we can all have freedom and plenty. The Stalingrad tractor plant will give you tractors next summer; the Dnieper Dam will give light to your homes and power for your farms in two years. To finish these great works we need great increase in bread. Can this be done if each peasant sits and decides when to plough? If the kulak sabotages and the farm-hands have nothing to eat? You must organize the farming of this township. You will get such help as can be given. More than that you have no right to ask."

Vera spoke up with intense feeling. "This is our second war. That first war was a murdering war. This war is not murdering but it is war all the same. It is war for the children of all of us. Two hundred families want to join with you. You must take them and give them help."

One after another the members of the Farm Soviet agreed. Ivan himself at last yielded: "We'll take them; we'll do our best."

"One thing more," cautioned Morosov. "Distinguish between friends and foes. You've been letting in kulaks. Farm hands even call you a kulak farm. I understand you think it's quite a haul to get them. Don't be naïve: they're not converted. Throw them out."

"They offered to put in horses and implements and food," said Ivan.

Morosov laughed. "In return for the chance to rule you. Where did they get those implements? Pre-war stuff is worn out; anything since then they got by stealing and by bribing officials. Hold a good cleaning of your kulaks and take the stolen stuff back."

The assembly brightened and even Ivan smiled. "Will you help conduct the cleaning?" he asked Morosov. The latter agreed.

Vera proposed a special meeting for women. "It's important to explain things thoroughly to them. Women are half the battle."

Hundreds of women turned out to the meeting. It was widely known that Vera came from Alexinko, one of their own hamlets, and had left her husband in a fight over collectives; this added to the interest. All Sunday the women asked questions about cows, babies, division of harvest; they wanted to know how this new farming would affect their daily lives. Vera's announcement that Anya Kosareva was studying in Kharkov in order to organize a special sugar-beet section made a deep impression; Anya's record vegetables were not forgotten.

Even more than Vera, old Artiukina stirred the meeting. Her inspired eyes framed by a black shawl, she spoke with the fire of old martyrs.

"If one is without milk, then all will be without milk. If one lacks felt boots, then all will go barefoot in snow. Maybe we will all die together. But maybe not; maybe we can learn. When I first began to read I asked what a certain letter was. They said: 'It is not a letter but a number.' I was so dumb I couldn't tell letters from numbers. That was only two months ago. Now I know letters and numbers. Perhaps we can learn still more.

"For eight years, since my man died, my children were hungry. This year I have thirty bushels of wheat—bread for a year for us four. Thanks to the Red Dawn I got it; they took me in and I worked in the harvest. We've learned little collective farms already; maybe we can learn big ones next. They say in other lands there are three hundred cows in one barn, yet all are fed." Two weeks later the women of Red Dawn chose the not-long-since illiterate Artiukina as their delegate to the Moscow Congress of Collective Farm Women.

In mid-December the Red Dawn Farm, now greatly expanded, held solemn session to examine its kulak members. Ivan, as president, sat in the centre of the platform, supported by four others: Morosov, one president of a small artel, a representative of the *Komsomol*, and a woman. These were the commission chosen by the meeting to judge thirty-seven citizens from ten hamlets and decide their membership.

A red-faced, choleric man in his late twenties took the stand: Mikhail Faber, youngest son of Old Man Faber. The Faber family, it was shown, had been anti-Soviet from the beginning. Old Faber had been "*Starshinoi* of the *Volost*"—head man of the township—holding drinking bouts with the local officials of the Tsar. In the civil war, his oldest son had joined a band which terrorised the countryside, killing peasants who were for the Soviets. The old man worked against the Government in a quieter way. "Plant only your own food," he urged the peasants.

So much for the family, but what of the youngest son? A farm hand put a question: "Didn't you say in 1928 that you would rather feed your wheat to your dogs than sell to the cursed Bolsheviks?" Young Faber reddened. Another witness testified that Mikhail had taunted the co-operative creamery for its early difficulties. A third stated that even last summer, after Mikhail had joined the *kolboz*, he swore that "the damn Red Dawn has too damn many lazy farm-hands." Could a man like this be loyal to the collective farm?

Mikhail Faber seemed on the point of an angry explosion. Watching him carefully, Morosov spoke: "Chief blame for the past attaches to the head of the family. Mikhail left his father a year ago in a quarrel over the girl he married. He worked well in the *kolboz* this autumn. He is too hot-tempered, but who is free from faults? My view is that he is young enough to change under the new environment, and may be admitted if he gives guarantees of loyalty. Let him put all his land rights, draft animals, and implements into Red Dawn as its undivided capital, without the usual right to withdraw it if he should leave. What do you say, Citizen Faber?"

Mikhail's brow cleared. "Sure! I always said half-hearted members were the trouble. Be either in or out, I say! My livestock's in for good. This farm will succeed."

Ivan, relieved, turned to the artel president beside him. "Mikhail is a hard worker. I thought Morosov would be tougher. This isn't so bad." The commission of five retired briefly, and brought in the recommendation that Mikhail be accepted. The meeting agreed.

"I'll have nothing to do with these scandalous proceedings," shouted a hard-faced man in his fifties, striding to the table. "I'm resigning right now and taking my property back."

"Not so fast, Citizen Penchelin," interrupted Morosov. "You can resign but we'll see about your property. Who wants to testify?"

Citizen Penchelin, it developed, had owned most of the land near Selidba before the Revolution, had operated a smithy with hired labour, and had employed many women for intensive work in his fields. Seven women declared that he had never paid the wages he owed them in 1914.

"He worked us so hard and fed us so little that we broke down and left in a week. Then he refused wages for the days we had worked. We've listed what he owes, with interest. We offer it as undivided capital to Red Dawn Farm."

Smiles swept the assembly. "A debt like that, with interest from 1914 at Penchelin's rate, should be worth a couple of Penchelin's horses," whispered the *Komsomol* member to Morosov.

Shubina told how Penchelin had treated her during the Revolution, refusing her the chance to learn to read. But lately Penchelin seemed to have been converted to collective farming. He had organized the Selidba artel and was its leading member, supplying it with many implements and helping get a tractor. What was behind this unusual change?

It developed that the implements had been stolen; they were some of those taken from the *Kommunar* Works. It was found that Penchelin held a mortgage on the tractor at exorbitant interest and had forced on the Selidba artel a constitution in which voting was by shares of invested property and not one man, one vote. Thus he exacted so much from the joint harvest that there was little left for those who did the work.

Hisses and sounds of wrath arose from the assembly. "What did I tell you?" Morosov reminded Ivan. "If a kulak joins, it's because he intends to rule."

"A fake artel working for Penchelin," he characterized it to the meeting. "The Government won't recognize such constitutions. We vote as human beings, not as property. We should not only expel Penchelin from Red Dawn but refer him to the police for theft."

The three days' cleaning expelled seven members and imposed special conditions on twenty more. It raised Red Dawn's prestige throughout the township. A new type of peasant almost at once applied for membership—the solid homesteads, each with a horse or two and a decent plough. They had hesitated long before joining, for they felt themselves above the poorer peasants who lived from hand to mouth. While they did not hire labour, and hence were not kulaks, they had hoped to become kulaks. Now they saw clearly that kulak rule was over and that Red Dawn Farm, having a majority of the peasants as members, would demand a reallotment of lands and take for itself the best. The way to prosper lay henceforth through Red Dawn Farm.

Ivan breathed more easily when these stable farmers entered. With their help the poorer members could be fed.

Four-fifths of all the farming families were now in Red Dawn. The new land allotment at once took place. By tradition all peasants possessed land rights rather than permanent pieces; lands were redivided from time to time. The new land division gave preference to Red Dawn, joining all of its lands in great continuous fields. Its eight thousand arable acres reached from Kichkas five miles north-west to Selidba, and four miles south-west to Alexinko Hamlet.

Kulaks still had land rights but were given the more distant lands. They raised an outcry that Red Dawn was ruining them.

"Certainly," replied Morosov coolly, "just as you once ruined the poorer peasants by controlling land allotments with the Tsarist police. We at least control for the majority."

Three days after the lands were allotted, Ivan was aroused from bed in the middle of the night before Christmas by a hammering at his door.

"Kulaks have burned the barn in Alexinko," gasped the messenger. "We had twenty-six horses; we only got out three."

Cursing under his breath, Ivan threw on his clothes. He knocked on Stesha's door, told her the news and added: "Get Vera. She's staying at Anya's. She comes from Alexinko and might be of help. Have one of the men come with you."

Then he was gone into the freezing darkness.

XIX

GREY CHRISTMAS DAWN was breaking when Ivan reached the hamlet. Nothing was left of the stable but glowing ashes and fragments of walls. Around it, in the ember-blackened snow, a panic-stricken crowd of men and women stood staring. The horses that had been destroyed had meant to them the hope of a good farm. Most of the women were wailing loudly; some were near hysteria. Superstitious dread had appeared in many faces.

"God's punishment is on us for joining the *kolboz*," moaned a pock-marked woman, turning away from Ivan to shiver under her grey knit shawl.

"The house spirits are all offended," pronounced a stocky matron, huddling into her heavy sheepskin and flashing on him bitter, terrified eyes of doom. "Not only of one house, but of all the houses. It is a mighty ill luck."

The younger men of the *kolboz* were shouting down the women's terror. One young fellow, whose soot-blackened face and singed sheep-skin cap proclaimed that he had been active in fire-fighting, declared loudly: "This wasn't done by devils or house spirits. Kulaks did it. I smelled the kerosene and heard them galloping away."

Ivan strode up to the speaker. "Collect any others who saw this." Then he turned to the crowd.

"Stop this panic!" he shouted. "All forces of the united Red Dawn Farm will help you with your ploughing. Those who burned the barn will be punished. Let all who can tell how the fire started meet at once in the schoolhouse. Let all the rest go home." His own heart sank, however; he did not see how they could endure this blow.

By the time they had gathered in the schoolhouse, Stesha arrived with Vera and Anya, who was home for the Christmas holidays. Morosov came with them and sat down on the bench near Ivan, who welcomed him with relief.

Swift inquiry showed that the stable had been entrusted to two farm-hands, Pavlovski, who had been absent on a personal errand, and Rochagoff, who had been found in a drunken stupor inside the burning stable. The latter stood before them in a shock of terror, which had sobered him sufficiently to tell a connected story. A kulak for whom he had formerly worked had given him the previous afternoon a bottle of vodka—"to drink to the birth of our Blessed Lord." Finding himself on Christmas Eve alone in the stable with the vodka, he had been unable to resist.

"Vodka's always been the ruin of me," he wailed, pulling off his sheepskin cap, and running dirty fingers through his tousled hair. Then, in a sort of stupefaction, he added: "But one bottle—who would have thought!"

"It's been the ruin of more than you to-night," groaned Ivan.

"Let's examine the bottle; there may have been more than vodka," suggested Morosov. But the bottle was buried under hot ashes.

Pavlovski was unearthed, a shuffling fellow, who continually scratched deep in his breast for lice. With querulous defiance, he explained that his former boss, Hackman, had offered him some cast-off clothing, telling him to come and get it on Christmas Eve. He had thought it all right to leave the stable in charge of his fellow.

"That's what comes of our taking members who have no sense of labour discipline," said Ivan.

"It seems a well-planned plot," remarked Morosov. "I doubt if Alexinko alone has people capable of directing all this."

Two peasants had seen a band of horsemen galloping away after the blaze started. The sound had aroused them from sleep but the band disappeared in the darkness before they could be identified or counted. No one had followed them, for all available men had hastened to fight the fire and try to rescue the horses. At the barn they had noticed a strong odour of kerosene. The fury of the fire, which made it impossible to rescue more than three of the horses, also indicated that it had been artificially fed.

"It may be hard to find the guilty ones," said Morosov.

"Why?" asked Ivan. "We'll start with the men who made Rochagoff drunk and enticed Pavlovski away."

"If you can find them," said Morosov drily. "They won't be at home waiting for us." When they went to the house of the two kulaks, they found that both had vanished during the night.

Gossiping with the peasant women, Vera and Anya had picked up indications of an organized band, including men from Kichkas and Selidba. Definite evidence was hard to get, for the peasants were afraid to testify and the district police were swamped with similar cases. An epidemic of kulak sabotage seemed to have broken out everywhere against the rapidly growing collective farms.

"I think I could handle this investigation," proposed Vera. "My husband is in the kolboz here; he put in one of those horses that were burned. His father is bitter and may have been mixed up in the plot himself. I can find out if anyone can."

"A good idea," agreed Morosov. "Take care of yourself. It's dangerous."

"I'll make headquarters at Anya's and keep all records there. That's far enough away. I can't stay at Pavel's house, anyway; his father won't let me. Pavel will visit me at Anya's and it will seem quite clear that I am hanging around Alexinko in hope of reconciliation with his family. That will cover almost anything."

Anya thought the investigation so important that she offered to help Vera even at the cost of giving up her school. Vera wouldn't hear of it. "I'm sheltered now by your home. If you gave up school it would call attention. Besides, your sugar beets are more important. We'll win our victory, not just by rooting out evil, but by bringing new wealth to the farms."

Anya spent the rest of her holidays organizing a sugar-beet department for Red Dawn. She secured from the Farm Soviet the best land for beets, formed several field brigades of women, arranged for implements and seed. Then she returned to her studies while the evidence in the arson case accumulated in her Kichkas home.

The burning of the barn was only the beginning of Red Dawn's troubles. Accidents happened entirely too often. The tractor on which Penchelin had held the mortgage was found one morning in broken ice at the edge of the rapids. It had been driven off the cliff and was badly wrecked. Penchelin, it was realized, must have kept a second key to the machine. When they looked for him, Penchelin had disappeared.

Almost more serious than the spectacular losses were the hidden influences. A dozen insidious and even contradictory forms of propaganda seeped into the farm, demoralizing its membership. The burning of the barn itself was held to prove different things: God's anger, the danger of opposing the kulaks, the inefficiency of collective farming.

Toward the end of January, Ivan went in despair to Morosov. "These kulaks are ruining us. They're cleverer than I am."

"Yes, they are shrewd. That's how they got ahead."

"I wouldn't have thought a handful of men could do it. But they know how to make use of every weakness. Many members owe them money; these debts they use both as pressure and bribe. Right now there's the seed campaign; we must get the seed wheat from the new members in time to trade for selected seed. It doesn't come in; the peasants are eating it. Kulaks tell them the Government must feed them, anyway. We're short enough at best. Unless we can stop this wrecking we'll all starve."

"In some districts they're deporting the kulaks," Morosov said slowly.

Ivan's eyes lit with sudden hope. "How is it done?"

Morosov hesitated. "There isn't any law for it yet. The central Government can tax kulaks, the village can reallot their lands, the State Police can arrest those guilty of crime. There's no law permitting deportation. There ought to be one soon."

"What's the matter with the Government?" cried Ivan. "We're law-abiding folk, but these animals wreck our life. Stalin himself said they should be abolished."

"Some districts are stretching the law a bit," Morosov admitted. "I'll speak to Party Headquarters in Zaporozhe." He was unwilling to say more and Ivan turned impatiently away.

To Stesha Morosov spoke more freely. Both had long been members of the *Komsomol* and expected soon to be accepted as candidates for membership in the Party itself. Stesha was so quick to understand, such a help, not only in the hard tasks of organizing, but in the even harder task of clear thinking.

Walking home with her from Kichkas one evening, he confided his deepest worry. "It's something I can't speak of to Ivan—the conflict within the Party leadership. The Conference decided against the kulak system two months ago. But Ryckof and the Right opposition hold the highest Government posts and delay putting the decision into law. The local authorities grow desperate; they take the law into their own hands in order to save the *kolboz*. It has to be done, Stesha. Unless the collectives succeed now we'll all starve next harvest. But we want law, not chaos. Zaporozhe asks for my report."

Stesha answered thoughtfully: "We can't sit idle while they destroy us. All the same we can't start civil war. The kulaks read the papers; they might resist with weapons if we enforce what Moscow has not authorized. I think we should prepare for the deportations; hold our meeting, make up our list of the wreckers, have Zaporozhe check it. But not actually deport until Moscow gives the law. We must make it a campaign to bring pressure on Moscow. After all it's not one-sided. We take the laws from Moscow but Moscow makes its laws from what we do."

"That warns the kulaks and makes them desperate," said Morosov, "but it's the right thing to do."

The snow crunched under their feet as they walked through the zero weather. They swung their arms, striking their bodies for warmth. Morosov suddenly seized Stesha's hand. "You haven't any gloves," he exclaimed. "You don't look after yourself properly." He rubbed her hands with his own. Then he gave her one of his gloves and thrust her bare hand together with his into his roomy pocket. "That's the way," he laughed, "to socialize one pair of gloves for two."

As he warmed her hand in his pocket, he felt a deep joy that seemed to increase his strength. "Stesha," he said tenderly, "it is good to be working with you. It is great happiness to be together. Do you feel it too?"

"Happiness is a small word. It is more."

"We must learn to keep such happiness."

For a time he was silent, while his life seemed flowing to join Stesha's through their hands. He broke the silence: "Stesha, in our time the fate of the world is being decided. It must be decided by us. We are facing a stern life of conflict. We will make it a life of victory, and I want to share that life with you."

She raised her face to his. It seemed to them both that their kiss enfolded the earth and the stars.

"Shall we have a Red Wedding, Ilyosha?" Stesha asked a little later.

"Whatever you wish. For me it is enough to go to ZAKS and register. But if you want more ceremony——"

128

"I'd like to show the peasant women how beautiful a wedding like ours can be. We'll write our own ceremony and pledge our joint lives to the building of socialism," she planned. "We'll have it at Red Dawn Farm with an orchestra and a feast! I'd like a day to remember, myself."

"When the seed is all in the ground, we'll celebrate that victory with a wedding," proposed Morosov. "We couldn't get a day off for it until then." Stesha laughed and agreed.

As they walked on, she began to speak of Vera. "There's another one that's happy. Pavel is helping her investigations; they're close as they've never been before. He's pulled completely free from his father's domination. I think Vera'll be in farm work now for good. She's a power with the women. You can't imagine, Ilyosha, how much I've learned working with her."

"What has she taught you?" he smiled.

"Not to let my husband make a housewife of me," laughed Stesha, striking him a playful blow on the lips.

He seized her hand and kissed the fingers. "It's a comrade I want, not a cook. How's Old Man Voronin taking it?"

"He's joined the farm, of course, but he's very bitter. He feels he was forced to go in; he would have been ruined without Pavel's labour and Pavel's share of the family goods. He hates Vera worse than ever. He acts as if she started this whole collectivization herself."

"So she did," Morosov said gently. "Vera and people like her. Young folks, wanting to be free." He hesitated, and then added: "It's hard on the old if they can't adjust themselves."

At Red Dawn they found Vera. "I've everything at last," she announced triumphantly. "Ten kulaks fired the barn; Penchelin and Old Man Faber were the leaders. Hackman was in it; we traced him to Rostov. Two others got away to Stalingrad; they'll be brought back. Most of them are still hiding near here. Part of the time Krotov hid them."

"Krotov!" ejaculated Stesha. "He always seemed loyal to the Government."

"That's how he screened the others," observed Morosov grimly.

"Old Man Voronin was in it, as I thought," Vera continued. "He told them how the stable was guarded. He knew it from Pavel." She made a grimace of annoyance. "Pavel says his father didn't know they would burn the barn, but thought they were just taking the horses and that he would get back the horse Pavel put in. That's as may be. We'll see how the old man behaves from now on. Pavel and I saw him to-night and gave him a chance to renounce the kulaks and give evidence for the State. He was pretty violent, but I think he may do it."

"Where's Pavel?" asked Morosov in alarm. "You've taken a terrible chance."

"He stayed to argue it out with old Voronin. Don't be angry with me. I hurt Pavel so much by my personal war with his family that I had to give him this chance to save his father."

"I'm not angry; I'm afraid of what may happen to you," replied Morosov quietly. "Don't go back to Alexinko till it's all cleaned up. That's an order. Leave any evidence you have with you here at the farm to-night. I'll go with you to Anya's."

"Can't she stay at the farm to-night?" suggested Stesha.

"Most of the evidence is at Anya's; we must take care of it," decided Morosov. "I have my revolver. We'll go at once. Tell Ivan to tighten up everywhere for defence against sudden onslaught. If Voronin warns the kulaks, we don't know what will break."

"I'm sorry to be taking you away from Stesha," Vera said, as they went out quickly into the night. "You have so few free hours."

"It's war," replied Morosov. "We have to protect all our own."

They came to a small grove just before Kichkas. Morosov put his hand on his revolver and they hastened their steps. They had almost emerged from the blackness of the wood when several dark forms were upon them. Morosov fired once, heard a man groan, and felt his arms painfully pinned. Violent hands dragged him off the road into the bushes.

Dazed by the blows that were falling upon him, he heard old Voronin's voice shrieking on the road. "Hellcat! Servant of Antichrist! Breaker of homes!" A string of obscene curses was broken by the sound of blows and a body falling. Vera's muffled moan died into stillness.

"Damned fool!" shouted a voice that he recognized as Faber's. "She's the one that had the evidence. We should have found out what they know."

"This devil of a Bolshevik will know all about it. He's the ringleader of the whole business," cried another. They converged on Morosov.

They tore his coat off roughly; it seemed as if they were tearing him limb from limb. He felt the prod of sharp knives.

"Jab it out of him!" said a voice cold with hate. "Where did that she-devil keep her information? Tell us if you want to live."

A harsher voice jeered: "Tell us if you want a quick death!"

Could he goad them into finishing him quickly, thought Morosov grimly, or would the torture be long? He fought desperately as long as he could move a limb. Knives hacked at him, cutting his clothing to bits. Helpless and half-naked in the grip of his tormentors, he bit his lips to keep from crying out from pain. A final shock of agony cut him to pieces. In his last moment of consciousness, he thought he heard yells of disappointment and the sound of horses on the road.

Through waves of pain he fought his way into daylight. Stesha sat beside him in the Kichkas hospital. Dimly he realized that something of him survived. Then he sank into oblivion.

She was still there when he opened his eyes again.

"When was it?" he asked.

"Night before last."

"Is Vera dead?"

"Yes. Ivan's boys barely prevented their finishing you."

"Did you catch them?"

"Two of them at the spot, and others later. The evidence Vera left at Anya's ties the group together, and we'll convict them all."

"Vera was a good soldier," said Morosov slowly. "She took her share of the enemy with her when she died."

Again he lost consciousness and again awoke to pain. There was something he had to say. "Dearest Stesha, everything that we hoped the other evening is over."

"No," sobbed Stresha. "No."

"I can never give you happiness. I can never give you children."

"That wasn't what you promised. You offered a stern life of conflict and to share it with me. You won't go back on that promise."

"You should have children, Stesha."

"The children of the Red Dawn Farm and the children of our great motherland will have to be enough for you and me."

It was not enough, thought Morosov, but he felt too weak to argue. Resting in the comfort of her presence, he fell into a long sleep.

XX

Stepan's gang drove into the middle channel, attacking from the left shore.

Tall and white on the bank stood the fourteen piers they had finished. But in mid-channel the untamed Dnieper flowed. The winter's task was to close the central bed by a cofferdam and turn the river before the spring flow. Concrete work was over for the season; they battled the freezing current now with logs and rock.

They thrust great bulwarks of logs far out in the torrent and filled them with rocks till they sank to the river bed. Tossing a bridge to this new outpost, they made it a fort to launch their next attack. Pier by pier they drove this bridge-like structure forward, while under its arches the water foamed. Five days before Christmas the workers from both banks met above the central channel, looked down at the ice-rimmed current, embraced each other and cheered.

Stepan celebrated by crossing the river that evening to visit the

Johnsons. He had a dozen questions to ask the engineer. He particularly wanted to satisfy himself, by seeing Mrs. Johnson, that he had been right in his quarrel with Anya. He had gone to the girls' barracks for a reconciliation but Anya had left the dam. Upset by this, he wanted to console himself by a talk with the woman who had broadened his aspirations beyond Anya's peasant views.

The Johnsons had not expected him but they greeted him politely. "Our hero, the concrete-pourer, has come back," Eva smiled warmly, adding in a low voice to her husband: "What shall we do with him when the others come for bridge?"

"He won't stay long after they come," Johnson assured her. "There are some things we'd all like to ask him."

Stepan sensed that something was interfering with his visit. As soon as the interpreter came, his hostess explained that two Americans were coming later for a game of cards, but that they would all like to meet him.

"You must really begin those English lessons," she urged. "Bob leaves me alone so much and I'd like something useful to do."

"I can come three times a week," Stepan answered happily. "I'm going on midnight shift and that leaves both days and evenings free."

Somewhat startled by the definiteness of his acceptance, Eva Johnson countered gaily: "Both days and evenings! But when do you busy Russians sleep?" Stepan blushed when these words were translated, for Mrs. Johnson's smile made of sleep an intimate personal habit, instead of a barracks routine that happened every night.

Eva Johnson was delighted by his blushing. English lessons with this handsome barbarian would be fun.

The American house was as perfect as Stepan remembered it, but Mr. Johnson seemed nervous. He burst out: "What do you think about this idea of delivering current in May, 1932, a year ahead of plan? Why are they passing all these resolutions? Are they trying to high-pressure us?"

Stepan, confused, decided that the interpreter had made a poor translation. He knew all about the "Finish in 1932" slogan. He had cheered it many times. Mr. Johnson could not possibly object to so excellent an idea. He began to explain in detail how the slogan had started, how all brigades had discussed it, how at last the administration had supported it and the Government had given the necessary priorities.

Johnson grew impatient; this wasn't what he wanted.

"Why did the Ukrainian Government hold a special session of Congress here at the dam last week?" he demanded. "I don't like mixing the dam with politics."

"I guess they all wanted to see the dam," Stepan answered, still not quite sure what the American meant. "Everyone wants to see it. It's the biggest thing in the Ukraine."

"Out of the mouths of babes," Eva Johnson said to her husband. "Don't worry about it, Bob. They weren't trying to do anything. It was just a darned good show."

Brushing her aside, Johnson continued to Stepan: "The chief of the American consultants has just stated officially that the dam cannot be finished before 1934. Our original plan was 1933, but your engineers are bureaucratic and your workers slow. You have remarkable competitions but that's not consistent, methodical work.

"Now, just as we decide on 1934, a lot of mass meetings begin voting for 1932. You hold a special session of Congress at the dam and decide that 1932's the date! What are they trying to do? You can't build a dam by mass meetings and act of Congress! I don't like this high-powered politics."

Stepan was disturbed. He had been thrilled by the idea of finishing a whole year early. All the farms and industries wanted power from the Dnieper; the whole country would go ahead faster as soon as the dam was built. Every brigade had carefully considered it. Did the Americans think it couldn't be done?

Two other Americans had come in; Johnson presented them to Stepan. The younger one at once asked: "I'd like to know the low-down on that trial of engineers they staged at the dam the other day. It seems to me they're terrorizing their technical personnel."

Stepan beamed, for the interpreter translated only the first of the two sentences. "Oh, yes," he explained. "You mean the 'gravediggers of workers' proposals.' You yourself said our engineers are bureaucratic. Well, our workers made suggestions for speeding up the work; some of the engineers just forgot them. Engineer Sharikov 'buried' a hundred and seven proposals; some other engineers were almost as bad. We held a trial and reprimanded the guilty ones. It was a big success. The administration at once made use of over a hundred good ideas that had been buried. The workers turned in two thousand more."

"What nerve!" cried the American. "What kind of court handles offences like that?"

"It wasn't a regular court. It was just a mock trial put on by the workers. We couldn't impose real penalties, but we printed it in the *Dneprostroi Worker* so that everybody knew about it. It was public opinion that got the results."

"How you workers persecute the engineers!" Eva Johnson threw a glance of amused admiration at Stepan.

The fourth American, a grey-haired man who had been listening with some amusement, now brushed the ashes from his cigarette and quizzed Stepan: "I wish you'd explain who you mean by 'we.'"

133

"Don't psychoanalyse the poor fellow," begged Eva Johnson, making a laughing gesture, as if protecting the youth.

Stepan felt puzzled and ill at ease under all the bantering. He tried to answer. "I mean all the workers on the dam. . . . Well, it includes engineers. . . . I mean the whole collective of the dam, all of us who want to see the work go ahead."

"That ought to include you, Harry," laughed Eva Johnson. "You're always howling about tradition-bound Russian engineers."

The grey-haired man took several puffs on his cigarette before he answered: "I wouldn't mind murdering them myself, but I don't like like that kind of mock trial. Sort of lets the whole profession down."

The interpreter had not followed this interchange. Stepan knew only that Mrs. Johnson was protecting him in a world of clever people whom he did not understand. He felt a sudden surge of warmth for her that almost worried him. He reminded himself that she was Mr. Johnson's wife.

Turning to Johnson, he asked through the interpreter: "It seems by the papers there's trouble in your country. They call it a panic on the stock exchange. What is a stock exchange and what is a panic? Does it mean that many people starve?"

"Oh, no," laughed Johnson. "They just dig a bit into their savings." Seeing Stepan's bewilderment, he explained: "The stock exchange is where they buy and sell shares in big enterprises . . . Like a dam or a steel mill . . . A panic? Well, everyone expected to get rich, and then it flopped."

Stepan struggled with the ideas but they seemed too much for him. "You mean," he said at last, "that they couldn't fulfil their plan."

"Something like that."

"But Americans have every kind of machine and skill," argued Stepan. "Why couldn't they produce what they planned?"

"They produced too much," laughed Johnson. "I don't think I could make you understand." He signed to his wife that it was time to end the discussion by getting out the table for bridge.

"I'm glad that's all it is," Stepan remarked politely. "Anyway, it couldn't hurt you Americans here."

"Not very much," agreed Johnson. "It only means that for some time to come I can't sell my land."

Eva Johnson was arranging the bridge table; Stepan saw that it was time to go. But he asked the interpreter twice over to explain Johnson's last sentence.

"How funny that sounds, to think of a private person selling land! Especially an engineer!"

Eva Johnson's perfume surrounded him as she went with him into the

134

hall and gave him his coat. Alone with her for the first time, he was deliciously stirred by her nearness, by the warm pressure of her long handclasp and the soft challenge of her eyes, which said more intimately than words that she desired his return.

Her bright lips were very close; he had to clench his hands hard to check a sudden urge to kiss them. Perhaps that warm red that sent such excitement through him was not natural colouring but exquisite art. Far from repelling him, the thought that she had painted her lips to increase their beauty made her seem for the first time humanly accessible. Would she be angry if she knew how much he wanted to touch her lips? Perhaps she would like it; perhaps American custom approved of married women's kissing! It was so hard to know what a foreign woman meant.

His breath came in gasps; his face and neck reddened. Then he recalled how she had stood beside him in those confusing questions. He made himself think of her only as his gracious champion. His eyes adored her; then he turned and left.

Eva Johnson went back into her living-room telling herself that it was a shame to have badgered this nice youth, who was so much more exciting than bridge.

The winter stars sparkled overhead as Stepan made his way across the new construction. The man-made stars around him were brighter. Once the lights had clustered close to the riverbanks; now they stretched from shore to shore. Below him the dark current of the central channel swirled between the new wooden piers. His gang would begin to fill the gaps to-morrow. As he neared the left bank he saw below him the great excavation where he had drilled and laid concrete for more than a year. Under the flaring lights men were clearing the site of machinery, preparing to remove the old cofferdam.

All this great work, this conquest of the river, had begun far back in brains of engineers. Mr. Johnson himself had talked of it in 1923. Lenin had made the plan still earlier. But even before Lenin, great Russian engineers had dreamed of it, making plan after plan. Stepan knew now —he had learned at trade school—that from 1905 onward projects had been drawn for a hydroelectric station on the Dnieper. Their realization had been prevented by two of the greatest landlords, one of whom was Grand Duke Mikhail, brother of the Tsar. Owning vast lands that would be buried by the rising waters, they had demanded such great sums for them that the dam could not be built. Only when the Revolution threw out the private landowners had the great creative dream of engineers been released!

To Stepan it seemed unnatural, even obscene, for an engineer to be a landowner. To engineers, the land, with its great cliffs and torrents of water, was material for work. Their work was the remaking of the earth, the powerful reshaping of its surfaces. What had they to do with selling little bits of land?

He decided that he himself must become an engineer, a greater engineer than Mr. Johnson, with all the American technique but with real respect for the dignity of his work.

How tragic for that lovely woman to be married to an engineer who sold land! She must have married when she was too young to know. She was just the right age now, with both experience and charm. She was interested in his country, his dam, his river. He would take those English lessons regularly, not only for the learning, but for Mrs. Johnson's sake. How wonderful to cheer her in her loneliness!

To the first lesson he took lists of the words he wanted translated: dam, crane, drill, concrete, and every kind of material and tool. He soon forgot these words for his teacher had other questions. Smiling, she asked: "What is my name?" "What is the colour of my eyes?"

When he replied: "Your name is Mrs. Johnson," she corrected: "My name is Eva." Laughing at the accent with which he repeated it, she made him say it again and again until he got it exactly, until it really seemed to be her name. She made him look in her eyes and tell the exact colour; he saw that they were light brown, with tiny green flecks and with long, dark lashes touched with some unguent which made the eyes seem large and deep. Never in his life had he observed eyes so carefully.

Then she shut her eyes and made him repeat the colour without seeing it. It was hard to think of eyes when the lips were so red and so near. That night he lay sleepless in the cold barracks, remembering Eva's eyes and lips.

By the third lesson, her eyes and lips seemed no longer foreign but a close, incessant disturbance. His kiss was an awkward explosion of pent-up desire. He feared at first that he had frightened her. But her lips moved delicately under his and her warm mouth opened. Then he knew that she wanted him and he seized her with hungry amazement.

But just as she seemed on the utter edge of yielding, she suddenly pushed him away.

"That's enough, you young barbarian!"

The words reproved but she did not seem angry. She seemed to be panting with delight. But it was very clear that she did not want him. Stepan felt bitterly humiliated; he had made a terrible mistake. It might even be that she liked Mr. Johnson!

"You'll have to behave if you take English lessons from me," she admonished gaily, inviting him to come back.

All night Stepan lay awake, with clamouring senses, trying to puzzle out what Eva meant. Passionately he denied that she was a wanton; she was the height of culture and charm. But what decent

136

woman would go so far unless she wanted to go farther? In what deep way had he failed her, that she began with him and would not go on?

Was it that he did not know how? He had disdained the loose women with whom some of his gang occasionally consorted. "I would not so spend myself," he had said, intact in virile pride. Perhaps that inexperience had made him too awkward for Eva. He writhed in mortification.

Or did Eva fear to divorce Mr. Johnson because she had no job? Because Stepan lived in a barracks and could not give her a home? No! This thought insulted her. So talented a woman could choose any job and any man she wanted. She must want Mr. Johnson after all. It had been his mistake from the beginning.

He went to the lessons again but he went timidly. He would not let himself be inflamed unless he was sure. Eva Johnson was a little piqued to find him so well-behaved, so controlled in study. She was able to stir him to blushes, to gasps, to trembling, but not again to kisses. She did not know that after every lesson he still had a restless night.

One night he woke from a light sleep to find himself shivering. Against the whiteness of a frosted window, Marin was jamming rags around the edges of a window frame.

"Cold snap to-night," he explained. "Winter has really come."

' I saw the ice forming last evening on the wooden dykes," replied Stepan. "Work will get tougher now."

When they went to work—they changed to the day shift next morning —the quieter parts of the river behind the cofferdams were covered with ice. They worked close beside and sometimes in the icy water, closing the gaps between the wooden piers. The cold smote them to their bones; the wind seared their faces. After a day of such work they came home aching in every part of their bodies. But Stepan slept like the dead.

Cold as was their work, there was a task yet colder. The second afternoon on the way home from work, they saw a small group of men breaking a hole in the ice above the dyke. The ice was already firm; it took a dozen blows with a crow-bar to smash it. Finally it cracked and water shone in the hole.

"Bring the bags," shouted the brigade leader. Two men brought heavy sacks of sand. "Come on now, the hole is ready." The words were blown from his mouth by a gust of wind and snow.

Stepan saw a man in a diving costume appear at the door of a shack not far away. "That's Pavel Orov, the famous diver," said Marin.

The diver put on his helmet and fastened it at the collar. Approaching the hole, he rapped with his palm on his copper head.

"Let's stay and watch," suggested Stepan. "He's signalling that he's ready to go down."

Picking up two sandbags, Orov disappeared into the hole in the ice. The rising wind blew sleet across the river, and covered the hole with a thin film.

"He's filling in the chinks at the bottom of the dyke," explained another diver. "This granite river bed is damned uneven. The wooden dyke doesn't sit firmly; unless the holes are plugged, the spring current might carry the cofferdam away. Orov and other divers have been chucking in sandbags for a month."

"Have you been down?" asked Marin.

"Only once since she froze. I can't take it like Orov. He's put in twelve thousand sacks and has six thousand more to do."

The shivering boys of Stepan's gang looked with awe at the filming hole. "It must be tough," said Stepan. "What's it like down there?"

"It's dark," said the diver, "with just a faint grey light from the hole. You're alone against the current, fighting to keep from being drawn under the dyke. You hear, far off, the dull blows of water on the frozen shore. But Orov says: 'We've conquered a lot of difficulties on the Dnieper and we won't be held up by this.' "

The Stepan gang hurried home in the rising wind; the cold blasts gave little chance for talking. In the dining-room Marin exclaimed: "What a man, that Orov!"

"With men like that we'll beat the American estimate," affirmed Stepan. "There's nothing men like that can't do."

"You bet!" cried Marin. "We'll open her in 1932 or bust!"

On January 20th, in the depths of winter, the last gaps were closed and the central cofferdam was finished. The remnants of the old cofferdam on the left bank were blown up, opening a channel between the fourteen piers.

Then, for the first time in its ages of history, the mighty Dnieper swung to the yoke that man had placed. It swirled under the ice and beat against the wooden bulwark; finding no outlet there, the river turned eastward and smashed its way into the left channel, bearing along the broken ice.

The day after this victory buried the site of his earlier work under the waters, Stepan entered the school for engineers.

XXI

BLOWING FROM THE EAST out of Asia the wind of March arrived. Warm from the Afghan hills and the cotton lands of Uzbek, gathering heat as it passed the sun-struck sands of the Turcomans, tempered by the waves of the Caspian, it rounded the Caucasus Mountains and drove for South Ukraine. Then, swifter than the wind went a humming of wires from Moscow to Vladivostok, that every newspaper in every little town might bear the tidings. The war for Soviet wheat had begun.

Anya looked from her window into a Kharkov blizzard and then turned back to the headline. "Sowing in Two Days." Far to the south beyond the blizzards she hailed the "first Bolshevik spring."

That was the way they spoke of it in Anya's school in Kharkov. The first Bolshevik spring! The first sowing under large-scale collectivization! The first farming of a continent on one united plan! On its success they staked their country's future. They would all starve together if this harvest failed. They knew that on every border—from Finland to Manchuria—and beyond those borders in the great world capitals, hostile powers watched like hawks for the famine that might give the chance to intervene.

From the far-flung southern front came war despatches as the spring marched north:

TERSK OBLAST: *March 6*. Warm wind from south-east blowing now for two days. Earth drying fast. Field work starts this week.

ALM ATA, CENTRAL ASIA: Sowing already started. Many farms badly organized; implements unrepaired; members do not even know the boundaries of their ploughing.

ROSTOV ON THE DON: The winter wheat of North Caucasus comes from under the snow in good condition.

ODESSA ON THE BLACK SEA: Warm sunny weather. Sowing delayed by Kharkov's slowness with selected seed. Hurry up, snowbound Kharkov. We are not snowbound here!

Cities still ice-locked awoke to the battle. From frozen Leningrad three hundred farm specialists entrained for the fields of South Ukraine. In Moscow and a score of northern cities the upper classes of agricultural colleges marched through the streets singing, with banners, bound south to organize peasants in the war for wheat. Here in Kharkov, the Ukrainian capital, forty thousand short-term students prepared to go home. They were young peasants who had come to town that winter for short courses in everything from running a tractor to managing a ten-thousand-acre farm.

Anya was one of them. In the overcrowded dormitory of an old university, she shared a room with a dozen girls. In an equally over-crowded classroom she shared experience with a hundred more. They made up for lack of textbooks by their desperate thirst for knowledge, seizing it from tired professors, scanty libraries, newspaper articles, and their own past. Stirred by the presence of thousands specializing, Anya had learned about sugar beets and their importance to the Ukraine.

At the end of March she went south to meet the spring. She felt herself a different person from the untried girl who had come last autumn from the farm. How full her winter had been of great changes! The greatest had been Vera's funeral—a Red Funeral at which people made pledges to carry on Vera's work. The farm's orchestra played the Revolutionary Funeral March and a long procession followed the red coffin—red, not black, to show that this was not the end of Vera, but that she was part of a struggle that still went on.

Standing beside the red coffin, Anya had firmly resolved to give herself to the fight for a better life for farm women—the fight in which Vera had died. She had also decided to join the *Komsomol* and later the Communist Party, that her life might be like Vera's, clear to a goal and brave. She had studied every waking hour in Kharkov; now she was going back to work.

The train was crowded with people of many professions, going south to help the sowing. Strange how many crafts were needed in this new farming! A group of young bookkeepers told her their services were especially in demand. Whole districts were being collectivized without bookkeeping! What scandal! Nobody knew his share of work or his wages. All this accounting and division of labour—how new and difficult it was for peasants!

There were even a dozen singers from the Moscow *Bolshoi* Opera, going south to "sing for the sowing." Thirty Young Pioneers, aged twelve, were going under adult leaders to "play with the farm children and teach them games." "We are beginning a new era in farming," announced one dark-eyed damsel. Everyone solemnly agreed.

A dignified, white-haired man approached Anya: "I hear you're from one of the big farms. I'm from Leningrad, a professor of astronomy, giving langern-slide lectures to the field brigades. Have you a horse and buggy? Could you give me a lift?" Anya replied that she would ask about it in Zaporozhe, but it began to seem to her that all these city people would simply be in the way.

They met the spring at Zaporozhe. March showers were turning the soil to mud. Anya's heart gave a bound of joy when she saw that Stesha had come to meet her. Stesha seemed closer than any other human being, since that dark winter night—was it only two months gone?—when she had lost Vera and Stesha had lost her hope of a full marriage.

The girls embraced. "I must ask at once," laughed Anya, "whether you have any use for opera singers and an old astronomy professor—complete with lantern slides on the starry heavens."

"Grab them at once," ordered Stesha. "We all want opera singers. We're ploughing early without the field blessing, but the peasants won't be happy without some ceremony. With city singers to open the sowing, they won't miss the procession."

"And astronomy lectures?"

140

"Just the thing for the field camps. This is no ordinary sowing; it's the coming of all the city culture to the farms. Besides, it's a weapon against superstition, a scientific lecture on the stars and the earth!"

"I seem to be out of touch with the new farming," laughed Anya, as the girls jolted out to Red Dawn in the springless *telega*, softened with straw. "I've heard nothing since Vera's funeral."

"There wasn't time to write," apologized Stesha. "You must have seen the murder trial in the papers. Seven convicted; Faber, Penchelin, and Voronin executed, the others sent north for five years. Later, when Moscow legalized it, we deported twelve more who were wrecking the farm; by that time we had wide support. We're building a Laboratory Cottage for farm experiments; it is named for Vera. Peasants give volunteer labour in her honour, outside their paid days of work."

"It's a miracle! Things looked bad in January."

"They looked worse in February," confessed Stesha. "The trial was the turning point. You might say it was Vera's death that saved us, by arousing the countryside. When the peasants were sure that kulak rule was over, they even 'discovered' fourteen horses that they had been sneaking out of the county for kulaks to sell. The *Kommunar* Works repaired the smashed tractor and got us priorities for two more; we've five all told. We're ready for the spring.

"Not all the farms are so fortunate. Just south of us the Glory Farm is in chaos. They used high pressure to get members; then they had to let them go. They're disentangling horses and lands on the eve of sowing. But Red Dawn was soundly built."

Anya wanted to ask about Morosov, but feared that it might pain her friend. Stesha brought up the subject.

"Last week Ilya came out of the hospital. We registered our marriage at once. We have a room at the farm, near the central office. He's not fit for real work yet, but he'll be with us when we take the field."

"We're lucky to have him at all," Anya spoke fervently. She admired Morosov and knew that his progressive views on farm specialization would greatly help her own work.

The Moscow singers shone in glory at the long open-air meeting that launched the march to the fields. No one in the county had ever heard such singing or seen such costumes. Processions led by priests were seen to be outdated. The artists themselves were exalted; never had they sung to such an audience as these peasants in a farm revolution!

Old Artiukina rushed to the stage where the Zaporozhe reporter was photographing the visiting musicians for his paper. "Photograph me too with the singers. Now I can die! I never thought to see such a day." The photographer obligingly took several flashlights of the singers with members of the farm.

Singing with the musicians, the farm members set forth in the night to take their posts in the fields, tested in the sowing rehearsal two days before. They dozed by campfires to the soft music of balalaikas. They began ploughing with the first light of dawn. The first day was a record—the greatest ploughing Kichkas had ever seen.

Anya supervised the ploughing for the sugar beets. She tested and distributed the seed. When it was sown she found that she could spare a fortnight to help Stesha with the ten-day nurseries, one in each hamlet. Here the older mothers looked after the children, freeing the younger women for field work. Two nurses made the rounds, supervising them. Anya had brought posters from Kharkov, urging fresh air for babies and the swatting of flies. Most of the mothers classed these posters with the opera singers, as too good for daily use.

As Anya walked from one hamlet to another the sowing thrilled her as she had never been thrilled before. This at last was the true symphony of man with his earth. Mile after mile of rich black soil lay in a single field—stretching beyond the horizon with all hampering boundaries gone. Over it worked the field brigades of oxen, of horses, of tractors, all moving by one plan.

"We have thrown away the wooden ploughs forever," boasted the leader of a horse brigade. "In the small artels the implements were bad. But when all the peasants joined we had twice as many ploughs as we needed, so now we use only the best. We have ploughed under the weeds of the old boundary ridges. We stop for nothing; if a man is ill or goes to market, another takes his plough."

"Put your hand on the engine," called a tractor driver, swinging lightly down for the change of shift. "She won't get really cold till the end of sowing. We work her twenty-three hours a day, stopping only an hour at midnight to let her cool a bit. We're doing twenty-six acres a day per tractor."

At night the fields were dotted with campfires, from which arose music of balalaikas and the singing of voices in many-part harmony. Political discussions one night were followed by motion pictures the next. The films were old and broke often; the operator was inexperienced and the projecting machine crude. What matter! They were the first motion pictures many of the peasants had seen. In a brigade near Selidba they stormed the screen and smashed it by attacking the villain; it had to be explained that this was make-believe. The white-haired astronomy professor gave a night to each camp. He was hard to understand but his lantern slides were novel and he won ovations. Everyone understood at least that the stars were great worlds, not merely candles to light the earth.

City people assisted in many capacities..Young Pioneers from Kharkov helped Stesha look after the children. Twenty-nine *Komsomol* members from Zaporozhe worked as volunteers in the sowing. They were children

142

of railway workers, who knew nothing of farming. The farm boys taught them to handle a harrow, and they taught the farm boys to organize branches of the *Komsomol*. They slept on the floor of the Red Dawn office and in the fields with the others. In this friendly interchange the old antagonism between city and country was breaking down. This, to Anya, seemed the most far-reaching change of all.

When sowing was nearly over, Ivan spoke to Anya: "It's time to plan your future home. Kichkas will be drowned out when the dam raises the water. Everyone else is preparing, but your grandfather has made no application to the resettlement office."

"Is there any emergency?" asked Anya. "I thought we had two or three years."

"The sooner the better. If you decide in time you can exchange your house for building materials. Red Dawn made its arrangements during the winter; we located our fields on the high ground in the allotment. After harvest we'll start building a model farm city a mile in, near the new centre of the farm. Many of our members are moving there."

When Anya spoke to her grandfather that evening, he stubbornly opposed the idea. "For seventy years no flood has touched this house. My father built it out of reach of the highest floods."

"You can see the dam they are building, Grandpa. It will make a lake eighty miles up the valley. The water will be higher than our house."

"You are young and easily convinced, Anya. You have never appreciated this house. When I was twelve years old I helped my father build it in the year the serfs were set free. It was the first free house in our village. It was built high and proud. The Dnieper will never take it. I'll stay in it till I die."

Anya told Ivan that her grandfather refused to move. "He's grown almost childish; he insists that the river cannot wash him out."

'He's out of his mind," declared Ivan impatiently. "We'll have him declared incompetent and build you one of the first new houses in our farm city."

Shocked at the suggestion, Anya looked at Ivan, summing up his actions of the past winter in a new light. "You're very efficient with property, Ivan, but you're rather callous with human beings. Grandfather has seen fourscore years of hardship and I won't be the one to force him now. He may not even live till the river rises."

Broken by the look he saw in Anya's eyes, Ivan stammered: "I didn't mean to harm him. I was only thinking of you. I want you to have a nice house, to have everything nice. Besides"—he hesitated awkwardly—"I wanted you near. I always hoped you'd like me. I knew you went to the dam because you hadn't decided. But I hoped your coming back to Red Dawn meant coming back to me."

"I'm sorry you hoped that," Anya said gently.

Ivan burst out: "It's still that Stepan!"

She shook her head: "There's nothing between me and Stepan."

"If you're not engaged to Stepan, I'll make you care for me." Ivan spoke with a feeling she had thought he could not show.

"Don't hope," she warned softly. "I know my own mind now."

Five days ahead of plan they finished their sowing. At the presentation of banners which signalized Red Dawn as first in the county, Nikolai Ivanovich came with a *Kommunar* delegation and made a speech.

"We are proud to have been your patron. You have grown up and you in turn must be a patron. Take on the Glory Farm. It is behind in sowing; go and help! Help also the single-ownership peasants with ploughing and selected seed."

"The single-ownership peasants," cried everyone in surprise. "But they are our enemies. We fought them and gave them the worst lands."

"Quite wrong of you," Nikolai Ivanovich corrected mildly. "The kulak was your enemy because he exploited you. The hard-working individual peasant is not your enemy. He is only a few months behind you, a not yet collective farmer. Show him that your way is better, but don't do it by smashing him. A strong farm like yours must help the harvest of the whole county."

The following day the tractors and draft animals of Red Dawn began work for individual peasants and the Glory Farm. It was a real sacrifice; horses were tired and machines due for overhauling. The *Kommunar* Works, aware of their difficulties, brought them sudden help from a thousand miles away.

"We're sending you six tractors for the week," Nikolai Ivanovich phoned one morning. "They're from the Crimea; they finished sowing there. They're bound for Siberia for a second sowing. Spring is late in Siberia, so we hauled them off their flatcars for a week."

Six tractors rolled into the Red Dawn yard an hour later. The men who jumped from them walked with a long, rolling gait into the farm office and asked for the plan of work. They set about it swiftly in two ten-hour shifts, adapting themselves quickly to the new conditions. They were the best workers Red Dawn had ever seen. That evening the members of the farm poured out to meet them in their field camp, anxious to get acquainted with men who could sow the Crimea and Siberia in a single spring.

"We're sailors," explained the leather-jacketed leader. "Demobilized last autumn from the Black Sea Fleet. We learned the trade of tractor driver during the winter and went to Simferopol in early spring. We sowed a hundred and twenty-five thousand acres for the State Grain Farm and ten thousand as a gift to the poorer peasants.

"The order to help Siberia came by 'lightning telegram' from Moscow. Our farm sent word by auto to the field crews ten to twenty miles away.

We got it at one in the morning; we were ploughing three shifts. We turned in the furrows and drove to the train. They're sending us at passenger speed, eleven days to Siberia. We'll sow for them—their spring's just starting—and be back in July to harvest our Crimean farm."

"Is this the way we'll farm from now on?" asked Ivan, a bit dazed.

The chief of the tractor drivers pulled from his pocket and carefully examined a sweat-dampened cigarette. "Shouldn't think so," he said. "The cost is terrific and it wears out machines. In a couple of years we'll settle down to a more economical method—when we make enough tractors for all our farms. This year's a regular war for maximum wheat."

Apparently he decided the damp cigarette would do, for he put it in his mouth and lighted it, inhaling deeply. Then he turned abruptly to the crowd around him.

"Say, boys, we like you but—give us our sleep."

Thus—March in the Caucasus, April in the Ukraine, May on the upper Volga, June in Siberia—the spring marched north across the land.

XXII

"HALF A MILLION is the slogan! Three times what we laid last year! We've got to shove the rock work ahead faster. The middle channel lags behind."

Stepan spoke to the five gangs under him. He was boss of a section now. His primary task was no longer drilling or concrete-pouring, but making construction workers out of unskilled peasants. Half of the men under him now were newcomers, rather apathetic, dislodged from the rural districts by the earthquake of collectivization. He had to make them into new people, conscious citizens, builders of a dam. Without such people—to make the dam and later to use it—the dam itself would be only useless rock.

Marin, Peter, Maxim, Andreyev—brigade leaders now under Stepan—took up the slogan: "Half a million cubic metres this year!"

Most of the newcomers remained uninterested; they began to complain. "The barracks where we live isn't finished . . . The food from the factory kitchen is rotten . . . Where are the rubber boots?"

Bormin, a stocky fellow with a furtive manner, generalized their discontent. "What have we to do with half a million? We're not concrete-pourers."

"You will be later if you stay," retorted Stepan. "Just now you're holding back the concrete-pouring in the middle channel. The rock work isn't ready for it yet."

"That's not our fault," grunted Bormin. "The cofferdam leaked."

"It wasn't our fault in May," agreed Stepan, "but the cofferdam's long been repaired. Instead of making up the month we lost, we're falling farther behind. Let's organize to correct the lacks you mentioned. You who complained about food, we'll put you on the committee to supervise the factory kitchen. What do you say?"

"T'hell with the factory kitchen. I'm going back for harvest when I've made my stake."

"Wherever you are," declared Stepan with some heat, "this dam is yours. It's going to send light and power to your farms. As long as you're here, put your backs into it." Some of the men responded and work improved.

Stepan conferred with his brigade leaders. "It's worse than I told them. The Donetz Cement Works isn't sending enough cement. The reinforcing irons arrive spasmodically. Rubber boots for the concrete-pourers haven't come at all. Most of our industries seem to be creaking a bit with the strain of the Five-Year Plan. We'll have to get after our suppliers. But the centre of the trouble is right here; it's the low morale of the middle channel. The turnover of workers is terrific."

"Watch that Bormin," warned Andreyev. "He's agitating against the dam."

"I've had my eye on him, but I haven't caught him in anything yet."

"It almost looks as if the Americans are right about postponement," said Peter. "Even the district trade unions agree that the season's programme must be cut."

"The Party doesn't agree," countered Andreyev sharply. "Nor does the *Komsomol*."

Stepan was a member of the *Komsomol* now. In a year or two, when he was sufficiently advanced, he would apply for membership in the Communist Party. He decided this without any great emotion simply because he was a worker and the Party contained the most energetic and intelligent workers, who drove the country ahead.

He turned to Andreyev. "There has to be a real storming of the middle channel; will the *Komsomol* lead it?"

Andreyev nodded. "That must be our summer slogan for the dam."

"Storm the middle channel." . . . "Half a million cubic metres. . . ." Under the twin mottoes, a great battle was launched in the central river bed. The administration and most of the engineers still doubted, but youth believed. . . .

Thousands of young people poured into the middle channel after eight hours of work on other parts of the dam, volunteering for four and sometimes for eight more hours. They went with songs and banners. Their enthusiasm infected the older workers. Office employees, engineers, and high administrators came after hours to add their bit in the middle channel. A newspaper campaign brought in volunteers from Zaporozhe. Even complete outsiders like tourists—students from Moscow, miners from the Urals, oil workers from Baku, taking vacation trips to the giants of the Five-Year Plan—caught the excitement of the battle for the middle channel and remained for a week or two of work.

One evening Stepan met in the excavation his old acquaintance the procurer, who had come with a group of Zaporozhe volunteers and was obviously enjoying the work.

Encouraged by the procurer's grin, Stepan shouted laughingly: "Come closer to the working class. I'll give you a nice job." He pointed at one of the wettest, dirtiest spots.

"You still here?" replied the procurer. "I didn't intend to sentence myself a boss." Jumping obediently into the designated place, he set to work.

"I'm glad you've come," remarked Stepan. "I hadn't time to go to you. I wish you'd check on a fellow named Bormin. From the Kuban. See if he really comes from the place he listed and what his past is."

"Disorganizing work, is he?" The procurer jotted down the name and address. "A pest of kulaks has flown out of the villages and is lighting everywhere."

The following day a gang of women workers from the left bank came to the middle channel to volunteer for four hours after their regular day. The leader, a black-haired, well-built girl in her early twenties, walked over to Stepan and flashed black eyes above a dirt-smeared grin.

"Hey, you folks of the middle channel! Everybody has to help you out." Her rich voice made a song of the challenging words.

"Because we're so important," laughed Stepan, assigning her a place to work. "Everything depends on us."

"You've a good opinion of yourself, haven't you?" The deep contralto shot up the scale saucily. As the girl walked away, she called back over her shoulder. "We're concrete-layers. We might work for you later in the middle channel, if you're as important as all that."

"No woman gangs for me," replied Stepan. "They're upsetting."

"I hope so!" the girl laughed, making a face.

Several times in the next four hours, Stepan found his eyes straying toward the place where the women's gang was working. He was surprised to find himself slightly annoyed by the excellence of their work. He took himself in hand; that shouldn't annoy him. It was a good thing that they had come.

The late summer sunset was flaming over the western cliffs when he saw the girl approaching, waving above her something which at first he took to be a pick. A long blade gleamed; he saw that it was an ancient sword. She tramped nearer, squishing the soft mud with her rubber boots. With a mock bow, she presented her trophy.

"Lost something, handsome? This seems to belong to you. What a sword!"

Stepan took it in his hand and brandished it, turning it high in the sunlight so that it flamed like a golden shaft above the opalescent river. Many implements and relics of the Middle Ages, even of prehistoric cave men, had been turned up in the digging, but this was the finest he had seen. He marvelled at the fine carving on the handle and the quality of metal in the blade that had resisted rust under the water for who knew how many centuries.

"We'll take it to the museum," he announced to the girl. "You might get a prize for this." Then he saw on her rough overalls a strange ornament of beaten gold.

Catching the direction of his glance, she smiled downward at the ornament. "That's for the museum too, but not till the end of the shift! It's a woman's. I found a whole pocket of them over there beyond the sword."

She turned to lead the way, hitching her overalls higher on her hips as if the tight, mannish cut caused some constraint. Stepan flushed and felt annoyed with himself for flushing. He had become suddenly aware of her well-rounded woman's thighs under the trousers. He had taken overalls on working women for granted before.

They went down into a depression in the river bed. Several of these strange ornaments shone dull gold in the sodden earth of a new hole. It was becoming hard to see them in detail. The shadows of the pit already wrapped them in grey dusk. The girl lifted the treasures and held them high against the sunset which still flamed in the sky above.

"How long ago were these made, in a world long before ours!" Her voice was a chant of wonder and farewell.

A sense of the sharpness and briefness of a life shot through him. His eyes travelled downward from the antique gold to the rounded arms and firm, pointed breasts under the coarse shirt. The girl smiled dreamily and looked at him. His arms went round her; he felt her breast against his as he pressed her firm, rounded thighs. Their lips met in a flame.

"Is that the prize you promised?" she whispered, and then pulled away, laughing, and started up the slope. "My name," she called back, "is Niura. Sixth barracks, third row, left bank."

As he watched her go the lights flamed on above the construction. With a shock he realized that he was still in the midst of a world at work.

The middle channel was ready for concrete-pouring ten days ahead of time. Its success raised the general morale of Dneprostroi. One section of workers after another adopted the counterplan for half a million cubic

148

metres; the engineers accepted it. Finally, the administration made it the official plan for 1930.

Dozens of new brigades entered the middle channel for concrete-pouring. Niura's was one of them; they worked under Stepan, making records as good as the men's best.

"I'm the best gang you have," she reported each evening to Stepan. "What's the matter with your men?"

Her teasing annoyed him. Every day for a week her brigade was highest of all. Stepan said to Marin: "Please beat her once at least." The following week Marin did. Stepan felt his masculinity appeased.

The contact established between Stepan and Niura by their kiss underlay the frequent exchanges of jest and comment at work. Their growing intimacy became manifest; Marin teased Stepan about his "concrete girl." Yet more than a fortnight passed before the kiss was repeated. They seldom left work together; Niura went home with her brigade while Stepan stayed to organize new volunteers. He found no time to go to Niura's barracks after his long hours of work. They met at trade-union meetings. The second time this happened, Stepan walked home with her.

Both had been talkative in the meeting, but they were silent on the lamplit road. When they reached her barracks they stepped with a single impulse into the shadow of the building. Stepan seized her. She thrust her hand inside his shirt and pressed his bare skin. Intoxicated, his lips moved swiftly from her mouth to her throat and then fastened hard on her breast. She gave a deep sigh of content, pressed his temples long between her hands, kissed him on both eyes and pulled herself gently away.

"How lovely you are, Niura!"

Then she was gone from him into the barracks and he heard her welcomed by the voices of her girls. As he walked home he thought what a delight Niura was to him. What sources of joy her warm passion had revealed. Into the warm, perfumed night stole a gentle breeze from the river. Suddenly he found himself wondering where Anya was and what would have happened if he had ever kissed Anya thus.

Not till the November holidays did Stepan find time to visit the Johnsons. By that time it was clear that the half million cubic metres would be reached. The whole engineering world was beginning to talk of the miracle of Dneprostroi. "Never in our lives have we seen such an avalanche of concrete," the chief of the American consultants stated to the Soviet engineers that very afternoon.

Again they held a world record, not merely, as in 1929, for a single month's achievement, but for the whole season. They had beaten the world in amount of concrete poured in a year. Stepan intended to make Mr. Johnson admit their triumph and the possibility of finishing the dam in 1932. Besides, it was weeks—no, months!—since he had last seen Eva. He was shocked to realize his neglect.

The two-day holiday gave him the breathing spell he needed. He telephoned ahead, smiling to recall how unaccustomed he had been to telephones when he first met the Johnsons and how casually he used them now. He found they had another visitor, an engineer named Wood, who seemed pleased to meet Stepan, and shook hands with an enthusiasm Johnson had never shown.

"Stopped over for the holidays to see this wonderful dam of yours. Work for your Government's Steel Trust. Most of the time on the road."

Stepan's heart warmed toward the newcomer, especially when he found that Wood talked a bit of Russian. Stepan exhibited his English and Wood was delighted.

"We're going to get on. I want to see not only the engineering side of the dam but the spirit of the workers. Will you show me around your section after the holidays?" Stepan readily agreed.

Towards the end of the evening the two engineers left to call on the chief of the American consultants.

Eva Johnson detained Stepan with a smile. "You mustn't go yet. It's so long since you've been here. I was lonesome when the English lessons stopped."

Her tone expressed greater interest than she had ever shown. She was surprised at the excitement she felt with the handsome lad's return. He had developed into a rather compelling man. How he had impressed the experienced Wood! Something—his work or a love affair—had made him more adult. She wished she knew his real life.

Motioning him to sit beside her, she offered the clove-flavoured tea that had thrilled him the year before. She challenged, smiling: "Are you so busy beating the world record that you have no time for me? Or has some other woman stolen you away? A man like you is rather dangerous to us women!"

She thought: Why, it's the truth that I'm speaking, but I mustn't let him know. There could be nothing serious between her and this foreigner who lived without comforts, perhaps still in a barracks. But why did he make her life with Bob so dull?

"There's no other woman I know that's as cultured as you are," breathed Stepan sincerely. "I judge all the others by you."

Then suddenly his vision of Mrs. Johnson was influenced by his growing relation with Niura. In a brief flash, as she bent over the tea-cups, and the deep vee of her blouse showed the curve of her bosom, he recalled how nearly he had once kissed Eva Johnson's breasts. How had he dared to seize so hungrily this alien woman, married, and so much older than he? No wonder she had called him a young barbarian. She seemed to him now an exquisite stranger, with gracious gestures, not quite human. He did not even want to stay.

As he went home by starlight across the construction—because of the twin holidays it lay more silent than he had seen it for months—he felt as if he were going home to Niura. For more than a year Eva Johnson's sophistication had affected his view of all women. Niura had seemed lacking by that standard, even while with each week her attraction grew. Now the importance of Niura's being like Mrs. Johnson had vanished. His heart warmed to think that he was approaching, on the left bank, not only his own barracks, but the one in which Niura lay sleeping among the girls with whom she worked. Niura was one of his own kind, a builder of the dam.

Next morning was the second of the double holiday. Demonstrations and celebrations were over; the whole twenty-four hours lay free. Stepan put on a new embroidered blouse— they were selling these things in the stores now—and went early to Niura's barracks.

He strode in while half the girls were in bed, lazily enjoying the rest from work. They yelled at him to get out; he retired to the door and shouted: "We're off to the country, Niura, for the whole day."

"You might ask me about it," she retorted. "You're not a husband to beat me yet!" The words tantalized him as he waited for her outside the door.

"Have you brought any lunch?" she asked when she joined him. Seeing his confusion, she jeered: "You men, I wonder how you ever managed to build the world."

She disappeared into the barracks and returned with a great hunk of coarse wheaten bread and another hunk of sausage, tied in a kerchief. Laughing, she stretched out her arms to the thin autumn sunlight. "What a day," she cried. "What a day!"

They strolled far beyond the settlement and came along the river to the frost-hard fields. Stepan pointed over the water to the high cliffs of the western shore. "I used to play over there as a child; later I bossed a gang of homeless kids. We had a cave that we called the 'Cossacks' Lair.'"

"Take me over," begged Niura. "I'd like to see it."

"Not now," said Stepan. "I don't want to go back. Some day I will."

He turned to go down in the *Plavny*, the wide area close to the river that was flooded each spring. Noticing her reluctance, he urged: "It's lonely and wild by the river, with great spreading trees and thick dead grass to sit on."

"I've always hated the river," she breathed, "but I'll go with you."

To his look of surprise she explained: "Every spring the Dnieper floods out part of our village—the part where I lived, for we were poor. When

I saw you standing so strong in the middle channel, I thought: He's beating the river; it will never drown us again! That's why I gave you the sword."

With his arm around her waist he drew her down the pathway. They came to the shore. Under a great tree the fallen autumn leaves and the long, grey grass made a soft couch for them. The high noonday sun gave a transient warmth to the autumn air.

"I'll teach you to love our Dnieper," he boasted tenderly, drawing her down to him.

"Not the river! You . . . the man . . . who conquers!"

With a happy laugh that ended in a panting sob, she threw herself into his arms.

XXIII

"I BET THERE'S SABOTAGE over there; I can spot it," said Wood to Johnson, looking significantly at some workmen who were draining the oil from a crane, testing it with their fingers, conferring over it, and carefully taking it away.

"You're as bad as the Russians," laughed Johnson. "They see sabotage everywhere." He turned to his interpreter. "Find out what's happened to Bogdanov; he promised to meet us here."

Stepan came up. "I'm sorry to have kept you waiting. They called me over to report about a fellow named Bormin. For some time our cranes have seemed to be wearing out faster than normal; we thought it was because we have so many green hands. Over the holidays we checked the oil and found emery dust. A sack of emery dust was discovered under Bormin's barracks."

"I hope you catch all the guilty ones," volunteered Wood. "Do you have much sabotage here?"

"Nothing very serious. Some kulaks get in on false documents and cause a bit of trouble. One was chief cook in the factory kitchen and poisoned the food. There were hospital cases but nobody died. Some of the higher engineers were in the Industrial Party that conspired to set up a dictatorship of engineers. They quieted down when their chiefs were caught in the Donetz; we had none of the ringleaders here."

"You make me feel quite at home," grinned Wood. "That's my job for your Steel Trust, detecting sabotage. They've a lot of it."

Stepan's eyes widened with interest. Johnson's annoyed voice broke in. "Look here, Bill, you don't mean you carry tales to the GPU?"

"Pshaw," expostulated Wood cheerfully, "you'd call it troubleshooting at home. The other day at a new rolling mill in the Donbas, I heard funny sounds in a big steel gear box. It wasn't easy to pry into that box; you had to shut down production to open her up. But next day was free day. I went back with my interpreter; I picked him because he's a Communist and doesn't take time off.

"We got a crane, took off the steel table above the box, and opened her. We took out nine pails of refuse, mostly steel shavings. No wonder there had been a funny sound! If we hadn't cleaned her when we did there'd have been a serious shutdown in about two weeks. Wouldn't you report that, Bob?"

"Certainly. To the director or the Chief Engineer."

"That's not enough. You're not always sure of your Chief Engineer. He might be in that Industrial Party that your Stepan mentioned—trying to make the Government look silly. I had a lot of trouble till I found the boys that really care about the works. It's what they call the Communist Committee; they've got one in every plant. They're green as grass on rolling mills but they know their people and they want to get things done.

"I reported to the director, the Chief Engineer, and the secretary of that Communist Committee: 'Nine pails of steel shavings couldn't get in that box by accident!' That was enough. Several important guys were yanked out of that steel mill a little later. I don't know how they picked the right ones, but I know she's working better now."

"Of course I have no sympathy with sabotage, but this Five-Year Plan is partly to blame for it," argued Johnson, as they walked slowly about the construction site. "They're spending money like drunken sailors; buying these gaudy new plants when they haven't enough to eat. All their best food goes out of the country to pay for machinery. That Stalingrad tractor plant is the biggest in the world, and they're building another like it and a third to make caterpillar tractors in the Urals. They're crazy. The tractors they're planning would take more steel than all their blast furnaces can produce!"

"Don't forget that they're building new blast furnaces," challenged Wood. "I'm on that job."

"They're taking them out of the hides of their people," insisted Johnson. "No wonder there's sabotage and discontent!"

"I haven't noticed any widespread discontent," remarked Wood drily. "I've noticed a lot of enthusiasm for work, and a few soreheads who act in the dark."

Johnson turned impatiently to Stepan, who had been following the conversation as well as he could, with occasional help from Mr. Johnson's interpreter. "You work pretty long hours, don't you? Fourteen or fifteen?"

"Eight on shift," answered Stepan, surprised.

Johnson shook his head. "You didn't come to our house all summer; you were working nights as well as days."

"If you count volunteer campaigns———"

"What do you get for it?" demanded Johnson. "I suppose you sleep in a barracks with twenty other men." Stepan nodded. "What do you get to eat? All the meat, butter, and sugar you want?"

"There's never been all we want of them, but there's more than my father ever had. We'll have plenty of everything when we get our new farms and industries built."

"If a fellow like you worked as hard in America as you're working," argued Johnson, "you'd get those things for yourself right away. Your whole country could have more butter and sugar and clothes if your Government didn't spend so much on new machines."

Stepan was disturbed. He had taken it for granted that to have plenty of goods you must first build the machines. It would be fine if there was some American technique for getting clothes and houses first.

"If you know a quicker way to get what we need, I wish you'd tell it to somebody on the election committee. We might put it in our instructions to the Government in the January elections. The workers cn the dam might elect you to go to Moscow and tell them how."

Johnson grunted. His conversations with Stepan always seemed to take an odd turn.

Wood began to guy him. "Here's your chance. Some Americans I know are likely to be elected to local Soviets in January. Beat them all; go to Moscow on an opposition ticket."

Johnson was not amused.

It flashed into Stepan's mind that Americans were not all of one kind and that Mr. Johnson's ideas might not be the only American technique.

After the Americans left, Stepan told Andreyev and Marin what had been discovered about Bormin. "He's brother of that cook that did the poisoning. The real name is Gusev. He was a kulak in the Kuban who got into a *kolboz*, looted their treasury, and disappeared. We found it out when the procurer sent his name and description; that led to an investigation there. The real Bormin was an honest fellow who 'disappeared' at the same time; they thought he had gone off to a job. It seems now that Gusev murdered him and stole his papers. They found the body. The fake Bormin's going back for trial."

"Nice guy we were working with!" remarked Marin.

"It shows we've got to be on the watch always," affirmed Andreyev.

During the final month of concrete-pouring—they reached, before the winter stopped them, 518,000 cubic metres, a hundred thousand more than the world record—Stepan saw Niura daily.

Their gay interchange on the job lessened; they no longer felt the need of the jests through which they had made their first approaches, and they did not wish it to seem that their personal relation distracted them from work. They went to trade-union meetings and production conferences together and often strolled late into the evening. Everyone took it for granted that they were sweethearts.

Once he took her to a concert, put on for the dam's workers by a troupe of the best Ukrainian artists, returning from the All-Union Olympiad in Moscow. Her dark eyes glowed with an ecstasy he had never seen in anyone before.

"They're singing my own songs, the songs of my village! I never knew they were so beautiful!"

On the way home she sang them again in a low voice. Stepan was deeply stirred by her rich, expressive contralto. That night was the highest point of their passion.

At times he felt a conflict between his work and his desire to be with Niura, and wondered what it would be like to come home to her every night. The picture had its attractions, but he thought it might spoil the real charm of their relation—its spontaneity and freedom.

He spoke to Niura once about Mr. Johnson's ideas, and asked whether she was content to live in a barracks, with twenty girls, with such shortages in food and clothing.

"Of course I'm not content. I don't particularly mind the barracks; it's rather sociable. The food isn't so bad since they cleaned out that cook. But I wasted five hours last week standing in line to get a pair of shoes, and they weren't very good ones at that. But you can't get everything at once. I was thinking at that concert: I myself would like to study music and sing our village songs like a real artist. That's more to me than a pair of shoes!"

Stepan told her how Eva Johnson gave all her time to being a wife. Niura made even shorter shrift of the idea than Anya had.

"I'd rather earn my living tamping concrete than pleasing a man. Seems more respectable."

Despite Stepan's preference for an untrammelled relation, he was not entirely pleased that Niura felt this too.

In midwinter Stepan heard that Nikolai Ivanovich was dying. For a year the old man had worked under an intolerable strain. To all of his other jobs had been added the task of making twelve thousand harvester combines at once. The rapid growth of collective farms created a demand for incredible numbers of these large machines.

No one in the *Kommunar* Works had ever made combines. They dismantled an American model, took over a shop that formerly made an

155

antiquated reaper, and began the manufacture of parts. A young American tourist, named Harris, helped them; he had stopped off between trains and was offered a supervising job on the strength of having driven a combine all one summer.

"The first Soviet-made combine"—the "*Kommunar*"—was finished in July as a sample to show to the Party Congress in Moscow. The best assembly men put it together in the open factory yard, amid an incredible confusion of hunting several thousand badly stored parts. They worked five days and nights with only snatches of sleep. When they took it to the field and saw that it actually operated, they rolled to the ground and slept sixteen hours.

Nikolai Ivanovich went with them but he did not wait to sleep. That week was only one of his continuous weeks of strain. His tuberculosis flamed up again but he had no time to be ill. The Congress cheered the new combine and asked for ten more to test at harvest. Then they ordered the *Kommunar* to build a new plant, with a capacity of twelve thousand machines a year. Nikolai Ivanovich stayed on the job, running a temperature.

The doctor ordered him to a sanitarium but he did not go. The twelve thousand combines would not let him rest. Twice he fainted quietly on reaching home; his wife gave up her job to look after him. By encouraging workers' inventions and insisting that the technicians correlate them, he worked out a scheme to beat the plan by four months. He fought it through to adoption and fell unconscious in the conference room. The doctor said he was dying but he rallied in the hospital and it seemed he might yet pull through.

Stepan felt he could not endure it unless he could see his old friend again. He telephoned and found that the patient would be glad to see him.

In the hospital reception-room there was a commotion at the desk. With surprise Stepan recognized Mr. Wood, in hospital clothing, arguing with the nurse. At sight of Stepan, Wood's eyes lit up.

"Please help me tell this woman I have to leave."

"The doctor does not permit it," the nurse explained. "This American is ill and wants to go to work. He's a regular Bolshevik who doesn't know how to stop."

Wood staggered against the wall. Stepan consoled him, helping him to his room: "It's fine of you to want to work, but your health is of value to our country."

The American lay quiet until he recovered a bit; then he smiled whimsically. "Don't make a hero of me; I'm not hungering for work. I'll rest at home; I can't afford to stay on here.

"Came down with pneumonia just after I saw you," he explained further. "Worked too hard; lost thirty pounds in two months. They sent me here and treated me fine. Might have been Rockefeller they were looking after; day nurse, night nurse, special-interpreter nurse, and a doctor all through the crisis. Between ourselves I haven't the money. My salary looks large, but I've a wife and kids in the States. They'll have to spread the bill over several months' salary. They won't even tell me how much it is."

Was the American raving? Stepan touched his hand. He did not seem feverish and the eyes were normal, too.

"Why do you talk about paying from your salary? The industry you work for pays for this."

"You're trying to calm me down," Wood insisted.

Before the American was convinced, the nurse arrived to say that Nikolai Ivanovich was ready for his caller.

The old fire was shining in Nikolai Ivanovich's eyes; it seemed to Stepan that he was not as ill as reported. Relieved, he told about the crazy American who worried over hospital bills. The older man grew interested.

"I've heard of his work. Bring him in; I'll convince him."

Wood came in and relaxed in a chair by the bed.

"From what I hear," said Nikolai Ivanovich, "you seem to like our country. You've worked like one of our own, clearing up those stoppages in steel. Did you really think we were such brutes as to let you pay for an illness caused by your faithful work?"

"I hadn't thought of it that way," replied the American. He seemed convinced by Nikolai Ivanovich. After a pause he added: "There are a lot of things I've wanted to ask a person like you. About your Five-Year Plan. It's tremendous but I don't see how you can do it."

"We have forces to call on that you do not know," asserted the man in the bed.

"I think I know some of them; your workers are wonderful in competitions."

Nikolai Ivanovich smiled. "Even we who organize them are surprised by what they accomplish. The world has never known what forces lie in the people, when once they are owners of their tools. . . . In every one of these human creatures who yesterday were serfs of a Tsar is a power to remake his bit of the universe. . . . Even out of the black night of our old Russia. How much more in your America . . .

"I would like to live another fifty years to see all men joint owners of their earth."

With shining eyes the American leaned forward and took Nikolai Ivanovich by the hand. "You have given me something to dream of. I wish I could see it like you."

After he left, the old man closed his eyes and rested. Stepan was torn with distress. Had he tried him too much? Yet his friend had seemed so full of energy.

"They send us some good people, the Americans," whispered the sick man, opening his eyes. "Worked himself ill in our industry. And without even knowing that we would look after him. That's one of the forces we often forget to count on—the loyalty of hard-working people who do not even understand us."

Stepan wanted desperately to pose the problem Mr. Johnson had raised. He hesitated to bother the sick man but it seemed to concern him too. If the country could be built more slowly, with less strain, with more butter and sugar and clothes while building it, wouldn't that save the lives of precious people, people like Nikolai Ivanovich? At last he put the question.

For some time the sick man waited; he seemed to be gathering strength. When he spoke his voice was strong and normal.

"There is no cheap way to build a nation. And we must be strong, not for ourselves alone but for mankind. Nations and systems will be crashing around us. We must be in that crash a sure foundation on which man's freedom can be built. . . . Shall we make ourselves of steel, or of butter? That is the choice we have to-day for those decisive years . . .

"I told your American that we have forces to call on. One force I did not tell—the power of iron will in us Bolsheviks. These foreigners think we should worry when rooms are crowded and food is scanty. No personal lacks can worry those of us who suffered under the Tsar.

"When I was about your age I was condemned to death for organizing workers. Every night for twelve nights they read the roll and took out my comrades to be shot, while I waited for my name. Then my sentence was commuted to fetters for life.

"Eight years I sat alone in a cell with chains on hands and feet. Every day in those years they manhandled my body. Sometimes only a jerk of the ear to show who was boss; every week or so they beat me up properly. Once a month they took me out and gave me ten minutes to bathe. In ten minutes I must unfasten the long row of specially placed buttons that made it possible even for fettered limbs to get out of clothes; I must bathe, wash my towel, and dress. Cold water always; never in all those years was I really clean. All those years my sentence read: 'Forever!' . . . As long as they held power.

"Do you think that cold or hunger or pain can hurt me after that? Now that we hold power and build our own new world? Can the whining of soft folk for this or that, or can death itself, turn us aside? Let them take all the butter and give us the Five-Year Plan three months sooner. Except for a little butter for our children, who must laugh in the world we build."

After a long pause, he spoke more softly. "Life can be very sweet without sugar. But that Anya of yours will be flooding the land with sugar while you are building our dam."

Stepan stammered: "Is Anya really——"

"Tsk! Tsk! You don't follow what she's doing. You're buried in that dam. Don't be a narrow specialist. Our world is wide."

"How do you find time to know everything?" Stepan marvelled.

"You'll find time too, Stiopa. But don't let it wear you out. Look at me! Less than fifty years and I'm finished. But I've had more life than many who live to a hundred. These years of ours count double. They are the years most worth living of any since time began."

He seemed so exhausted that Stepan rose penitently. "I'm tiring you," he apologized.

"No, stay another moment. What is strength for but this? We won't meet often; possibly not again. Our Five-Year Plan will use up a lot of us old ones. That's nothing to worry about. It is making a lot of new ones like you who will carry us on."

"We can't do without you," cried Stepan, clenching his hands to hold back sobs.

"Oh, yes, you can," smiled Nikolai Ivanovich. He closed his eyes and sank into a light sleep.

Watching under the low-turned light the fitful breathing, Stepan knew that when he should apply for membership in the Communist Party, as he hoped they would let him do in a year, it would not be only because he was a worker who could see and think and fight for a workers' country, but because he must carry into the future a torch that came to him down uncounted ages, and that was placed in his hands by Nikolai Ivanovich. Could he be worthy to inherit that flaming will?

After a time he thought of Anya and wondered how he had lost her. The old man had said "your Anya"; the old man knew. He remembered how Anya had written: "Most of all he loves the river," and how this, together with Nikolai Ivanovich's intercession, had won him the right to work at Dneprostroi. In that quiet hour by his sick friend all the long-buried pain he had had from her rose to the light and vanished. She had not dealt the pain; it was part of his fight into life. He knew at last what the turmoil of work had hidden, that Anya—whether or not he saw her—was a deeper part of him always than Niura could ever be.

Niura had taught him the joy of unquestioning, unashamed passion. But Anya—how far back and how simply she had touched the springs of his life!

XXIV

DNEPROSTROI WAS IN THE midst of the municipal elections.
When Stepan returned from the bedside of his sick friend, Marin met
him with congratulations.

"The workers of the middle channel proposed you to-night as their
representative in the Zaporozhe City Soviet."

Stepan was taken aback; in his worry over Nikolai Ivanovich he had
forgotten that meeting. Then his heart bounded at the thought that his
fellow workers trusted him with their city affairs. It would be a heavy
responsibility to add to his work at the dam. The campaign would
prevent his intended immediate visit to Anya. But the old man had
urged him to widen his horizon. And how fine to go to Anya as an
elected deputy!

The news of his old friend's death two days later confirmed his
decision. He must do his part to replace the activities of that irreplaceable
man.

As the largest hive of workers in Zaporozhe, Dneprostroi was buzzing
with political activity. Its thirty-nine outgoing deputies had to face their
constituents—at some two score meetings—and be heckled on the record
of their two-year term.

The sorest point of the dam's workers was the lack of a street-car or
even a decent bus line to the centre of town. "We ordered this two years
ago," the voters fumed at the deputies. "We're wasting thousands of
hours walking to town."

"Tourists from all over the Soviet Union come to admire our dam and
have to pay fifteen rubles for a rickety cab from the station," declared
a voter.

"If you bureaucrats can't get us a car-line, we'll elect representatives
that will," cried Marin, supporting Stepan's candidacy. "Our banner
winners know how to get things done."

Stepan's name was one of two hundred nominations made in these
meetings. The election committee reduced them to a slate of fifty-nine,
on which Stepan—already known as popular and energetic—was
included. His achievements in work and in the fight against illiteracy
were printed in the special election issue of the *Dneprostroi Worker*. He
himself made many speeches about the need of arousing all citizens to
take part in city politics. He said nothing about himself or what he
would do if elected. This would have been bad form; if the voters chose
him, they would tell him what to do.

Most of his time went to helping compile the *Nakaz*—the voter's

160

instructions—which set the task of the city government for the next two years. Every mass meeting was urged to submit ideas for this; every housewife was canvassed in her home.

Stepan spent several evenings calling on housewives. In one ancient hovel he came upon an old woman who had never thought of voting in her life.

"What honour that the Soviet Power should call on me," she fluttered. "And what do you want of me, my dear?"

"You must take part in government, Grandma."

"How shall I govern? I am old and cannot work. I am dark and cannot read."

"You are a citizen, Grandma, and an owner of our country. Tell the Government what the people need."

She looked around the shabby room, through which it was hard to move because of the double line of laundry hung to dry. "And does the Soviet Power want my instruction? Then see, my dear, how I do my laundry. Four people live in this room and it's bad for the baby's health. We must build more laundries; that's what I tell the government."

Stepan noted the woman's instruction and duly turned it in to take its place among fifteen hundred similar ones gathered from Dneprostroi voters. He worked on one of the many committees which sorted and condensed and finally printed the list. After all these preparations, the slate of candidates and the *Nakaz* went through the final elections almost unchanged.

During the campaign, Stepan hardly saw Niura except at meetings. She was studying music after work and had progressed far enough to play in one of the bands that enlivened the election assemblies. Several times Stepan, on the platform, saw her among the musicians. When they met she teased him by saying "Comrade Deputy" with mock formality; he retorted by calling her "Honoured Artist of the Republic," to be which was her dearest dream. They no longer took special pains to be together. Niura's first attention was for her music, while Stepan's thoughts were for the elections and for Anya.

He had hoped to go to Anya after the elections but every evening was taken with the immediate business of the City Soviet. A *Nakaz* of four thousand instructions had at once to be considered, since all demands that concerned the central Government must be forwarded, with appropriate comment, to the All-Union Congress in Moscow, convening early in March. After this, they settled down to municipal business. Stepan, assigned to the street-car and housing committees, formed a group of his fellow workers at the dam to investigate housing. All this took time, but the number of citizens a deputy could rally for municipal work was a measure of his success.

Anya was almost equally busy with the Kichkas election. She was on the village clean-up committee; she distributed paint and whitewash. "Clean up to make the election a festival day," was the slogan sweeping the Ukraine. Anya took enthusiastic part; it was her first election.

Cleaning up Kichkas was not easy. Its electoral district extended as far as Alexinko and included several small hamlets. The villagers nearest the river were moving to homes farther away. Many families had either dismantled their houses for materials or left them for temporary use by the dam's construction workers. Both the old and the new homes had to be made presentable for the festive day. A house-to-house campaign cleaned the yards and collected a lot of old implements and scrap iron for the nation's industries.

"We can do most of the rest with whitewash and bright-coloured paint," remarked Anya to old Artiukina. "I managed to get both yellow and pale blue in addition to white."

Artiukina peered shrewdly at the younger woman. "Folks say you'll be one of the candidates, because of your sugar beets."

"The *Komsomol* is recommending me," confessed Anya. "But the candidates are not as important as the *Nakaz*. Everything in the village has changed since the last election. We must all be thinking up new ideas for improving our life."

"We'll keep Marya Kurkina for president, won't we?" asked Artiukina anxiously. "I bragged about her in Moscow at the Congress of Collective Farm Women a year ago. Only one village in five has a woman president."

"I think Kurkina and most of the Village Soviet should be re-elected," asserted Anya. "They're all of them honest; the drunks and grafters were thrown out two years ago. There may be better talent but the present members have experience. I think we should replace only the three that are leaving for study."

"I'm not so sure about re-electing Bobrov," said the older woman doubtfully. "He's not been popular since he argued against poor peasants and took in kulaks."

"We all make mistakes in times like these," Anya answered. "Ivan's a dependable worker. We need him in the Kichkas Soviet."

Anya spoke that evening on the district radio hook-up, in which the villages exchanged reports on the coming elections. Marya Kurkina introduced her, stating that she wished to give her radio time to one of the new candidates, who had something important to say to the district. Anya had worried some about her first radio speech, but when the time came she did very well.

"Our country needs more sugar," she urged in a low, clear voice. "Now in the election is the time when we must all of us help plan for the country's needs. In the past this district has not grown many sugar beets.

But our Red Dawn harvest has shown that you can get twelve tons per acre here. If you want to plant beets, our records are open to you through the Vera Voronina Laboratory Cottage. Let's flood the land with sugar!"

The Kichkas peasants, listening on their recently installed loudspeakers, were thrilled to hear the voice of two local women coming over the air.

On a day in late January, Marya Kurkina called the final election meeting to order in the presence of a representative of the county election board.

"We have 325 present of our 335 voters. It is 97 per cent; we consider that we can proceed."

After the choosing of a præsidium and the reading of the election law, Kurkina presented the slate of candidates—the nominees of the *Komsomol* and the Party. Several names were added from the floor.

"Why isn't Morosov in the new Soviet?" demanded Artiukina. "He suffered most of all for us."

"I think we should make him village president," contributed a bearded peasant.

A murmur of protest rose from Artiukina and from several women. "We want Kurkina for president!"

"Let me explain about Comrade Morosov," said Ivan, rising. "He is in Kharkov at the Agricultural Institute. As soon as he returns, Red Dawn Farm wants him as president; he has agreed to take the post for a year. Red Dawn is larger than Kichkas Village and Morosov will not have strength for both. He writes that he thinks it important to continue a woman in office and that he votes for Kurkina as village president."

Amid general applause, Kurkina retired from the stage, while her name was voted on, and then at once returned. Ivan Bobrov's name came next. "He did good work as chairman of the committee on roads," said the man who proposed him. Then silence fell.

"Speak up," urged the county representative. "This is the time to tell Bobrov what he has done well and what badly. I see you are just dumbly electing him."

"Not dumbly," protested Artiukina. "Under him Red Dawn has grown to five hundred families and we got more food from this last harvest than we ever got before."

Two-thirds of the hands were raised for Ivan; no one voted against him. "Well, Comrade Bobrov," said the county representative, "I wouldn't call them enthusiastic, but it seems you get in."

With varying percentages the meeting elected others, the peasant, Pankrassin, who had just come back from a course in village finance, the doctor, Zharkov, who had improved the local hospital, and a woman whom everyone knew as Claudia and who was declared "energetic, but with too sharp a tongue."

163

Such a forest of hands went up for Shubina—also a candidate for re-election—that the chairman could not count them. "It will be simpler," she remarked, "if those who didn't vote for Shubina will raise their hands." Five workers from the new creamery raised their hands and one of them explained their position. "We've only recently come here to work and we don't know Comrade Shubina well enough to vote for her yet."

Anya took no part in the discussion; she felt especially shy because she was a candidate. Her name came last, nominated by the Kichkas *Komsomol*. She was surprised to find that more people wanted to speak for her than for anyone else except Shubina, who had been two years in village politics.

A stocky matron, with a child in her arms, asserted, "Kosareva did a lot for the summer nurseries."

"That not the main thing," argued a solid-looking peasant. "She's the leader in sugar beets in the district. We should tell the Village Soviet to elect her to the County. We should send her as high as possible—to Kharkov, even to Moscow—to promote beet-growing. It's the best Kichkas has to give the nation."

Many people were applauding and demanding the floor. Kurkina asked one of them: "Speaking about Anya Kosareva?" The would-be speaker nodded. "Going to criticize her?" demanded Kurkina. "No? Then we'll omit your praise. So much of it will spoil the girl. She isn't twenty yet."

A smile passed over the audience. The hands they waved in voting gave Anya praise more glowing than any speech.

Relieved and proud, she sat back in her seat and listened to the discussion of the *Nakaz*. Anya knew what was in it; as one of the better-educated villagers, she had spent several nights with the election committee trying to reduce to coherent form the unlimited desires of the countryside. Demands for better crops had been referred to Red Dawn and requests for light and power had been sent to Dneprostroi.

For the Kichkas Soviet there was still a formidable document, including a score of ambitious demands, such as a multigraphed newspaper, a small airfield, a history of Kichkas, new public baths with a laundry, barber shop, and tea shop, the conversion of Faber's confiscated house into a library and village club.

The Kichkas Village Centre, including school and hospital, was ordered transferred to Red Dawn's new "farm city." Transport was to be furnished for the household goods of all villagers who moved there; all houses were to be wired for electric light and radio. Nor were these demands enough for the insatiable assembly. "A well-equipped fire department with branches in every hamlet" and "a dentist in our hospital" were added from the floor.

As the secretary was adding these instructions, Artiukina demanded the floor. "What did the committee do with my instruction to give us peaceful work and no more war?" Several women applauded.

"That doesn't depend on the Kichkas Soviet," explained Kurkina, "but we'll send it to Moscow if you like."

"Tell them we haven't forgotten what we suffered from the Poles and the Germans here in Kichkas before. Tell them to make our Red Army strong and to keep out invaders! We're getting a good life now and a fish could live without water better than we could live without our Soviets. We want peace for the rest of our days, but if those enemies come in with their bayonets, I'll fight them in the front lines myself!"

The schoolhouse rocked with applause and friendly laughter.

As the meeting was closing, messengers came to report elections from outlying hamlets included in Kichkas Soviet.

To everyone's surprise, Alexinko Hamlet had chosen Pavel Voronin to represent them in the Village Soviet. The Party had recommended another candidate, thinking that Pavel's lifelong submission to old Voronin, the murderer and traitor, did not speak well for his fighting qualities. The villagers had been moved by a young man who declared: "Since Vera's death, Pavel has been our best fighter for the *kolboz*," and by a woman who pleaded: "He needs a lot of public work to express his feelings about what happened to his wife."

With head erect, Pavel strode to the platform to present his credentials. The county representative congratulated Alexinko on "a good election, showing popular initiative," and added: "Your local Party members seem to have lagged behind the peasants in discovering new talents."

When the assembly broke up, Anya shook hands with Pavel. "I've had hard thoughts about you," she admitted. "I'm glad you're working with us now."

"You were right to think badly of me," answered Pavel, in a voice firm but full of pain. "I can never atone for what I did to Vera. But for my long submission to my father, and my demand that she tell him her discoveries, Vera would be alive to-day."

"We must make her live in the lives of all of us," said Anya. "All of us owe her very much."

The members of the new Soviet remained for a brief session in which Marya Kurkina was made president while Anya Kosareva was elected deputy to the County Congress of Soviets.

When at last Stepan came on a Sunday to Anya's cottage, he found only the grandfather and a strange middle-aged woman at home.

"Where's Anya? What's happened to her?" he cried.

Grinning, the old man reassured him. "Our Anya's gone to Moscow. They sent her through the county to the province to the Centre! She's elected to the All-Union Congress! Kichkas pays a woman to stay and look after me so that Anya can spread sugar beets all over the country."

Stepan congratulated the grandfather sincerely, but he felt a shock of dismay. How out of touch he had been with Anya! How far she had gone ahead! For the first time he feared that he might lose her, that he had come too late.

XXV

A NYA WAS THRILLED by the special train to Moscow. She ate in a dining-car and slept in a berth! And what fascinating passengers! All of them elected to the Sixth All-Union Congress, and doing such exciting things.

Her compartment mate, Natalya, bossed a big tractor station "manned" entirely by women on the high steppe of South Ukraine.

"We furnish farm machinery for thirty-two villages! Our tractors work twenty-five hundred hours a year, four times the American average. But our time-keeping worries me; nobody has a clock. Isn't that just like our country?" laughed Natalya. "A more than American mechanization held up for a simple clock!"

What an interesting crowd in the Moscow railway station! Hundreds of deputies were arriving from different republics. Anya saw many dark Asiatic faces and brilliant costumes, and heard the chatter of strange tongues. The drive through the decorated streets left her breathless; there were so many energetic people, all going somewhere. For an old city, there was a great deal of new construction; they seemed to be making over the town. She had hardly time to notice the picturesque brick wall around the Kremlin before she entered the Grand Hotel.

From her bedroom window she looked into history, past tall towers into the Red Square, where the fantastic, many-cupolaed church of Ivan the Terrible stood colourful against the pale blue sky. Above the Kremlin wall she could see the Red Flag on the white-domed building of the Government offices, where she would meet the men and women making history to-day.

Three of them were her room-mates. Late into the night, the women got acquainted over many glasses of weak tea. Anisia Ustinovna, a kindly, middle-aged woman from Siberia, was the oldest of the group and the most experienced. This was her third term in the Congress; she was one of the leaders of the Siberian delegation.

"How did you first go into politics?" inquired Anya, thinking that the large woman in the shapeless home-made gown of dull red cotton, was like a village mother.

A smile lit up the lined but placid face. "I'm a widow with four children and I used to be a potter. I helped with famine relief in the Hungry Year. When I told the County Congress how bad things were in our village, I was afraid they would be angry with my harsh unpleasantness. But they sent me instead to the Provincial Congress, 'to tell very strong how bad things are in our country.' The Provincial Congress sent me to Moscow to tell how bad things were in Siberia. Since then I work at politics instead of pottery."

"This is my first term," announced Dunia Ostrova, a thin wisp of a woman from Leningrad. "I've been active in the textile workers' union since 1919. That was my year of great joy."

"But that was a year of typhus and hunger," protested Anya. "Didn't you suffer from these?"

"We hungered all that year," Dunia admitted. "But that was the year when I learned to read and write and my husband began to respect me as a citizen. For the first time we had a whole room for ourselves— my husband and I with our children—for we took over the houses of the rich in the Revolution."

"How much you older women endured." Anya's eyes were soft with sympathy and admiration.

"You young girls can't realize your freedom," said Dunia. "You don't know the slavery you escaped."

"Some of us do," declared Shadiva, a golden-skinned creature from Samarkand. "I was sold in marriage at the age of ten and violated before I was a woman. Fortunately I had no children, so when my chance for freedom came, it wasn't too hard to run away."

Anya stared in awe at the fiery slip of a girl who—still only twenty-two —had undergone such experiences. All evening she had wondered how this gay, fascinating being, with the green velvet cap over her long black curls, could be the famous deputy from Central Asia, whose name was in all the papers. But now, as Shadiva, passionately eloquent even in tea-table talk, stamped across the room with her black shiny knee-high boots clattering with energy, it became credible that wherever she went in Central Asia women came out by thousands to cheer her—a symbol of their own new freedom.

"I ran away from my husband to study in Samarkand," Shadiva related. "He sent me a letter of divorce. He wrote: 'Take note that I am marrying Fatima, who, thank Allah, cannot read or write.' But I had my revenge! When I finished school, I went back to the village and taught Fatima also to read!"

All of them looked at Anya next. She felt very young and inexperienced. "Each of you has won in a hard fight," she said. "I feel that I have hardly lived at all."

Anisia consoled her. "Each generation has its struggle. Ours was the fight for equality and freedom; yours is the fight for production. I understand you've accomplished something with sugar beets."

Under her sympathetic listening, Anya's story of beet-growing again regained its importance.

"We're planning a beet industry in Siberia," volunteered Anisia. "You and I must go around to the *Peasants' Gazette* for the latest data."

With Anisia as guide, Anya found the *Peasants' Gazette* in a large rambling building near the centre of town. She exclaimed over the "Voice of the Peasant," the name given to a library of several million peasant letters, all classified and put at the disposal of the Congress, so that its members could know what the peasants were thinking about marriage, the family, the crops, as well as every kind of farm and government problem. She learned with surprise that her harvest of twelve tons per acre, more than double the average Ukrainian yield, was far below what could be raised with better cultivation.

"Twenty tons is quite possible," declared the editor, giving her several pamphlets on sugar-beet growing and the methods used in foreign countries. "Specialize! Farming is a dozen different professions. You'll advance by science and specialization."

She tramped through the snow that evening to the decorated opera house, presented her credentials to the tall Red Army guard, and entered the rapidly filling hall. She paused in the confusion of the aisles as she saw before her the flag of her country, enormous across the back of the deep stage, rich red against the hangings of soft grey. In front of it was the long red table for the præsidium, the white sculptured head of Lenin, a great green globe of the world, and "Workers of the World, Unite!"

Around her the deputies were finding their places. Most of them were in everyday clothes, but the gay kerchiefs of the women added colour to the gathering and not far away were the gorgeous silk robes and giddy gold caps of the Central Asian representatives. A lustrous glitter filled the air from the golden sweep of the theatre's many galleries, filled with three thousand men and women from Moscow's factories and offices. Lower down were the boxes of the foreign diplomats, formal in evening dress or military uniforms, and the great crimson trench for the foreign and Soviet Press between the deputies and the stage.

Deeply moved by the thought: "I, Anya Kosareva from Kichkas, am a part of this great Government," she seated herself with the Ukrainian delegation. There was a sudden rush to feet as the music of the "International" broke from a symphony orchestra, then a thunder of applause as the leaders of the Government appeared on the platform.

Anya strained to pick out the faces: Kalinin, Molotov; yes, there was Stalin himself in khaki. President Kalinin declared the meeting open and began reading names for the præsidium. Stalin smiled a greeting when his name was mentioned and the whole audience rose again to cheer. A peasant woman with black cotton shawl walked firmly in her high men's boots up the crimson runway; a sailor in a tight blue blouse rolled after, followed by a Tartar in a bright green hat, and the famous cavalryman Budenny with Red Orders covering half his chest.

How fast everything happened! In the first twenty minutes half the reports—including some on industry and the Army—were thrown off the agenda. "We all support the Army, anyway, and we'll read the report in the newspapers," said the Ukrainians, while the Caucasian delegation added: "In a week the spring sowing will be in full swing in the south and we must get back to lead it." Molotov, Chairman of the Council of People's Commissars, plunged at once into the main report of the Congress, which Anya had not expected until the following night. Kichkas could learn speed from the central Government.

Anya listened intently to Molotov's painstaking analysis of two years of world history, especially of Soviet progress in industry and farming contrasted with the economic crisis shaking the capitalist countries. How solid his arguments were with statistics and facts! Almost more exciting were the days of discussion that followed, in which nearly two hundred much shorter speeches from as many deputies revealed the aspirations and achievements of all parts of the Soviet land.

A new railroad had been completed across Asia, connecting Siberian wheat with Turkestan cotton. Wild nomads of the plains were settling in collective farms. The greatest iron and steel city in Europe was growing in the desolate plateaus at the foot of the Urals. Even the tribes of the Arctic, once exhibited in cages at the zoo as half-human creatures, were holding Soviet Congresses, building new polar towns with schools and universities. Many difficulties and demands were mentioned and rapidly referred to the appropriate committees.

Inspired by the great panorama of her tremendous country, Anya met with a sub-committee on beet crops. Anisia and many other farm women took part. Anya's campaign proved to be only one of many attempts to meet the country's need of sugar. They compared notes on problems and methods. The yield must be increased and beets spread to new areas!

In the midst of a hot and highly technical discussion on crop insurance for sugar beets in new regions a stocky man in a khaki blouse entered and walked diagonally across the room to sit at one end of the speakers' table, so unobtrusively that only after she saw his face did Anya realize with a start that this was Stalin.

She looked at him carefully so that she might tell everyone at home in

Kichkas what Stalin was like. He looked strong, with bronzed face and greying hair. His eyes were grave yet kind, penetrating and yet assuring. He seemed neither tired nor particularly energetic, but like a man who has worked very long and can go on working much longer, because he knows how to use strength—quietly, with no waste motion. Most of all, he seemed confident and calm.

Stalin did not take the chair or make a speech. He only listened very intently. From this intent listening it became clear to Anya that the increase of sugar beets—which Stalin seemed to find important—was not only useful in providing food for the Soviet poeple but played its part in the balance of world forces that determine history. She felt that she herself must say only those things which were most significant and that she must think these clearly and say them fast.

When it was her turn she told how the Red Dawn Farm had secured twelve tons of sugar beets per acre. "This is more than twice what we got in the past. All the same it is not nearly enough. I learned at the *Peasants' Gazette* that it is possible to get more than twenty tons. One must cultivate eight and nine times during the season, much more than we ever thought of doing. We shall do it on our farm this summer and get twenty tons of beets!"

Stalin interrupted with a direct question, looking straight at her: "Has your soil a good enough history to compete with those foreign records?"

"No," admitted Anya, "but we shall make up for that by fertilizing. Twenty tons is not really the highest possible. When we've built up the soil we shall go even higher."

"How many acres does your farm assign to its sugar beets?" asked Stalin.

"Two hundred and fifty last year," replied Anya. "This year we'll manage to get more."

"Does that satisfy you?" Stalin's words came slowly. "Three hundred acres for sugar beets . . . is that enough?"

What did he mean, Anya wondered. Then she felt his eyes appraising her, encouraging her, as if he wanted the most of which she was capable. She knew what she wanted now.

"We must bring sugar beets to new districts. We must flood the land with sugar! We must raise twenty tons per acre everywhere in the Ukraine!"

"How will you start it?" asked Stalin.

"Right here! I pledge you personally that I'll get twenty tons on our Red Dawn fields, and I challenge all the beet-growers here and all the others we can reach to do the same."

"I accept your pledge," Stalin agreed gravely. He turned to the secretary of the committee. "Let the papers take note of this contest."

Then he smiled at Anya. "The eyes of the Soviet people will be watching you this summer, Comrade Kosareva."

As Anya sat down she saw that others were signing up for the contest, and she realized what she had done. How easy Stalin had been to talk to! But how quickly things had happened! Now there would be a contest in sugar-beet growing across the country!

They all went together into the delegates' dining-hall. Stalin stepped to the long buffet and brought back to their table a huge plate of sandwiches—thick slices of French bread with cheese, sturgeon, or caviar. Embarrassed that Stalin should be waiting on them, several of the women jumped up and went for apples, mandarin oranges, and chocolates wrapped in tinfoil, heaped them on the table, and went back for glasses of tea.

Everything was very informal. Stalin referred half-jestingly to the days of the matriarchy, when "mothers were chiefs of society," those "years before history, before the settled life of farms and the division of labour began woman's long enslavement." He added, looking at the group around him:

"Our socialist country is producing a new kind of woman. After generations of slavery, of feudalism and capitalism, our new Soviet women arrive, builders of socialism equally with men, to avenge the heavy centuries."

As Anya was thinking of the world-binding shackles, heavy with history, which it was her joyous task to shatter, Stalin turned to her directly.

"It seems you are the first time in Moscow, Comrade Kosareva. I think it will not be the last."

She began to tell him how happy she had been to come to Moscow and "see all our leaders."

"But now you also are a leader." Stalin's eyes twinkled.

"Well, yes"—Anya was breathless—"but I'm happy to see you, anyway, Comrade Stalin."

He laughed at that and it seemed to Anya that her words had been stupid, that she had spoken without thinking. But the laugh was friendly and it did not matter if the words were stupid, since he knew what she meant.

"Leaders come and go," he said. "Only the people are immortal."

Anya saw him glance around the dining-room at the great crowd of deputies. But was she, Anya Kosareva, one of those people called leaders? Was this the way leadership happened, by growing sugar beets with the peasant women of Kichkas and then suddenly beginning to grow them with the farm women of all the Ukraine?

"I think you are barely twenty, Anya Kosareva," smiled Stalin.

"Not quite," she breathed.

"And here you are in the Congress that leads the country! The art of leadership is a serious matter. One must not lag behind the people, for to do so is to become isolated. One must know how to lead a movement forward, but one must not rush ahead either, for this also is to lose contact with the people. I think you have judged rightly that the time for this contest has come."

Rising, he joined another group of deputies.

With mounting excitement, Anya was thinking: How had the contest really started? Had it come out of her? Or out of all the women deputies? Or even out of peasants as far away as Kichkas? She did not know. But she knew she had uttered the words that released it, and that now it would be done.

And with this, she knew herself part of a great surge of life that would go on forever, far beyond her own short years.

XXVI

WINTER-LOCKED MOSCOW was left behind her; before she reached Kharkov dark patches discoloured the melting white of the fields. Farther south the snow was already gone. Trees were budding and birds singing; peasant carts laboured heavily through mud. Anya was surprised to find herself thinking, not of the important tasks before her, but of an earlier season of mud in Kichkas Village, when the short legs of a girl child tried painfully to keep up with the swinging legs of a boy.

How far back it seemed; how long forgotten! Just before she left Moscow a letter from Shubin had told her that Stepan had been looking for her. The spring mud, following upon the letter, recalled that ancient clash and pain. It had never been really forgotten; deep down it had spoiled her relation with Stepan. Now the hurt was gone, not only because Stepan had been to Kichkas, but because of the strength the past year and especially her trip to Moscow had brought her. At last she knew her way of life.

When Ivan and the other members of the farm met her at Zaporozhe, she found herself quite absurdly expecting Stepan and regretting that he was not there. On the long muddy road to the farm she conquered the feeling completely. She mustn't let her hopes run away with her. How could she think of Stepan when everyone around her demanded a complete account of Moscow all at once?

Laughingly she begged for mercy. "I'll tell you all together when we get there. This cart tries to jolt my head off my shoulders every time I turn to speak!"

At the Red Dawn office they crowded around her. She told them how the sugar-beet contest had been launched "together with Stalin. He said the eyes of the Soviet people will be on our farm this summer." She looked up suddenly and saw Stepan standing at the door.

For a moment he seemed hardly real but the personification of her morning's dream. Then she saw that he was embarrassed at being there, and she realized that he had never been to the Red Dawn Farm since Ivan had organized it and that he had come now because of her. Her face was radiant as she nodded a greeting.

"I want to congratulate you on all your successes." He came forward a bit awkwardly.

"You're doing a few things too," she laughed happily, rising and reaching out her hand. The others all greeted Stepan and began to joke with him on being a deputy in Zaporozhe. He responded pleasantly but turned the subject back to Anya.

"It's you we want to hear about. You've been to Moscow and you've made a pledge to Stalin and you look just the same as before!"

"Why not?" she laughed. "No, really, I feel as if I'm a quite new person. But I'm glad to be home."

Stepan sat down beside her, still holding the hand she had given, until she unobtrusively took it away. For more than an hour he listened with the rest to her vivid account of the Congress, the women she had met, Stalin, and the new possibilities for sugar beets. At first he took it for granted that she would soon finish and let him see her alone; she must know that this was what he wanted when he had come so far. But time went by and the members of the farm still kept dropping in, not only to hear about Moscow, but to ask for various kinds of information and help from their deputy.

Pavel Voronin came to ask if the *Peasants' Gazette* would send its educational aeroplanes to their farm, and what size airfield would be required. Olga, their new librarian, wanted to know what books she had heard about in Moscow. Had she ordered any for them? Ivan and the farm's managing board wanted to plan with her for the sugar beets.

"We won't settle things finally till Morosov comes next week and we have the general meeting, but we should talk over at once how much land you can use and how we will re-allot the machines and labour power and get the seed."

Across these demands of work, Anya from time to time sent a glowing smile at Stepan. He saw that she was glad he had come, but that it would be some time before she could break away from the office. He was determined not to leave without the quiet talk he had come for, but he hated to wait passively while she was busy with a hundred things. Unless he claimed some share in her now, these mounting demands might sweep her away from him entirely.

173

"I'm going to look around the farm until you are ready to go home. Then I'm walking to Kichkas with you. Can you tell me about when that will be?"

"Give me another hour," she begged. "Olga might take you over to the clubhouse and library. We're very proud of what she's done. I'll meet you there when I'm through."

He had meant merely to use the time till Anya was ready, but his interest grew as Olga took him rapidly past the farm's central buildings —the machine-shop, stables, granaries, and the poultry farm. He was pleased by the newly whitewashed houses with pale blue or yellow trimmings, "decorated for the election." "Anya helped with that," Olga said. She pointed out the great yard, still full of debris from the scrap-iron collection, and told him that in return for the metal they had salvaged for industry they would soon receive one of the new Stalingrad tractors, a 15–30, bigger and stronger than the Putilov 10–20's they already had.

He stayed longest in the big stone house, once Faber's, now a club and recreation centre. In the very room where Yeremeyev had drunk bootleg *samagon*, a health exhibit from Kharkov gave graphic lessons in village sanitation and hygiene. The programme for the winter's activities posted on the blackboard showed an amazing schedule: lectures on natural science and care of livestock, mock trials on political subjects, amateur plays. There were a string orchestra, a chorus, and study circles of many kinds. Two excursions had been made, to the dam and to the *Kommunar* Works; the children's essays on these trips were proudly displayed.

"Some of this was done before we had the building," explained Olga. "The programme will be even better next year. Our main addition is the library. We have seventeen children who carry books from house to house to encourage reading, and forty young people who give regular evenings to reading aloud to the illiterate. People are reading Pushkin, Tolstoi, and even foreign classics like Shakespeare."

This, then, was Anya's life; these were her friends and the activities of her farm and village. It was a good life, many-sided. While the dam and the new industries had been re-making the city, the farm had not remained as he had known it. It had gone if anything even more swiftly ahead.

"I am stunned by your farm and its activities," he exclaimed to Anya when at last she joined him. "Everything's so changed!"

"Yes, many things have changed," mused Anya as she fell into step beside him. For a time neither had need of further speech. Stepan wondered if she felt, as he did, the intimacy growing through their silence and the mated rhythm of their bodies on the road.

A wide band of saffron lay on the western horizon when they came into the market square. The last glow of sunset transfigured the little white houses and the onion domes of the village church. "Do you remember when I first saw you dancing here?" asked Stepan. "You were the loveliest thing I had even seen."

"I remember something earlier. The first walk I took with you on this road."

"I hoped you had forgotten that. I was an unmannerly brat. How you must have hated me for the way I dragged you through the mud."

After a moment's thought, she answered frankly: "It hurt for a long time—but no, I didn't hate you. You were something gorgeous out of a wilder world."

He captured one of her hands and touched it gently with his lips. She laughed softly. "It's some time since it stopped hurting."

"You more than paid me back when you ran away from the Lair. That finished Kichkas for me. But later you gave me the best thing in my life. I think it was you who said—when the procurer was investigating my past—'Most of all he loves the river.'"

"Yes," admitted Anya, surprised.

"Those were the words that gave me the chance to stay here and work on the dam. The procurer had planned to send me north. I might have been at Bear Mountain to-day instead of here with you."

She drew a deep breath and pressed his hand softly. "I'm glad you're here and that I helped. When they asked me about you, I remembered how you ran up the rocks to shout at the sun. That seemed to me what you were most: a wild, free boy loving the wild river."

"I've not been back to the Lair since you told me it was only a dark old cave. I didn't want to see it again until I go there with you. I'll make you like it there!"

Startled, she looked at him, but he was staring at the road ahead. Holding her hand tight, he sought the right words. "Ever since I saw you dancing in the village, you have been the dearest person in my life. I haven't always known it. Often I didn't know what I wanted. Down deep, when I was getting ahead on the dam, I was always thinking that some day I would come to you and show you what I had done. Then I heard you had gone to Moscow, and I thought: 'How far she is beyond me! Shall I ever get her back?'"

They turned down the long road that led through dusk to Anya's cottage. The fresh breath of the river came to them now, mingled with the odour of locust buds. Anya lifted their clasped hands, pressed Stepan's gently against her cheek and murmured: "Still the same male pride you had when you first pulled me along this road."

' Pride?" ejaculated Stepan. "When I've just told you how afraid I've been of losing you?"

"That's just egotism in reverse," smiled Anya. "What has this talk of losing or going beyond to do with comradeship? Must you have either possession or worship? I think that equal companionship between man and woman is the best relation of all, and the hardest to reach."

"Would you help me reach it, Anichka? Could you love me?"

"I have always loved you," she answered gravely, but she held him gently away when he moved impulsively to embrace her: "Our equal comradeship will not be easy. Your life is on the dam, mine on the farm."

"But now, with my present job, they'd give me an apartment——" he began swiftly. Then he stopped. She was right about his egotism. He had thought she would give up the farm to come to him. Give up the people who had made her deputy to Moscow? Give up a sugar-beet contest planned with Stalin? He had been mad to think of that. It was equally impossible for him to leave the dam for farming. Not even for Anya would he give up his chosen work.

"We will find ways to bring our lives together," she assured him tenderly, "but it will take some planning. Clearly I must be on the farm all this summer. I have the contest and my work as deputy, and I must look after Grandfather. It would be better not to think of marriage until autumn."

"I want you in the Lair at spring high water!" he urged passionately. "How cold you are to speak of autumn!"

She laughed softly, drew his head down to her, and kissed him on the mouth. His arms held her to him; his lips pressed insistently until she began to tremble. When she pulled away she clung to his arm, for she could hardly stand. Stepan's blood was singing.

"Now will you give me the springtime?" he demanded.

"What a boy!" she laughed, still trembling. "I'll give you whatever you ask."

Glad strength flowed into his limbs; his heart shouted at the completeness of her submission. But she added: "I still think you will make it hard for us both if you insist on starting our new relation just now when I have so many things to do."

He brushed aside her caution; he hardly heard it. "It will be spring in the Lair and the water will be over the stepping-stones and I'll carry you in," he exulted. "There where you ran away from me—that's where I'll make you want to stay!"

"What an outlaw!" she laughed, trying to turn into mirth the response she felt to the passion of his tones. "All my friends will want a Red Wedding and a party."

Some of the joy drained out of him. "I want to be alone with you by the river—not with the deputy, with the woman."

This time her laughter was sincerely merry; the trembling had passed
176

and she felt happy and controlled. "Romantic boy, we'll be alone by the river. We'll register the marriage by ourselves and go to the Lair. Next day we'll come back and have the feast."

"Only a day?" he protested. "I thought at least a week. It's easy to get vacation now; it's slack time on the dam."

"I warned you there'd be trouble," she admonished gaily. "A day is enough for you in the sowing season. You can come for week-ends all summer. Even then the Lair is not my choice for a home."

Laughing with her, Stepan reflected that the one-room cottage where Anya lived with her grandfather was also not an ideal home for their married life. He resolved to secure an apartment in the city, for the time when Anya should come to the town.

He went by row-boat to the Lair a few days later to prepare it for his marriage night with Anya. The cliffs were as wild as ever but the view of the river was changed by the jagged arc of fifty half-finished white piers two miles upstream. Budding bushes grew fragrant over the log he had placed for Anya's last visit; some of them he cleared away. The cave seemed lower and darker than he remembered. As he brushed out dead leaves and placed blankets and food under shelter he saw that the fuel he had stored so long ago was still there.

The whole place had a deserted air like something left behind in a former existence. He thought of all the hunger and hope that had once changed this cave into a stronghold of free Cossacks. Tenderly smiling at the incredible and vanished dreams of the boy who had lived here, he admitted that the cave was still transfigured by them; they had made it his first real home.

The air was warm with sudden spring when he took the trail to the Lair with Anya. Over the high prairies the sun sank gently through a warm haze of afternoon. The earth stretched soft and black to the horizon; it was all Red Dawn land, ploughed the previous autumn and ready now for seed. When they had last been here it had been unturned sod, matted with weeds. Now the warm scent of fallow soil filled their nostrils; the trill of the meadowlarks proclaimed insistent joy. Even the old trail had been covered by the ploughing. They laughed gaily as they plodded through clinging, fertile earth.

"I'm getting this land for my beets," boasted Anya. "It's rich; see how it sticks."

"I'll think of you working hard here this summer when I'm taking it easy on the dam," he bantered. He wanted no thought of work in the splendid languor of the afternoon.

They found the stepping-stones covered. "See how the water tumbles, Anichka! It's the highest I've ever seen." Lifting her, he carried her triumphantly over. He set her down and gave her a long kiss that searched the springs of life in her body. "Now, Anya, the door is locked by the river. Nobody can come in. No friends, no constituents, not even your thoughts about sugar beets. To-night we'll think only of each other. If the river rises higher," he threatened, "I'll have you here all spring."

"Wife-beater," she laughed, pretending to fear him. She ran away from him, passed the cave, and scrambled up the cliff. He overtook her on the point of rock. "I wanted to see if this was really the last view of the sun," she panted.

The long level rays of sunset came to them through a narrow gap in the cliffs and struck the water far out, gilding the other shore. Anya exclaimed at the wonder of the view, but Stepan was watching the light in her golden hair. "It is really worth shouting for," she cried, turning. The look in his eyes left her breathless, and she raised her face for his kiss.

Next morning, they found the river still higher. Stepan grew concerned. "I was joking last night about the flood. This begins to look serious. There'll be trouble on the dam this spring."

"Who's thinking about work now?" teased Anya, and both of them laughed.

The wedding celebration that evening was held in connection with the ceremonial march to the fields. This year there were no opera-singers from the city, such as had helped in their difficult first spring. The farm had its own orchestra now and a chorus of forty voices. Stesha came home for the event. Morosov, the farm's new president, was already there. In the midst of the community gaiety he announced that they were also to celebrate a wedding.

Marin came forward—he was unusually clean and shining, in an embroidered blouse and new corduroy trousers—and told what a fine fellow Stepan was and what good work he did on the dam. "And not only on the dam, but he organized the first contest to wipe out illiteracy. We elected him to the Zaporozhe Soviet and he's going to build us a street-car line. Any girl that gets him gets a champion!" Everyone laughed and applauded.

The eyes of the assembled villagers judged Stepan strong and handsome. But it was Anya they knew and loved. They applauded still more when Stesha told of her work for the farm and assured them that marriage would not take her away—not yet at any rate—and that all must help her celebrate her new status by working hard in the beet contest this summer.

Morosov made a brief speech about the difference between the old and the new marriage. "Formerly the priests told wives to fear their husbands. We consider this nonsense to-day. Both should be equal comrades. We feel sure that Anya and Stepan, who have already done much useful work for the community, will together be able to accomplish more for the good of us all." Anya, watching him, felt that he did not speak with his usual facility; she thought with a pang of the Red Wedding Stesha and Morosov had wanted and knew that he thought of it too.

Stepan and Anya came forward and pledged their joint lives to the swift building of socialism—"that in the world of our children may be peace, security, and plenty for all." Afterwards, everyone congratulated the newly married pair.

The party in the village club went on till midnight. There were dancing and singing to accordions and balalaikas. A table was heaped with refreshments: huge sandwiches of many kinds, several varieties of soda pop, wine, and ice-cream. The heavy drinking of vodka, customary at pre-Revolutionary weddings, was frowned on by Soviet youth. They dispersed after midnight but few went home. Sowing was to start at dawn; they went from the club to their camps in the fields. Anya wished to inspect the ploughing in the morning; she went with Stepan to the field. They made a deep bed of straw a little distance from the campfire, where their friends were singing.

To Anya this second night seemed her true, complete marriage. The night at the Lair had been wild, romantic, passionate, overwhelming her with surging sensations in which joy was hardly to be distinguished from pain. Under the overhanging roof of the cave, by the dark roar of the rising river, she felt ravished away from the quiet life of her girlhood to an alien universe where she existed only through Stepan. But to-night, under the stars, with the campfire glow on the straw and the voices of friends singing in the distance, she gave herself to her man joyously and completely, untroubled by any shock of newness, feeling that they were part not only of each other but of a wide and friendly world.

To Stepan, the night in the field was not as perfect as the night in the Lair had been. The sense of a near-by encampment seemed to him a constraint. It took away the sharp triumph he had known that first night when Anya, always so sure of herself, so ringed by chaste self-possession, awakened to the first throb of passion in his arms. He had not shouted his joy but he had known that if he shouted no one would hear but Anya, the river, and the cave. He had been tender with her even in the height of passion, but it had increased his exaltation to know that if he chose to take her roughly she was in his arms with no one to interfere. Here in the fields, he felt he had to share her with the social life of the farm.

Before dawn, he was awakened by the roar of the new Stalingrad 15–30 as the enraptured Ivan started it down the field. Soon he must leave to reach the dam on time. Anya stirred too; her work began at dawn. He buried his face in her breasts before he left her and kissed with hard, fierce kisses until she was rosy and trembling. He sighed to think that he must go to-night to a bunk in the barracks while this warm loveliness lay in some camp in the fields or in the grandfather's cottage—unpossessed.

She saw his eyes darken and sensed his feeling. "Don't let it be hard, dear. I shall be wanting you too." He gazed deep in her eyes and turned away abruptly, knowing that in spite of her quick response to his passion she would not let him interfere with the work she had pledged herself to do.

XXVII

Not until May Day could Stepan return to his wife. The highest flood in more than half a century rushed down the Dnieper gorges, roared through the rapids, and tore madly between the piers. These already stood high above the onslaught, but below and around their unassailable concrete the wildest water Stepan had ever seen smote at the cofferdams that guarded the locks on the left bank and the power-house on the right.

He worked day and night with a furious energy that left him exhausted. When he dropped dead-beat on his bunk in the barracks, he thought in a brief flash of the events he would tell Anya when they met. Almost before he thought of her he was asleep.

Ten days they fought to save the locks and failed. The water broke over and through the dykes and buried them under the flood; it was impossible now for the locks to be finished in time. Turning from this defeat, Stepan joined his gangs to the fight on the right bank for the power-house. The effort of thousands of workers preserved this vital spot in a partial victory. Work here was delayed two weeks, but this could be made up.

He spent the double May Day holiday with Anya—his first rest for weeks. She welcomed him joyously; it was brilliant weather. They strolled lazily along the shore under the fragrant locusts. On the second day, feeling rested, they chased each other down little ravines into the *plavny*, where the receding river had left great pools of water lilies just beginning to bloom. Muddied and mosquito-bitten, they mingled gay kisses with teasing laughter. How delightful, thought Stepan, to leave all the struggle behind, to find this rest and reward at the end of a month's hard labour!

Anya's labour he hardly thought of. She would have been the first to admit that her steady toil in the fields was not as exacting as the battle with the river he described. She had watched the ploughing and tested the seeds. The first plants had broken the surface a week before May

Day. She had had much responsibility, but only one period of heavy physical labour, the five hard days of hoeing just accomplished with fifty women around young and thriving shoots.

Her season was only beginning but it was beginning well. Since the work was important to her, she tried to talk about it to Stepan, but found it hard to interest him in it. However their conversation started, it always ended either with laughter and love-making or with an account of Stepan's fight with the river. She was content to listen to his exploits, which were so much more vivid than her own.

Anya had not thought it necessary to tell Stepan that Ivan had continued his proposals to her up to the moment of her marriage. But perhaps Stepan surmised this; he seemed more interested in Ivan's present courtship of Shubina than in anything else Anya told him about the farm.

"I think they were made for each other," she laughed gaily. "Ivan was too wrapped up in work to know it. It was Shubina who decided that something must be done. As soon as she knew, last winter, that Ivan would be head of the tractors instead of president, she took a course in tractor driving herself. She succeeded so well that they gave her the Stalingrad tractor for the second shift. That made Ivan notice her; she was the best driver under him.

"Such an amusing rivalry developed. Both are in love with each other, but they're also in love with that tractor. They call it '*Lomka*'—'Little Scrap Iron'—because it came to us in return for scrap iron. Ivan takes it on one shift, Shubina on the other. Neither will trust *Lomka* to a third person. They've lengthened their shifts to ten hours so as to have *Lomka* all to themselves, without an intruder. They're trying for the all-union record in acres ploughed per tractor."

"They're both good workers; they might make it," judged Stepan.

"That's all very well," opposed Anya. "But *Lomka* won't let them get married! She united them but now she separates them. She takes all their time. When Ivan comes in from his day with *Lomka*, Shubina goes out and spends the night. They get no time together because of that jealous machine. Neither of them will let a third person touch *Lomka*. Only they have the right to caress her, to feed her with fuel, to grease her parts. If either would give up *Lomka*, they could spend their evenings together. But neither is willing to change to an ordinary Putilov tractor."

"That's a real love rivalry of our modern days," laughed Stepan.

Anya felt happy in his laughter; she ruffled his hair and incited his kisses. The holiday passed joyously, bringing to both of them rest and renewal of love.

"We'll have wonderful week-ends all summer," prophesied Stepan confidently. "Both the work on the dam and my tasks as deputy are settling down to routine." He reckoned without the demands of Anya's work.

As the young beets grew, they increased their exactions. First came the thinning; it was all-important to select the best plants of each clump, and give them enough space but not too much. Then came the ceaseless cultivating; not a single weed must be allowed to get started to drain the strength from the beets. Instead of hoeing three times during the growing season, as she had done the previous year, Anya determined to hoe steadily, covering the fields eight times from end to end. She toiled in the physical labour and supervised the work of the others. With each week Stepan found her more exhausted in body and mind.

There were hours of sharp ecstasy. Life ran high in them both and the exhaustion did not last. If on the first night of each week end Anya was too tired to respond fully to Stepan's affection or listen with full interest to the tales of his work, a day's rest worked wonders. She was her own gay self before he left. Passion was still young in them; under his caresses, her beauty increasingly flowered. Even her fatigue was a healthy weariness. The rhythm of each week with its work days and rest day, its open-air labour, its sunlight and love-making, gave her a glowing life that her friends all noticed.

"Marriage agrees with you," commented Stesha one Monday morning, meeting her in the fields.

Anya laughed happily. "Marriage and work together take every minute of time and every ounce of energy, but I've never felt so happy in my life. Every bit of me is living." A sudden compunction smote her to be making merry with Stesha to whom this happiness was denied. "Oh, Stesha," she whispered, "I wish that you . . ." She gave her friend a quick hug.

"Don't worry about me," Stesha assured her with tranquil eyes. "I'd rather have Ilya to share life with than anything else I know."

Yes, thought Anya, Stesha had her own way of happiness. For a brief flash she almost felt that her own joy was incomplete. Stepan and she shared ecstasy denied to Stesha, but they did not yet share life. Stepan had shown no interest in the work she was doing; to him it was only a hindrance to their marriage.

Joy between Stepan and Anya continued through early summer. Then everything seemed to happen at once. July was unusually dry; at the end of the month the leaves of the beets began to wilt. Every evening Anya watched in the fields to see if the plants would revive with the dew. Five times the cool night repaired the ravages of day. On the sixth night a dry south wind prevented the dew and wilted the leaves still more. Anya's spirits drooped with them. Another such twenty-four hours would wither her hopes.

The members of her brigade were turning home hopelessly. "Come back!" cried Anya. "This is the biggest crisis our farm has faced. We're not prepared for irrigation but we'll do it. Some must collect buckets and tubs from all the hamlets; others go to the field brigades to ask the help of the men of the fire department. I'll go to Pavel Voronin for the portable pumps and to make the plan. Three of you come with me to round up Pavel's helpers. Everyone be back here ready to start at dawn."

As she sped through the night she thought of other plans for the morrow and put them aside. Two reporters were coming from Moscow papers, one from Kharkov, one from Rostov—part of a continuous procession who observed and reported the progress of her beets. "I won't have time to talk to them. Let them find their way about and photograph the irrigating."

Stepan might come to-night; she dreaded his disappointment. For the first time she hoped that his work on the dam would keep him away. He was waiting at her home when she returned at three o'clock in the morning. Her heart leapt with relief when he expressed no annoyance; he had learned of her emergency from others. She dropped her exhausted head on his shoulder and fell instantly into a deep sleep.

He woke her before dawn. "I'm going to help you irrigate. You have a husband who knows how to handle water," he teased.

Pavel was waiting at the shore with two pumps and most of the men of the fire department. Not all had come; some couldn't be spared from distant fields.

"I'll take one of the pumps," offered Stepan.

"Hey, boys, we've got a Dneprostroi champion!" cried Pavel.

Anya's heart bounded to find Stepan working beside her. It was the first time he had taken an interest in her work, the first time they had been joined by anything but love.

The women hoed long trenches rapidly between rows. The water from the two pumps followed them and the thirsty soil greedily drank it. Bucket brigades were formed to reach the farthest end of the field. An hour after sundown the irrigation was completed; twenty thousand pails of water had been poured on the field.

"This will be in all the papers; it's a great story," chorused the reporters. "We've taken photographs."

As Anya went home with Stepan in the twilight, they passed the part of the field that had been watered first. The trenches were dry again but the beets had revived. Their large glossy leaves fanned out erectly.

"We've saved them, Anichka," Stepan congratulated her. "You've a good fire brigade and a fine bunch of girls."

Before they reached home the first stars were shining. A crescent moon hung golden in the west. Fireflies twinkled in the garden and a nightingale trilled from the ravine. Refreshing coolness blew from the river. Stesha had come to Anya's and prepared their dinner. Morosov not only joined them with congratulations but asked Stepan about the dam.

"We're reaching the final stages," explained Stepan. "The dam is a unit now, connected both below and above. I've been crossing by a wide tunnel—wide enough for an auto if an auto could reach it—that cuts through the piers from shore to shore. Between the piers you come out on a series of bridges across the spillways, and look down on the river and up at the top of the dam. This week I came by a new bridge across the top from pillar to pillar. Right and left banks hardly exist any more in our work; Chief Engineer Winter speaks of a 'single storming crusade for the final curbing of the Dnieper.'

"My gangs are filling in with concrete the spaces between the piers. We're working below the level of the water; we shut the current off with metal shields. They're over forty feet long; there's no experience to go by, for nobody ever used such long ones before. We've had a devil of a time holding them and making them fit. The chief gave us hell for our slowness but we've got the trick at last. We'll fit the last shield next week and the water behind the dam will begin to rise."

"When can you stop working in the water?" asked Anya.

Stepan laughed. "The higher we build the higher the water rises. We race the river. Some of the time we keep ahead and work without protection; in the autumn rains the river will catch us up again. That will be the last fight—the fight to close the comb."

He went back to the dam in the morning and Anya went back to her hoeing.

A great cloud of moths came out of the south, carried on a dry wind, dimming the sun with its approach. Like an evil snowstorm they whirled over the fields, alighting to lay their eggs. The women were terrified. The larvæ from so many eggs could eat the field in a single day. They chased the moths with nets, smashed them with hands, stamped them into the earth with feet. The moths flew into the women's ears and nostrils. They swarmed countless and relentless.

For several days and nights Anya did not leave the fields. Morosov came for her with a horse late one evening. "You are killing yourself," he reproved her gently—her face was black from the sun and thin from sleepless nights. "I've come to take you home for a rest."

She looked hopelessly at the moths and got into the cart, her whole body sagging with despair. As they passed the field where the tractors were ploughing for summer fallow, she saw moths clustered in dense clouds around the spotlight that Ivan had installed on the Stalingrad tractor. Shubina could hardly drive because of them. Anya stared dejectedly; these moths seemed to be plaguing every farm operation. Then her eyes widened with a new idea.

"Take me back at once!" she commanded Morosov. "Help me get the women together. We'll try building fires to attract and burn the moths!"

All along the edge of the field the women kept the fires going. The moths flew into the flame and fell singed in great heaps. The women shovelled the bodies into the fire. It was a filthy task; the smoke was stifling and the stench nauseating. All night they worked. Dawn showed the fields infested only by a few stragglers.

At Anya's house Stepan waited. He had come that evening full of triumph. He had fixed the last three shields between the piers. The water had begun to rise behind the dam; it would keep on month by month until it washed over Anya's house and Kichkas Village. He had been very happy in this house but he would not regret its passing.

He intended, this Sunday, to take an excursion with Anya to run the rapids. As a boy he had done it at much risk. There were safe boats now piloted by daring boatmen. The hundreds of tourists coming in the past few days for the last chance of that famous excursion had reminded him that the rising lake would bury the rapids forever. It would be a thrilling trip with Anya—their joint farewell to the old life that used to be on the untamed river.

Anya was not in the house, though the sun was setting. "She's out in the fields chasing moths," exclaimed the grandfather with patronizing amusement. "It's funny the way folks farm now. Women don't even cook their men's meals; I brought mine from the central kitchen."

He offered Stepan a large hunk of brown bread and a share of the pot of soup, adding: "You might as well have her share. She's probably eating in the fields. She ought to be in pretty soon." Assuming that some trivial problem delayed her briefly, Stepan sat down to wait. After a time the grandfather went to bed.

Stepan paced the floor restlessly. What was the mattter with Anya? He had been glad to help her with the irrigation; it had been a pleasure to feel that she needed his help. But she shouldn't have an emergency every week. This devotion to work was praiseworthy, but it was becoming preposterous. She should give her husband some of her time. Irritable, he lay down to rest. When he awoke it was nearly dawn; Anya had not come.

He found her sleeping in the field, under an evil-smelling smoke from a pile of ashes. Several women lay nearby in ungainly attitudes. She was dirty and dishevelled; her arms were foul with unpleasant grease, which some move of her hand, possibly during sleep, had smeared across a cheekbone and through a lock of hair. Pity smote him for her exhaustion, but was swallowed up in anger. This was the day when he had planned to exult with her in the sunlight on the foaming crests of the rapids.

He shook her awake. "Come home and wash yourself. Why can't you rest decently in bed? I had a fine excursion arranged for to-day and now look at you!"

Dazed from the onslaught, she came to her feet still swaying drunkenly with sleep, not knowing quite where she was or what Stepan meant. Then she smelled the smoke and saw the fields. The air was clear of moths above long rows of glossy leaves. Sighing with relief, she turned to the sound of movement behind her and saw that two of the girls, aroused by Stepan's voice, were pulling their clothes into order and rising. Her mind, which had been stunned into inaction by Stepan's anger, slipped easily into the habitual routine of work.

"It's all right now. Go home and take a good rest." She spoke to the girls almost automatically.

"Can't you give even one day a week to a husband?" demanded Stepan bitterly, his anger growing because she had spoken to the girls and not to him.

Shrinking under the attack but still half asleep, Anya raised her hand, pushed back the hair that had fallen into her eyes, saw the filthiness of her arms, and wiped them on a large beet leaf. Every motion seemed to Stepan an evasion.

"Can you come on the river even this afternoon?" he insisted.

"I can't tell until after I've had some sleep."

"I'm not going to stick around all day waiting. If this is the way it's going to be week-ends, perhaps I'd better not come out until you have time for me."

"Perhaps," she assented dully. Then she saw him fling back his shoulders, sensed his rage, and forced herself to a last attempt. "I'm really too tired to discuss it. I told you it would be hard this summer. I'm going to bed and I want to be left alone to sleep. We'll talk about it later."

In early afternoon she awoke rested but with a vague sense of loss. The morning's events came back slowly, like fragments of a half-drugged dream. Had Stepan really spoken in such anger? She would ask what the matter was and set it right.

Stepan was gone and her grandfather was dozing. From moment to moment she expected her husband's return. Hadn't he said something about running the rapids? There wouldn't be time for the whole trip, but there might be for the latter, most thrilling part. She put on a crisp embroidered blouse and a clean scarlet kerchief. It would be fine on the river after the exhausting worry and dirty work of the week.

Supper-time came. Somewhat dispirited, Anya went to the central kitchen and brought back three portions. Waking, her grandfather told her that Stepan had left at midmorning to run the rapids alone. He sided with Stepan. "Good farming is all very well, but a woman must hold to her man." The fault must be hers, thought Anya. She must organize her work better. She would say this humbly to Stepan when he came for the night.

Slowly the swollen moon sank behind the village. When it was gone, the abandoned stars shone with a sharper brilliance in the purple night. Anya knew it must be nearly morning. There was no longer hope that Stepan would come.

Morning would bring new tasks, not only for her, but for the brigade of women who awaited her instructions. She lay down quietly without tears and fell asleep. Dawn found her ready for the next day's work.

Twice in the following week, Anya fought moths all night in the fields. Then the pest lessened and she gave her brigade and herself two full days' rest. She awaited Stepan in better condition of body and mind than she had been for weeks. Instead of coming, he sent her a letter.

DEAREST ANICHKA,—You were right in saying we should not launch our new relation when you have so much on your mind. I have the chance to take my six weeks' Army training now instead of later in the autumn. When I return, Marin and three others are going into the regular Army, and I shall have to find someone to take their places. This and my work as deputy will use the time until your harvest. I shall not come until then.

After harvest I hope you will spend the winter in the city; in November they are giving us a three-room apartment overlooking the river. Here we can establish the married life that seems impossible this summer.

Your own,

STEPAN.

The trip down the rapids was spoiled because you did not come.

Anya stared at the letter until she could have repeated it verbatim. How he had thrown her words back at her like a blow! This was not what she asked when she urged a postponement of marriage. The marriage had begun already; this was a break that meant a constant pain. He had not even said that he would miss her, except in that backhanded slap about the rapids.

The letter at least had freed her completely for work. The Red Dawn Farm and the Soviet people waited for her beets. Whatever else was clouded, this was clear. Whatever else was left behind, this must be done. Stepan would know this some time, if not now. He was a worker, a champion, a loyal son of the Soviet motherland. His personal anger would pass; personal hurt would be forgiven. But if she failed in the pledge given to her country, the respect in which he held her would falter. If she made him an excuse for that failure, he could never trust their love again.

The road to a good life together lay in faithfully doing the tasks of her life apart. She wrote him: "My dearest: I shall miss you. I should be glad to see you. But it is true that I cannot be sure of my time until harvest. This winter we will try your way."

XXVIII

FOR STEPAN THE RED ARMY camp was relaxation. It was a rest to leave the responsibility of the dam and to be free from all decisions about Anya. Because of his important work in industry, he was called up, not for two years' regular service, but for summer training as a reservist. The camp was not far from Kharkov, on the banks of a sizable stream.

The military activities were not entirely new to him, although this was the first of the five summers he would spend in camp. For two years, as a member of a voluntary defence association, he had participated in sports connected with defence. He was a fair marksman, and had long since learned to hike across country carrying a heavy pack. Many of the recruits were similarly proficient; the human material of the Army had completely changed since Stepan, as a boy, had followed those brave but half-educated fighters for the Revolution.

Hardened by his work on the dam, he was not exhausted by the six hours' military practice every morning, but was ready after lunch to enjoy the rest of the day. They ate in the open-air pavilions, each seating a thousand men. For the afternoon they were free to choose their activities and to wear whatever they liked. Since the weather was hot, most of them wore bathing trunks, in which they swam, played basket-ball, studied, and loafed. Just before dinner, they gathered under the trees in groups of thirty or more—their sun-bronzed bodies stretched out informally on the grass—for classes in politics, discussing the principles behind collective farming or the Five-Year Plan. Just now they were especially concerned with the international situation; Japan had marched into Manchuria and was rapidly advancing toward the Soviet frontier.

"The political lessons are as important as the military," declared the political commissar the first evening. "To teach men to march, shoot, and manœuvre is a fairly well-established routine. To make the Army an intelligent part of our country's life is more complicated. We must fit our political education to local, national, and international events."

As part of this policy, Stepan was taken on several trips to Kharkov, where he visited a locomotive works, a giant plant making electrical equipment, and admired the daring sweep of the new fourteen-story Government buildings—"the first skyscrapers in the Ukraine." He also became acquainted with a nearby camp of fifteen hundred Young Pioneers, city boys and girls spending a month's vacation in the open air; they exchanged visits with the Army and secured from it some of their doctors and instructors.

Good relations between the Army and the city were cemented by the "patronage" which the municipality of Kharkov had taken over the summer camp. The best city architects and engineers had devised the advantageous use of stream and hillside, diverting the water to form swimming pools, shower baths, and a decorative fountain, and planting alleys of poplars as boundaries between the regiments. The trade unions of the large factories had each "adopted" a regiment and helped provide its recreation facilities.

Stepan was especially attracted by the many club-houses of all shapes and sizes, from tiny summer pavilions serving tea at three kopeks a glass to motion-picture theatres accommodating several hundred men. These structures were planned and built by the men in their leisure time, with materials supplied by their civilian patrons. Regiments vied with each other in making them functional and artistic; there were places for chess-playing, for reading, for sun-bathing, or simply for a beautiful view. All over the camp, men were working during the afternoons on club-houses, putting up ornamental screens, painting posters, irrigating plots of flowers from the river. Stepan enjoyed the miniature construction and his talents with concrete were much in demand.

During his last week the municipality asked the Army's help in an emergency. Kharkov was building a tractor works "outside the Five-Year Plan." The growth of collective farms—far beyond the Government's expectations—had caused a demand for more tractors than the Plan would supply. Kharkov, a city of civic pride and the capital of one of the most important farming regions, undertook the stupendous task of constructing a huge new plant when every bag of cement, every machine, and almost every nail and plane of glass was allocated five years in advance.

By arousing patriotic Ukrainians to produce machines above the Plan in the supplying factories, Kharkov had succeeded in buying equipment. To make up the shortage in construction workers, the city's population donated rest days from factory and office work. Trainloads of volunteers puffed to the tractor plant daily—Kkarkov was on the unbroken week with one-fifth of the people free each day—and marched with bands and banners to the tasks of hauling dirt or carrying wood blocks for floors. In a succession of crises the construction went ahead. But no civilian help could dig that trench—seven kilometres long and a metre

189

deep—for the pipes of their water supply. The city authorities called on the Red Army for aid.

"Kharkov has done a lot for this camp." The political instructors seized the opportunity. "It's our turn to help Kharkov now. We'll also be helping supply machines for the farms from which many of you come."

Stepan marched as one of seven thousand men next morning to the site of the tractor plant; all were equipped with trenching tools. They took positions along the seven-kilometre line, one man to a metre. At the bugle signals they began digging a trench, each man making a hole in front of him a metre deep, a metre wide, and a metre long. By noon the seven-thousand-metre trench was finished. Stepan and the others spent the afternoon in celebrating with such of the construction workers as were not on shift.

The weeks in camp opened new vistas to Stepan. Instead of concentrating on the details of a single construction job, he had seen the dam in its relation to a hundred enterprises, some of which he had visited. His mind was expanded even beyond the limits of his country. A lecturer from Moscow on the Far East had given him a new respect for China's forty centuries of civilization and a keener cynicism towards the League of Nations, which had failed to hinder the Manchurian adventure of Japan.

Uplifted in spirit and strengthened in body, he returned to the dam. His quarrel with Anya now seemed to him very petty. Such small things, he was sure, would not trouble him again. Warming towards her, he was willing to let bygones be bygones. Besides, he wanted to see her; he hardly admitted to himself how much. He thought of going to Kichkas next week-end, despite his threat to stay away till harvest.

At the dam he was swept into a vortex of furious activity. Petrov challenged: "You've had it easy in the Army. We're two months behind in concrete-pouring and three months on the building of the high-tension switching station. All work on the locks is shut down for want of labour. Even the roofing of the power-house goes slowly and we can't install generators until it's done. I hear you put in a trench for Kharkov. We could use a couple of Army camps here."

Plunging into the work, Stepan missed Marin even more than he had expected. He felt bereft of his closest companion and best assistant. For the time—lacking Marin to take his place—he had no more rest days. His evenings went to catching up with his tasks as deputy. It was harvest after all when at last he went to the farm.

Anya and her brigade were the centre of a triumph. The harvested beets, weighed by impartial judges, averaged just over twenty-one tons per acre. She had kept her promise to Stalin and the Congress. More important than her own harvest was the contest she had started across the land. Hundreds of large farms claimed the proud rank of twenty-tonners; thirty tons was the goal set next. Anya had helped change a whole nation's farm practice in sugar beets.

Newspaper reporters and farm delegations gathered around her and the brigade that shared her glory. The nation's Press carried the chronicle of her labours. Nine times her women had hoed the fields from end to end; it was featured as if they had fought nine battles. Eight times they had cleared the fields of moths by setting fires at night. Stepan learned how that evil-smelling smoke and those grease-fouled arms were regarded by the country.

She welcomed her husband joyously. The two months' separation increased his ardour; her triumph made her seem again a prize that must be won. She had a new deftness, an ability somehow to draw Stepan into sharing her success. In their personal relations there was a poise, almost a hint of reticence which, had he understood her better, might have told of the hard nights in which she had fought and conquered loneliness. Stepan noticed only that it made her more desirable. It seemed a maidenly reserve which had revived through separation, renewing for him the thrill of conquest in their love.

"My harvest share is tremendous," she told him. "I can hire a woman to look after Grandfather all the time. I'm going to Moscow for a two weeks' session of the Congress but I'm on no standing committees; I won't have to stay. When I come back, I'll live with you in Zaporozhe. They've offered me a scholarship to study further but I've decided to let that wait."

"The deputies from all the land will be loving you, while I'll be longing—alone," he protested, but his eyes told her that he was tremendously proud.

Two weeks later he carried her over the threshold of the little flat in Zaporozhe, tossed unceremoniously into a closet the brief case and handbag she had taken to Moscow, took off her coat and hat, and mussed her golden hair.

"At last you're mine alone, Anichka! Now begins our real honeymoon. I'll not let you go again."

She was still full of the Moscow November holidays and wanted to tell about them. From the tribune under the Kremlin walls, she had watched a million Moscow workers storm the Red Square. Ten columns from the city's ten districts, they entered as a great advancing wall of marchers, sixty abreast. They surged over the Square like an irresistible tidal ocean, under a foam of red banners. Out of them rose the beat of a thousand factory bands, buried under their marching . . .

Standing all day with the Government leaders of her country, she had known that her summer's work was part of the onward march of those great columns that passed beyond the Square and down the years.

It was something she would always remember. But Stepan wanted to show her the flat now, and she wanted to see it. Postponing her story, she looked about her new home.

Proudly, he led her from the small square hall into a large bright room with shiny hardwood floor and cream-coloured walls. They walked past the central dining table and stood at the triple window to admire the view. The long wooded slope of the *plavny* dropped southward to the distant bend in the river. By the windows stood a desk for Stepan's work. A door led them to a smaller, similarly finished room where an oak wardrobe stood beside a white enamelled bed—springless but with boards comfortably padded by a thick mattress. The bedroom windows looked west to the sunset and straight into the heart of the construction where Stepan spent his days.

To Anya, the kitchen across the hall seemed at first sight very tiny; she was used to cooking on a vast brick stove in the main room of the house. Stepan showed her how to light the shiny black gas stove; she had never seen one before. She exclaimed over it and over the running water. At Grandfather's cottage she drew water from the river for washing, and carried drinking water a quarter of a mile from the village well. She was thrilled by all the conveniences and particularly by the bathroom, where water ran easily into a white tub—as much as you wanted—and could be heated with little trouble by a gas-heater.

"They're making these modern flats for all the permanent workers," boasted Stepan. "Some of them are in apartment houses like this one; some are in small houses for one or two families alone."

"I wouldn't want a small single house in a city," declared Anya, wrinkling her nose. "A big apartment house is much newer and more fun. It's just like a hotel in Moscow!" She hugged Stepan and danced with him from room to room to admire it all once more. Noticing the many-coiled yellow radiator, she ran across and patted it with delight. "There is even central heat—a regular hotel!"

For several weeks the flat was a delight to her—a new and beautifully elaborate toy. When Stepan was at work she spent her time in the big department store of the Socialist City, as the new residential section was called. It took some time to equip her home. Money was not lacking; her harvest income, added to Stepan's wages, was more than she had ever dreamed of having. But furniture and cotton goods were scarce; they were rapidly bought up, since everyone's income had increased. She had to wait in long lines for the things she wanted. Luckily, she reached the furniture department one morning just as a shipment of davenports came in. Being first in line, she bought one immediately. With this in the dining-room, she could invite her friends from the farm to spend the night.

"What a convenient flat!" exclaimed Stesha on a two-day visit.

"We must have something like it in our new farm city." Anya's interest in the flat and new furniture had been lagging but revived at the praise.

After Stesha left, the flat seemed to Anya even emptier than before. She was accustomed to steady work in social relation with many people, comfortably filling the corners of space and the moments of time. The gay little flat was delightful for a honeymoon or a vacation but it didn't seem like life. It was only for evenings with Stepan. There was nothing to fill the long days.

It was good, of course, to have time for study. Three evenings a week, except when some emergency detained him, Stepan went with her to the trade school, where he learned engineering. Anya enjoyed the courses in history and science, but had no opportunity to study her own specialty, which she still considered sugar beets. At first the lack seemed hardly serious, for after the long hard summer she was glad to rest.

Once a week she spent the night with her grandfather, giving the day before and after to the problems of her constituents. Old friends dropped in; the life of the farm and village seemed to flow through the little cottage. She would begin to make plans with Morosov, Stesha, and others, and would realize with a shock that all this activity, of which she had been a vivid part, was going ahead very rapidly without her. She was startled to discover that all week in the city she longed for those days on the farm. Not even her love for Stepan and her daily discoveries in the life of Zaporozhe could fill the hours from which essential work had vanished. Stepan took no interest in her village life. She felt that she was becoming two persons, who did not agree with each other.

Suddenly Stepan grew busier. The onset of winter found the concrete work far behind schedule. Most of the engineers did not believe it possible to pour concrete after the freeze. The younger men, including Stepan, held that it could be done. The Party supported them and gave a new slogan: "Close the comb before spring flood." Concrete-laying in winter presented new difficulties which Stepan felt in honour bound to solve.

He began to come home late in the evenings. He was too tired to talk. If previously he had ignored the farm, now he did not even discuss the dam. When he came home he wanted only food and sleep. Anya craved tenderness to justify the empty waiting of the day. Increasingly, Stepan treated her as the keeper of the flat whose function was to furnish meals whenever he might appear. Her trips to Kichkas made him irritable; however little she could count on the time of his arrival, he wanted to reply on her presence whenever he might come.

"I'm under heavy pressure at work; things must move smoothly at home," he declared. But in his important work she had no share.

Anya at last admitted to herself that she was lonely and that Stepan's love did not fill her life. Even if he could be with her oftener, even if he were tender and considerate, she wanted her own work.

In February she believed she was with child; in early March she was sure. She waited to tell Stepan until she felt certain; then she waited for some moment of understanding and mutual tenderness. Her restlessness grew, centring around the child. She tried to assure herself that her pregnancy made her see things too tragically, but for the first time she wondered if her relation with Stepan had the enduring quality of marriage. It would be sad for the child if the marriage failed.

Week by week on her trips to the village, she saw that the water was rising. The time was at hand when the cottage would be flooded out. Her grandfather had grown more childishly insistent on remaining. Anya was worried by what seemed a change in his delusion. His stubborn but not unnatural belief that the river would not reach his house, because it had never reached it, was changing—now that the water was actually in the yard—to an irrational faith that as long as he stayed he could by sheer denial hold it back. His defiance of the river was passing beyond the border of sanity. The woman who looked after him complained that, since everybody had moved away, there was no company and no help if an emergency should arise.

"I must stay with my grandfather until I can move him," Anya told Stepan. He was so annoyed and considered her departure so exclusively from the standpoint of his own convenience that she found it impossible to speak of her pregnancy before she left.

At the farm it was almost time for sowing. Stesha told her that Morosov had been asked to work for the county and Ivan would soon take over the presidency of Red Dawn Farm again. "We felt that he wasn't quite up to it when the farm expanded. But he's grown and he was always a good manager. Ilya has built the social relations within the farm and its connections with the county. We'll still live here, for I'm working in the hospital. But other farms need Ilya more."

Anya found herself accepted as the head of the sugar-beet work returned from a winter vacation. She told Stesha about the child, explaining that she would be unable to do such heavy work this summer.

"That's more than balanced by your experience," Stesha assured her. "We need you at the Vera Voronina Laboratory Cottage. The farms all around come to us for advice."

Anya brightened at the thought that people needed her. "I'd like to try a new method of fertilizing on part of the fields," she ventured. "I got the idea in Moscow last November and I've read up on it since. Instead of putting dry fertilizer on the field once in the spring, we'll make a solution, diluting it to avoid burning, and apply it several times during the season in small doses near the roots."

"There, you see," cried Stesha. "You'll manage beets from the laboratory." Anya saw that what her friends took for granted might indeed become the truth.

She began to go back and forth to the laboratory and was glad to see that this seemed to make her grandfather more contented. Special attention to his needs had worried him with the thought that she considered him ill. His failing mind at times forgot her marriage, but his long peasant years made her steady work seem to him normal.

Anya wondered about it. "Is work instead of love the root of life? Does it go deeper, and last longer?" Passionately she rejected this conclusion, telling herself that the twin roots were equally work and love.

She discussed it with Stesha. "When the farmers come for advice I feel that I'm living again. Yet I want Stepan badly. Only I can't be just his housekeeper; that destroys both my own growth and our marriage. How can I manage? I won't give up Stepan and I won't give up my work."

"A child will give you some work," remarked Stesha.

"I'm glad of that," said Anya softly, "but that doesn't settle it. I'm no child specialist. The child should spend his days in a sunny nursery with other children, not all the time in the little flat with a grown-up amateur. What could be worse for the child than a restless mother fussing with it all day?"

"You must give up something," smiled Stesha. "Everyone must."

Anya thought it over. "Then I'll have to give up something from both my work and my marriage. Keeping both, I can't have exactly what I want in either. . . . I'll have to keep adjusting; life will be compromise after compromise."

"That's true," agreed Stesha, "but your work will enrich your marriage and marriage will enrich your work."

Anya recalled the vision she had had in her talk with Stalin. She was going to smash the shackles that bound women! "It takes longer than I thought," she sighed. "It will be easier when our country grows stronger, when working hours are shorter and connections better between the dam and the village. But it will never be completed in my life."

She joined the Red Dawn Farm in its march to the sowing. Peace came to her when she watched the camp fire fade and lay down to sleep with her comrades under the friendly stars. Here were her life's roots; here was her work and here had begun her marriage. When Stepan had time for love, he would find her here.

If he did not find her, she must find the way to him. Not merely to his flat at Zaporozhe, but to the marriage he must help her build.

XXIX

THE FIGHT TO HARNESS the Dnieper entered the final stage. The spring flood was rising fast; the intensity of the struggle increased. "Compete for the honour of laying the last bucket of concrete!" This slogan aroused all brigades to beat even their former records. Victory lay ahead —first in weeks, then in days, then in hours!

"To-day, the twenty-eighth of March, at five-twenty in the afternoon," announced the *Dneprostroi Worker*, "the last cubic metre of concrete will be laid by the following workers, all with world records." The list included the prize-winning brigade in each operation. The last batch of concrete would be mixed by the winning groups in the mixing works, hauled to the spillway by the winning locomotive crew, hoisted by the winning crane men. The best concrete-layers would put it finally in place.

As prize-winning foreman, Stepan had gone to the dam before midnight to supervise the last night and day of work.

"Good boy, Maxim!" he cried when he saw that they were all there ahead of time. "I'm coming down on the block with you. You'll start her off and Peter will finish. Both from our old first gang!" His heart was warmed by the thought that Maxim, that former thief and ne'er-do-well, was one of the winners. How the men who conquered this river had been themselves remade!

They hastened into the spillway between Piers 34 and 35. The rush of water was very strong, swirling above the knees of the carpenters who were building the forms.

"Go to the shore for a high-volt pump," Stepan shouted to one of the men. The pump came but took some time to install. By four in the morning the strength of the water was such that the carpenters could not work. All hands offered their help to the pump men. Everyone breathed more easily when pumping began at five o'clock. In the lessening water, the men worked silently and rapidly and the forms were prepared in an hour.

The pump suddenly stopped working; the forms began to fill with water. Despair seized the concrete men; they were ready to hurl themselves on the pump men for delaying their work.

"Stand back," ordered Stepan. "Give them a chance." Then he spoke to the pump men. "Get hold of yourselves. You've done it before; you can do it again." Twenty minutes later, the pump worked again. Everyone prepared the forms with tripled energy.

At seven o'clock, they hailed the first concrete with cries of excitement; they placed concrete steadily for an hour. Then they turned the working place over to Peter. Maxim's brigade had completed the task set for them. Stepan stayed on for the next shift.

Peter's brigade were in tremendous spirits. They had come an hour early and had restlessly awaited their turn. Well above the water now, they laid concrete without a pause. All of them knew that to-morrow their names would stand in the newspapers from Moscow to Vladivostok, linked forever with the history of the dam.

An hour before the time fixed for the formal ceremony, the concrete-pourers were ready for the last bucket. They had to wait until the chiefs of the administration, the delegations from the Zaporozhe factories, and the workers' bands arrived. Stepan had been invited to stand with the chiefs of the dam; he had declined the honour. Chief Engineer Winter had understood and had looked at him almost enviously. Stepan wanted to feel with his own hands and feet the concrete that finished the last spillway.

From both banks of the river and from the piers overhead he heard the music of bands and the roar of cheers. Above the din rose the triumphant toot of the locomotive bringing the last bucket. The bucket was swung into place by the crane. Stepan and Peter sprang to it, opened it, felt the fresh mixture rush about their feet. With shouts, all the members of the gang jumped on it, stamping it into place. Withdrawing at last to the solid half of the spillway, they proudly surveyed the damp but finished work. With a shout louder than any before, they seized Stepan and tossed him into the air above their heads, catching his outstretched body several times upon their lifted arms.

They set him down, dizzy, dishevelled, and happy. They tossed Peter next. A round silver ruble fell out of his pocket, tinkled on the hard concrete, and flashed in the sun as if fell far down to the river.

"Stop it, fellows! This is costing me money," yelled Peter. "I'll throw you down to fish it out!"

"They're charging you for the tossing. I got mine for nothing," laughed Stepan, smacking Peter hard across the shoulder. He started up the ladder to the top of the pier.

All the way to the shore, he was surrounded by congratulations. For a time, he mingled with the celebrating crowd. Then the strain of the last few days, and especially the two shifts of high-pressure work since midnight, made him sleepy. Soon after dark he went home to bed.

The flat seemed lonely after the day's excitement. For a week he had hardly noticed Anya's absence. He had worked all his waking hours and had eaten at the central dining-room. But Anya should have been here to share this triumph, he thought with drowsy resentment, as he drifted off to sleep.

Next morning he decided to go and get her. His day was free. As he crossed the dam, he saw that the water stood higher against the concrete they had laid. From the high bridge, he looked far up the valley. For the first time, he felt the dam not as a daily struggle but—in its relation to the river—as an essentially completed thing. Above it, the Dnieper had risen, widening until it could hardly be called a river. The rapids he had run the previous summer had been covered long ago. A new lake, more than a mile wide, stretched to the north far beyond the limit of his vision. Had it reached Dnepropetrovsk, the great steel city? Probably not; the water level was well below the tops of the spillways. Eventually the Lenin lake—they called it that in honour of the man who had planned this dam in the darkest hours of the Revolution—would reach that distant city, over fifty miles away.

Along the shore of the rising lake he strode triumphantly toward the abandoned village. Sowing had begun. Far off he heard the rumble of tractors; he smelled the warm damp scent of broken earth. On the high banks the spreading locusts were at the edge of bloom. Half-submerged in the milky water, the soft grey balls of the pussy willows were fully swollen. When he passed through the torn rubble that had been the village, he caught a sour whiff of rotting boards and old dung heaps. The new lake flowed over the clay foundations and the broken bricks of the ovens, gently washing down the deserted constructions of man. The life had gone to a higher site.

At the farthest end, beyond the grove of locusts, the grandfather's cottage still stood. The water was over the threshold; it rippled knee-deep in the yard. In front of the house, in the midst of the water, sat the old man, firmly planted in his chair. Anya stood beside him with the water swirling around her; the hem of her skirt was pulled up and tucked in unevenly at the waist. She bent over her grandfather, urging him to come with her away from the water.

"It's going down, Anya. It can't harm the house as long as I stay here. Don't you see that it's going down?" The high, querulous voice rose on the soft spring air.

Stepan walked impatiently into the water. Brushing Anya aside, he seized the old man, chair and all, and carried him out of the flood to the top of the bank. The grandfather fell from the chair and shrank away from Stepan, moaning.

Anya rushed to his aid. She was shaking; tears stood in her eyes. "You brute!" she attacked Stepan.

"You're too sentimental, Anya," declared her husband firmly. "Stop pampering his delusions. If you couldn't get him to a proper place in all this time, I'll find a place to-day and put him there. You're wasting too much time on him."

All the disappointment of the past winter boiled up in Anya. Half-hysterically, she turned on Stepan. "You understand nothing of people. You never care how anyone feels. When he was a boy of twelve he helped his father build this house in the year when serfdom was abolished. It was the first free house in the village and it made his life a part of history. If you ever put your life into a building and see it destroyed, you'll know. But now you think only of your own strength and your triumphs, regardless of anyone else!"

Stepan recoiled under the shock of surprise that Anya could thus attack him. Furiously he shouted back: "I'm putting that strength of mine into something worth while. I wouldn't build my life into an old hut; I've built it into the Dnieper Dam that will last a thousand years!"

Anya turned her back on him and began to minister to her grandfather. Already half-ashamed of her outburst, she was trying to control her irritation. Soon, she looked up and saw Stepan waiting awkwardly. Her heart softened, for she thought he was standing by to help.

"Your presence only worries him," she apologized. "Perhaps you'll go to the farm and tell Stesha and Morosov to come."

"I'll ask them for a place to put your grandfather," replied Stepan. "You've had enough of this; I'm taking you back to-night."

Amazed, she stared at him, realizing with a shock how far apart they had drifted in the brief two weeks. It had not entered her mind that he had come to take her to town, nor had it occurred to him that she might be working at the farm.

"I'm not going back just now," she explained. "I'm in charge of the laboratory here."

"I thought you were my wife!" he raged.

She was silent, fearing to lose her temper again. Turning, she waded to the house. Stepan saw her disappear in the dark doorway. Soon she came back bearing pillows and blankets. Angry with himself that he had not thought of doing this, he was angrier with her for not asking him.

"You make it quite clear that you don't want me," he accused, but she offered no reply.

She thought with dull hopelessness: "Oh, I do want you but why is it always so difficult?" She began spreading out the bedding and pillows in the sun, for her grandfather to rest. Stepan strode haughtily away.

He was still angry when he reached the city. Let Anya come to herself and understand her duty as a wife. If she didn't, well—he shrugged his shoulders. He thought back over the winter. Somewhere in the long months the glory that had been theirs had vanished. What had happened to their marriage?

In early afternoon Morosov came to the flat, reporting: "The old grandfather is dead."

"Did Anya send you?" asked Stepan sharply.

"Not exactly," replied Morosov in surprise.

"Then thank you for coming so far to tell me. Perhaps you'll stay and have some tea?" There was an uncomfortable silence. Stepan was pleased to see that his aloof politeness embarrassed Morosov. You with your farm taking my wife away, he thought, I'm not one that answers your call.

"I have to go back," Morosov broke the silence. "Aren't you coming with me?"

"No!" The word was like a blow.

"Why not?" Morosov stammered.

"She'll blame me for the old man's death," said Stepan sullenly. "Besides, she's taken up now with your farm."

Morosov lost patience. "Stop thinking of yourself. Think of your wife, who is left alone. If you can't think of Anya, think of your child!"

"My child . . ." exclaimed Stepan, bewildered.

Morosov looked at him with sudden pity. "Stesha told me. Didn't you know? What kind of husband are you, anyway?"

After a long pause Stepan reached for his hat and coat. "I'm going back with you, of course. I don't know what kind of husband I am; I've never thought about it. It's true that I didn't know."

They crossed the dam in silence. As they reached the other shore, Morosov spoke seriously but gently. "I can't leave you alone in this. Anya's happiness and work mean too much to all of us."

An hour earlier Stepan had resented the work that Anya did with Morosov; there was no resentment left in him now. "There's something pretty wrong with us if she didn't tell me," he admitted slowly. "Perhaps she doesn't love me any more. Something seemed to happen to her last winter."

"Anya has loved you since she was a little girl," persisted Morosov. "She doesn't change easily. What did you do to make her change?"

There was silence while Stepan thought this over. Finally he confessed: "It wasn't her fault that she didn't tell me. She didn't have any chance to talk to me. I was always busy on the dam."

"The dam is worth being busy on," declared Morosov. "Was Anya busy too?"

"She had the flat to look after and she went to evening courses. What else she did I really don't know."

"Your Anya was doing great work for our country. Didn't you feel, as we all did, her glad and vivid life when she fought to give more sugar to the land? That was the woman that aroused your love. You made her a housewife with three rooms to look after. She couldn't be interesting as a housewife, not even to you."

As Stephen considered this, he saw above the road the houses of the American colony. "I think I know where the trouble began," he guessed. "Ever since I visited the American engineer I've wanted what I called an American-style wife. Mrs. Johnson gives all her time to making a lovely home for her husband; she keeps herself beautiful to inspire him. Anya quarrelled with me when I first told her about it."

200

"It began long before the Americans," smiled Morosov. "Don't blame it on them. It began when man first subjugated woman, and then lost love for the thing that he had made. It's a very old male desire—marriage has been based on it for ages—to take the finest woman you can find and make her a possession. It's one of the things we have to fight to-day."

When they reached the fallow earth the tractors were nearer than in the morning. Horses worked with the tractors, moving across the field in a co-ordination which Stepan, newly aware of the farm now, realized he had never seen. It was not the painful plodding of the single horse driven by one peasant, in the heavy toil that had crippled his youth. Nor was it the great mass drive of tractors fighting for a record, as when the Red Dawn Farm strove to master its machines. It was a subtle rhythm in which each tractor knew its place and the place of the horses, in which the harrows followed the ploughs and were followed by the seeders, and all were adjusted to the size and shape of the field and the quality of earth.

"Why, it's like music," he exclaimed, struck with atsonishment. "See that lone horse in the last narrow corner with the harrow, and the pair over there. Each of them works unhindered yet follows a common plan."

"Yes, it's a good farm," Morosov nodded. "They've pretty well mastered the mechanism. . . . That's the music Anya hears."

Feeling for exact words he went on: "It's a changing relation. Each field is different, each crop is different. It's not something you learn just once; it's something you learn daily. That's our life, too. Each finds his own adjustment and it differs from to-day to to-morrow. What forced me to find it was the fact that I could never make of Stesha a possession in the usual sense."

He turned to the left at the half-submerged ruins. "Our roads part here. I'm going to the farm; you'll find Anya near the cottage. You've grown a lot, Stepan, in the past four years. Once I wrote in your characteristic: 'He wrecks everything that he cannot boss.' You've got over that now in your work; you're a fine workman. You'll get over it in your marriage, too."

So it was Morosov who had written that damning characteristic. Stephan had often wondered but now it no longer mattered. It had happened in a different life to different people. How everyone had grown since then!

"Thanks for everything, Ilyosha." He seized Morosov's hand at parting, giving him for the first time the friendlier name. "All these years I never knew or liked you. It was my loss."

The air was sweet with perfume when he passed the locusts; the warm day had opened the first buds. Beyond them he saw Anya's golden head. She sat on the top of the bank, where the long light of the setting sun struck full on her unbound hair. She was watching the wide lake grow out of the turbulent river on which her forebears long ago had built their home. The old house was sagging into the water that now flowed freely through the door.

She looked up and smiled a welcome. He sat down and gently took her hand.

She said: "I'm sorry I was angry."

"Sh!" he reproved. "Who has a right to be angry with me if not my own wife?" Both of them laughed and their laughter joined them more subtly but no less deeply than a kiss.

There was something that must be settled before he could feel at ease. "You don't think I killed him, do you, Anichka?" he asked.

"I only know," she said, "that his life was already over and his time had come to die."

He put his arm around her shoulders. After a long while he spoke. "But ours . . . has come to live, Anichka." She nodded, her head on his breast.

XXX

Forty-six waterfalls leapt from the spillways and fell into rainbows, foaming in the August sun. The sight of the tall piers and tumbling water smote Stepan with a shock of pain. He stared through the long glass wall of the engine-room that overlooked the dam and the river. He closed his eyes for an instant, then opened them to look again along the great white arc from shore to shore.

Always, since the day when the river first broke over the spillways the majesty of the dam had given him a satisfaction that no familiarity could dim. The mighty arc, which had cost so much struggle, which for four years had been such a battleground of torn rock and arrested water, stood now as calm and complete in beauty and strength as if it were a part of Nature, as if it had been there from the beginning of time and would be there forever. Always it had been to him the sign that man's work goes on beyond his lifetime. But to-day he strove to etch each line of the structure on the mind behind the eyeballs, as if the fragile brain might make immortal the perishable rock.

He turned abruptly back to the engine-room. "I thought it would last a thousand years," he said heavily. "It's been there not quite ten."

The tall blond youth to whom he spoke pulled a grimy rag from his pocket and wiped the streams of sweat from his brow. "We'll be finished by midnight, Comrade Superintendent. We're taking out the last one now."

Stepan looked past the foreman of the engine-room and saw the gleaming walls, with their black panels, and the eight torn gaps that wrecked the polished floor. At the far end of the room, in the blue-green light that came through the glass wall—sunlight reflected from the river —the ninth generator, the last one, was surrounded by a dozen busy men in overalls.

"Make it by nine o'clock or sooner, Vladimir. We can't tell when the troops will need the bridge."

"I'll let you know when we have the last of it loaded. Where will you be?"

"In and out of the office all afternoon. I'll drop in here again this evening."

Stepan went swiftly out of the power-house and up the steps. He turned north by the tree-lined boulevard that ran along the bank of the river. He saw beyond the dam the dark green lake, with Greater Zaporozhe on the far shore. There was the aluminium works, Europe's greatest. There was a machine shop more than a mile long under a single roof. There lay the largest ferro-alloy works in the world. Around and beyond these giants, and far beyond the limits of his vision, stretched the great new city of parks and apartment houses, and schools and hospitals, and halls for study and laughter, where there had been naked steppe ten years ago.

He found it hard to pass the end of the dam, because of the hordes of people who were pouring over it toward the east. Across it ran a bridge in two levels, bearing the railroad and the wide, international highway that came from far beyond the Soviet borders, past storied Kiev to Zaporozhe, and, crossing the Dnieper here, led eastward to the Urals and the Caucasus, and southward to the shores of the Black Sea. Along this way the armies of Hitler were advancing; they had already crossed the Dnieper far to the north. The flank had been turned; the great river bend at Zaporozhe was no longer tenable. The last escape to the east for a wide region lay over the dam by the double bridge.

A month earlier the main flow of traffic had been westward, carrying troops and Army supplies. Now life flowed in reverse, eastward, in a great tide. It flowed swiftly but without panic; long since had the forms been organized. Trains of mothers and small children; trains loaded with school-children and their teachers; special trains for whole factories or great farms; trucks, tractors, horse carts moving shorter distances. All were loaded not only with people but with the people's possessions, clothes, cattle, machinery, and the equipment of giant enterprises, which would resume their tasks in the Urals or Central Asia, more than a thousand miles east.

Pushing across the stream of people, he continued along the shore of the lake. Off to his left, some distance from the water, the greatest throng of all seethed around the railway station. He thought of looking for

Anya there; she might already be with the special train of the Red Dawn Farm. When he saw the size of the crowd and the number of trains, he judged it impossible to find her. She would reach him more easily at his office. Turning sharply up the bank, he entered the large building which ten years ago had served the dam's construction and had since handled the distribution of power.

He found Marin waiting in his office. It was good to have this old friend with him. Marin had remained in the Army; they had met but seldom in the past ten years. Now their paths came together; everyone was part of the Army to-day. Marin's chin was sterner than of old, and two months at the front had lined his face, but he stood erect in his captain's uniform, and his smile was as warm as ever.

"Is there any hope at all, Marin?"

"For the dam? No. The enemy will be here in less than twenty-four hours. It's merely a question of how much we can take away. That's why I'm here." He saw the pain in Stepan's eyes, and added, sympathetically: "The whole Soviet people will mourn it, but it must be especially hard on you. The dam was your life."

"Something more than my own life, Marin," Stepan spoke calmly. "Each of us connects with the life of the world through something. To you the dam was one achievement of our vast country. But to me our country was the widening of Dnieper Dam." He added furiously: "I'll blow it up with my own hands before I'll let Hitler use it to enslave our people. But I wish I could carry it stone by stone to the East!"

"But you've worked elsewhere?"

Stepan nodded. "One year on the Volga, one at Angara. The years that Anya went to the Agricultural College. Both of us wanted to come back here. This seemed our centre. Here in the electric heart of our Ukraine."

"We're taking most of the heart out," declared Marin. "I hope your generators are ready."

"Eight of them loaded. The ninth will be ready to-night."

"Then eight, at least, will get over; hurry up the ninth. The troops will be crossing all night, but especially after midnight. I'll be back about dark to check our final arrangements. I'm going now to the Red Dawn Farm to cover your rear."

"You'll save time by waiting for Anya. She's been helping with the farm's evacuation. She'll know where the rest of them are. I'm expecting her any moment."

Marin sat down. "She's been with the farm all these years?" he asked. Stepan shook his head.

"She supervises sugar beets for the district. We live on this bank in one of the old American houses. She covers the region by auto. But her roots are still at the farm."

204

Anya came in ten minutes later. She moved with such sureness and calm that Stepan relaxed. She was only a little heavier with the years but she was clearly tired from working in the August heat. The blue-figured kerchief stuck damply to her hair; the bare, rounded arms and linen shoulder caps were soaked with perspiration. Smiling a welcome to Marin, she answered her husband's inquiring look.

"I couldn't drag the children through the crowd. You'll see them at the train. We're at the north end of the station. Seventh in line among the civilians."

"Don't leave your train after dark," warned Marin. "Some time to-night you'll go through. Probably about midnight."

She put a large parcel on Stepan's desk. "Food," she explained. "You'll have no time to get any."

"So you had plenty of time," he said with soft irony. "Why did you make so much? It's enough for ten."

"So that you'll remember me to-morrow! And perhaps even the day after," she smiled. Then she added in a matter-of-fact tone: "I was putting up lunch for two hundred. What's half a dozen more?"

She turned toward Marin. "Is the Army ready for our auto? We're through. Everything's on the train."

"Shall I use it to go to the farm?" he asked. "I'm giving the boys their first assignment."

Anya laughed grimly. "Go on foot across fields if you want to get there. All road traffic comes this way. Keep well south of the wheat field; it's burning. We soaked it with our last gasoline. You'll find the men waiting for you at Ivan's cottage. It's the only building left."

She looked out of the window, winking back the tears. Her voice was shaking as she said to Stepan: "You'd better appreciate that boiled chicken. It's the costliest you ever ate. Shubina's breeding stock, the last of her forty thousand hens. The rest—are retreating with the troops."

"Inside or outside?" asked Marin with a grin.

She flashed him a grateful glance for his saving humour. "Don't ask me for military secrets. We gave them yesterday to your quartermaster. Along with eighty cows and two hundred pigs."

"Keep the receipts," said Marin easily. "You'll get something on them in the East."

She shook her head in fierce denial. "We'll get them right here when we come back to rebuild our land!"

Smiling approval, Marin rose to go. "See you to-night," he said to Stepan. He raised his hand in salute to Anya. "See you . . . later!"

She went to the door and locked it behind him. Sitting on Stepan's knees, she gently rumpled his hair. "I like your Marin. I hope he'll be with you for the finish," They sat close for a time in silence, until she asked: "Am I keeping you from anything that is needed?"

205

He shook his head. "Vladimir handles the power plant, and Maxim the other equipment. The dynamite is laid. I must be on call here, but my work is chiefly to-night. I'll have no sleep till late to-morrow. This hour is the rest I need." He drew her cheek against his, as he added: "Just you, without even the children now."

After a time he felt that she was sobbing. "Cry it out," he said. "It's been a strain. The farm, of course, is gone."

"You couldn't even imagine how completely. Stables, cow barns, piggery, Shubina's prize-winning poultry farm, and the incubators that changed the breed for the whole county. All burned or delivered to the Army. The same with the harvested grain. The standing crops are burning. All the tile-roofed cottages of Ivan's proud farm city that the Kharkov architect designed. And the running-water system that was only two years old. Even the old wells are filled with earth, and the green apples knocked from the trees. 'They shan't ripen for the robbers,' Ivan said."

"Your sugar beets?"

"We drove the tractor ploughs over them and cut them to pieces before we gave the tractors to the Army."

He felt her shaking in his arms. Then the trembling passed and she continued calmly. "I hadn't suspected what a streak of sentiment there is in Ivan. He kept his house till the last; the partisans meet there to-night. 'I built it. I'm the one to burn it,' he said. 'But not until Shubina has gone from it.'"

"I don't feel that way about our house here," mused Stepan. "I took out your picture and the children's, and what clothes and camping stuff I need. Your things went out sooner. Let the Army handle the rest; it will go up with the other buildings. Your life and mine have been outside it—on the dam and on the farm. It's been a good life. Where else in any land in all past ages could we have known ten such years?"

"It's still a good life," she asserted. "The farm is gone. The dam will be gone to-morrow. But you and I go on."

He looked at her sombrely. "You bragged nicely to Marin. Don't deceive yourself and me."

"About returning? That's as may be. Marin knows it as well as you. This may be our last time together. All the same, we go on. Our children will be safe in the East."

Close in his arms, she spoke softly: "You remember what Petrov told you? Eleven, no, twelve years back when you stole that crane? The left bank was your bigger gang; you must work to make your bigger gang win. That helped me a lot when we destroyed the farm. Only now our bigger gang is beyond our country—all of freedom-striving peoples of the world. That's hard to feel. Life widens—painfully. But it's still our life."

"I'll think of that to-night," he said. "And at to-morrow's dawn."

Just before dusk he stood with Marin on a rise of ground beyond the power-house. Marin checked and approved the detonator that connected with the dynamite under the dam. The point had been chosen because it gave a view of anyone approaching; it was the rise from which Stepan had looked back to evade pursuit long ago, when he stole the sack of grain for the Lair.

How the landscape had changed since then! To the north-east, where once the wild rapids had been, the dam shone white against the opalescent lake. The air shook with the rumble of troops crossing the upper bridge. Due north, instead of the village of Kichkas—it was long since under the lake—was the crowded railway station, and behind it the office building of the dam. The fields to the west, once matted hard with weeds, were soft with years of ploughing, and ravaged by the recent passage of tractors over the beets. Beyond them, on the north-west horizon, great clouds of smoke arose from the Red Dawn Farm.

"The boys from the farm will watch all approaches to-night," said Marin. "They're resourceful; the Nazis will hardly pass them in the dark. Daytime's another matter. Not even our troops can hold the Germans then. We should have till dawn to pass over. I'll be with the trains at the bridge. I'll come to you when they've all crossed. If by any chance the Germans get to you first, blow her up without waiting for me."

"Whatever is on the bridge?" asked Stepan.

"Whatever's on it. In that case, wait till they practically have their hands on you. Can you fix it so that if they snipe you at dawn from a distance your fall will set off the detonator? That's one thing that mustn't fail."

Stepan nodded. "I can fix it."

"Chances are I'll join you here and we'll make the Lair. Where are the horses?"

Stepan pointed down the rise to a clump of trees, under which two horses were tethered.

"All set then," approved Marin. "Are you going with me to the station to say good-bye?"

"Later," Stepan answered. "I'm checking the generator first."

He lent a hand in the power-house. The windows were curtained heavily for the last blackout, for the enemy air bases were near. There was a scuffle with parachutists—soon over. By ten o'clock, everything was dismantled. He stepped behind the dark curtain and looked once more at the dam. It was the last time he would see it from this place, his own particular view. Coming back into the room, he walked with young Vladimir to the door. His jaw was set firmly and his eyes were grim.

"Don't take it so hard, Comrade Superintendent. When we come back, we'll built her again better and faster than before!"

"Faster? Certainly. Better? Maybe. But what we built you'll never build. What we built was built once only. We're not destroying it. It will never be destroyed."

He laughed at Vladimir's look of sudden worry. "Don't be afraid about my job to-night. I'm not flighty. You'll know what I mean some day when you've built your dam in the east."

It took some time to find the train in the crowd and the blackout. He had a moment of panic. How could all these get over the bridge before dawn? Would he have to blow it up with people on it? With Anya's train, the train with his own children? He forced his mind to the search. In the dark, he ran into Morosov, who was looking for the hospital cars on the same train to say good-bye to Stesha. They found the train together.

Anya stood by the car steps, with the nine-year-old Stepan. She greeted her husband and went swiftly to get the other two children. "They're sleeping in one of the nursery cars. You mustn't go in."

Stepan took the boy in his arms. "Mummy is boss of the whole train," boasted the youngster. "Why aren't you going too?"

"I'm staying in the Cossacks' Lair to fight the Nazis," the father explained, looking deep into the boy's gleaming eyes.

Then Anya came back, leading seven-year-old Anna, and carrying the baby, Ilya, in her arms. Stepan kissed the children good-bye and wished them a good journey. "Study hard so that you can rebuild all that we are destroying," he admonished the two older ones. "Work honestly for our Soviet Power. Remember what it cost."

After taking the children into the car, Anya returned to Stepan for a last embrace. "For the first time in my life," she told him, "I wish I were joining you in the Cossacks' Lair."

"So Anya and the old outlaw gang are reconciled." He was deeply moved.

"Does it mean so much to you?" she asked, surprised.

"More than you'll ever know. It was the one part of my life you wouldn't enter. But now you're with me there."

In leaving the station, he stumbled in the darkness into the mixed freight and passenger train on which Vladimir had just loaded the last bits of the ninth generator. They were covering the machinery with tarpaulins. The boxcars were crowded with workmen, technicians, and their families, who would set up a new plant in the East. Vladimir shook hands with Stepan and took his post on a flatcar, sitting on a tarpaulin over the machines that he guarded. The three-bell signal was given muffled from the engine, and the long train moved eastward. It was going out among the first. Anya's train would be considerably later. Refugees from farther west preceded it; they had waited longer and were in greater need.

Crouching near the detonator at midnight, he checked it over once more and then sat back to wait. He tried to count the trains that rumbled over the bridge. Shortly after one o'clock, German bombers came over, and the earth shook with explosions. They were feeling for the railway station; one of the bombs seemed close. Anya's train, he thought, was not yet over the bridge. The bomb must have been near her, then.

He heard men approaching from the west, plodding heavily in the darkness of the broken field. Fixing the detonator so that if he fell it would explode, he trained his rifle on them and shouted: "Who goes there?" If they were Germans and he fell now, Anya's train would be caught this side of the river. Perhaps he had miscounted; perhaps she was already safe. The approaching men replied that they were Ukrainian farmers from farther west, fleeing before the Nazi advance. They had left the road to escape the bombing. Stepan did not know them. He kept his rifle trained on them as he directed them to the railway station; he stood tied to the detonator until they had passed.

He had lost count of the trains now. He could not even guess about Anya and the children. Perhaps it was better this way. That's Marin's job, and the job of the farm's armed partisans, he thought. They'll do it. I can do nothing. He would know her fate when Marin came in the morning, if both Marin and he survived.

How long the fire of the Red Dawn Farm burned in the north-west! How long it took to die. What a great farm it had been, as great in its way as the dam! Great dams in other lands had already surpassed in size this one on the Dnieper; Boulder Dam in Arizona was higher, the Grand Coulee Dam in Washington was larger. But no other country in the world had a farm like the Red Dawn Farm. Its flames died down toward dawn, and the night grew black. Only the white arc over the river was faintly visible under the stars.

The sky paled toward morning. Far off on the horizon, a new red glow appeared. Was the dawn coming? Marin had not come. Dawn would give swift passage to the Germans; the Red Dawn irregulars could not hold them during the day. No! He must have been confused with watching. The glow was not in the east but in the north-west. The Red Dawn Farm was flaming anew.

Ivan's cottage, he thought, they're leaving it. The Nazis have come.

Looking toward the dam he saw Marin approaching, a dark grey form against the pale grey sky. The thin, uniformed figure walked swiftly and easily, as if everything were in order. Anya, then, was safely over, and the trains all gone. Stepan turned toward the detonator. For days he had dreaded this moment as the end of more than his own existence. Marin stood beside him and nodded. It was only a great relief that he felt as he made the connection and threw himself flat on the ground behind the hill.

For miles around they heard the roar of the explosion. Red Army men, digging in all night on the eastern shore, heard it; their faces grew set and grim. Refugees, approaching the station from the west, heard it; an old woman in a cart crossed herself many times as she turned back toward the pursuing death. Four horsemen, turning down a gully, heard it; hot tears ran down their swarthy cheeks. "Hurry," cried Ivan. "There's barely time to reach the Lair before the flood." The dying echoes reached the trains that were slowly pulling eastward, shunting on many sidings to make room for Army trains that still advanced. Anya, still only a few miles beyond Zaporozhe, straining her ears at dawn for this last signal from Stepan, caught the far trembling of the earth and air and knew that the Dnieper Dam was gone.

Stepan lay flat behind the hillock, while the fury of the blast swept above him; he heard the deafening roar as the wall of water and broken rock smashed through the gap in the dam and smote the river bed. Then he raced with Marin down the slope to the horses. As they galloped southward on the high bank the sky grew rosy. Behind them, a great tidal wave flooded into the basin below Zaporozhe and broke with whirlpool fury up the shore.

"It has to fill that two-mile basin first," he yelled at Marin above the tumult. "We'll make it. But it sounds like the end of the world."

The first waves were breaking over the stepping-stones when they reached them. Stepan checked his horse and guided it firmly over. Marin followed. In that brief interval, the water already swirled higher. Marin's horse fell, floundered, and Stepan helped him through. They hurried up the other side to the cave. The water rapidly followed.

"No Nazis will get by there till the flood ebbs," laughed Marin. "We'll make our war plans in perfect peace."

In the outer part of the Lair, Stepan was startled to see his nine-year-old son, eating a piece of bread and meat. The boy looked at him in excitement mingled with reproach. "I waited most of the night for you, Daddy. Uncle Ivan came and gave me something to eat."

"How did you get here?" demanded the father.

"The children got away with Mother," said young Stepan, nonchalantly. "But I came back to fight the Nazis with you."

"You little bandit! Does your mother know you're here?"

"Anna promised to tell her after the train left. She couldn't come after me, anyway."

Marin laughed. "Here's a new Stepan!"

"He deserves a thrashing," declared the father.

"He'll get it," agreed Marin, "but not from you. He's starting to war a year younger than you did. These kids to-day are good."

Stepan spoke to the boy. "You might have killed yourself in that river. You'll take orders now. This is war. We'll let you watch the horses and hide them under the trees when the Nazi planes go by."

The boy seemed disappointed by the assignment. "Uncle Ivan thinks I'd make a good scout to visit the villages. You did that long ago."

Stepan compressed his lips grimly as he thought what the boy was asking. "We'll settle that later," he said.

"Come on, kid," called Marin. "We'll show you where we hide the horses. We found the place when we were only a little older than you."

Stepan took the boy on his horse and they rode together along the side of the cliff till they came to the gully with the creek. Dismounting, they led the horses through the bushes and along the ledge to the hidden gap. Young Stepan almost shouted his delight when he saw it; then he clapped his hand over his mouth. They climbed up the hidden gully and came out in the little glade. Six horses were there already. As they staked theirs out, Stepan softly whistled a Cossack song.

"How naturally you take to it, you old outlaw," grinned Marin. "One wouldn't think you had blown up a dam to-day and said good-bye to your family."

Stepan looked across the glade at his son, who was investigating the horses. He spoke slowly: "When all of your life, all the good of it and the bad of it, is welded together at last in a single weapon, and you take it up in your hands for the final war—there's a great freedom."

Marin looked across the glade, not quite understanding. "Even that time we stole the gipsy's horse comes handy."

"Yes," agreed Stepan. "And Anya—and the boy——"

Back in the main cave, they met for the conference. The child slept, exhausted by the night.

"I'm here as contact man between your partisan bands and the Red Army," announced Marin. "We're safely hidden in the Lair during the flood water. When it ebbs, the front will have passed to the east. We have here delegates from six villages, and one from the dam. Let them proceed to report."

Ivan spoke. "We've food for the winter for three hundred. Buried in four places. All from the Red Dawn Farm."

Stepan stated: "The boys from the dam supply the ammunition. That's hidden in three places, too."

Marin asked: "Where's Morosov? He's the only one not here."

"He went with five men and grenades to the woods beyond Alexinko," replied Ivan. "Nazi motor-cyclists were coming through and might have reached the dam from the south. They didn't come on. Morosov didn't either. We'll find out about him after the water ebbs."

Discussion and planning went on all day in the Lair. Outside the flood roared in undiminished fury, foaming to the very mouth of the cave. The river had risen twenty-seven feet.

Ivan and Pavel Voronin got dinner, over the fire close to the water. Stepan brought out the parcel of food from Anya. "She knew what I needed better than I did," he said. "Here, Ivan, are the last of your chickens."

"No," retorted Ivan. "I've one that's later." Lifting a freshly dressed hen from the pot, he dropped it back in the boiling water. "I found it in the yard just after I set the house afire. Stayed behind when we gave the rest to the Army. The little traitor was waiting for the Nazis. We're cooking it first."

They finished the meal and relaxed about the campfire. The boy went to sleep again on a straw pallet next to Stepan's. After a long silence, Ivan spoke.

"It's a long time since we met here, Stiopa."

Stepan agreed: "Half a lifetime away."

"It seems we're back where we started," said Ivan disconsolately. "We've burned the farm and blown up the dam, and destroyed everything we built in twenty years. We're back in the Cossack's Lair again. Only"—he smiled wryly—"we've lots more grub."

The faces of the group grew sombre, as they thought of all that they had lost. Marin looked at Stepan, and waited. Would he be leader again? The campfire was dimming when Stepan replied.

"No, Ivan, we're not back where we started. We're two hundred million lifetimes ahead. We built not only the Red Dawn Farm and the Dnieper Dam. We built the people that burned the farm and blew up the dam in the war to save the world."

The sombreness of the faces changed to grim determination. They began to prepare for sleep. As the campfire died, Stepan strode over the sleeping child to the mouth of the cave, and stood watching the raging river.

"It has stopped rising," he said. "We will be ready. It should begin to go down by dawn."